THE CENTURY EARTH SCIENCE SERIES

Kirtley F. Mather, Editor

FUNDAMENTALS OF
Earth
Science

FUNDAMENTALS OF

Earth
Science

By HENRY D. THOMPSON

Hunter College

Second Edition

825

New York: APPLETON-CENTURY-CROFTS, Inc.

FOREWORD

THE EARTH SCIENCES comprise a closely knit body of facts, principles, and theories, knowledge of which is essential to human progress. An understanding of the physical factors in the environment is moreover an especially valuable contribution to a life of personal satisfaction and enjoyment. This particular scientific discipline should therefore occupy a central position in any broad program of general education. At the same time, it embraces many enticing opportunities for specialized professional careers. With either objective in mind, a course of study designated by the title of this book, or organized along similar lines, should be considered as embodying the application of the principles of physics, chemistry, astronomy, and biology to the all-important task of comprehending the earth as the abode of man.

Whereas in the past, in many institutions of higher learning, it has been the custom to separate the several subdivisions of earth science into special courses, dealing for example with geomorphology, mineralogy, geology, geography, or meteorology, the need for intellectual synthesis and academic correlation has become convincingly apparent. No better starting point for general education in science can be found than a study that integrates and unifies these subjects. Doctor Thompson has recognized that opportunity and in his book he has provided the means for meeting its challenge. His selection of material and method of presentation are worthy of high praise. His survey is broad, but not superficial. He introduces the student to all phases of the many ramifications of the science of the earth and at the same time digs deeply enough in each to uncover its real essence.

A course of study based upon this textbook should prove highly appropriate, at approximately the freshman level in college, to provide for the cultural needs of the general student and at the same time to stimulate further professional studies on the part of those who may later specialize in the fields of geology, geography, or meteorology. In comparison with the very few other texts that have had somewhat similar aims, this one is especially notable for its clarity and sustained interest, as well as for its presentation of the latest results of recent research in several important subdivisions of the field. Conspicuous, also, is the extensive use of aerial photographs, an important feature in a time of great expansion in use of the airways.

v

All in all, the book will impress those who have had long experience in the teaching of earth science as refreshingly new, rather than just a rehash of the old familiar story. From whatever perspective it is appraised, it rings true. Its use should prove a real stimulant not only to a more extensive understanding of the subjects with which it deals, but also to the acquisition of those scientific habits of mind that are essential in modern life.

KIRTLEY F. MATHER

PREFACE

THE SCIENTIFIC INVESTIGATION of the earth is progressing at a rapid rate. Much new knowledge has been gained in the thirteen years that have elapsed since the publication of the first edition of this book. Progress has been most marked in the fields of geophysics, geochemistry, oceanography, and meteorology. The explorations in those fields have greatly increased the available information concerning the general structure of the whole earth, the absolute ages of the rocks in the crust, the configuration of the ocean floors and the nature of the materials that underlie them, and the directions and causes of the movements at different levels of the water in the hydrosphere and of the air in the atmosphere.

The second edition includes many of the recent advances in the above-named fields as well as those in other branches of earth science. Changes have been made in the text wherever necessary to take into account significant new developments. The main purpose of the book—to give the beginning student a comprehensive picture of the planet on which he lives—has been retained.

The manner of use of this book will vary with circumstances. Most will read it to gain information that will meet the requirements of a certain course in their academic institution. Some may read it for the pleasure of understanding. In either case, since the coverage is broad, all or part of the text may be useful. For example, we use this book at Hunter College as a basic text in the first term of geology, with laboratory work on topographic maps, minerals and rocks, structure sections, and block diagrams. The sections on weather and climate and on historical geology are omitted by us because we have separate courses in these subjects.

Great improvement in the quality and effectiveness of the illustrations will be noted. The photographs have been drawn from many sources. For most of the drawings, I am indebted to Robert Balk, Marie Bohrn, John Dean, Virginia Edwards, Erwin Raisz, and Fred Young. Others have been obtained from governmental agencies and are so acknowledged.

Before the revision was undertaken, Anastasia Van Burkalew critically read the entire text of the first edition and made numerous valuable suggestions. John Dean made special contribution to the reorganization and elucidation of Chapter 7. Fred Young helped to reorganize and to

vii

expand the old Chapter 25 into the new Chapters 25 and 26. Kirtley Mather, Editor of The Century Earth Science Series, made valuable suggestions for changes and additions at several places in the text. Even though I have received important advice from many sources, I take full responsibility for the statements that appear in the text.

For the typing, pasting, and indexing I wish to acknowledge the efficient work of Susan Berger, Margaret Clifford, Carla Reidel, and Alice Vrbsky. Without their help the revision would have been long delayed.

H. D. Thompson

Hunter College

CONTENTS

CONTENTS

— 1 —

Scope and Development of Earth Science

SCOPE OF EARTH SCIENCE

THE EARTH is man's home. Here he was born; here he lives and dies. Man has the opportunity to discover and the capacity to interpret the phenomena of the earth. In so doing he learns to understand and enjoy the world about him and to use wisely the resources of his habitat.

Earth science, in its broad meaning, deals with the whole earth, not merely with one part or one aspect of it. The earth is composed of concentric shells of material, arranged according to density. The outermost, all-enveloping, shell is the *atmosphere*. Next is an incomplete covering of water, the *hydrosphere*. Beneath the hydrosphere in the ocean basins and projecting above it in the continents is the solid *crust* of the earth. The crust is much thicker in the continents than in the ocean basins. Beneath the crust is the *mantle*. The innermost part of the earth is commonly called the *core*, and is divided into an outer core and an inner core (See Figure 4-1). The interrelations and interactions of the constituents of these shells, as well as some aspects of the organic world, all come within the legitimate field of earth science.

Animals and plants are the builders of a variety of rocks and are responsible for many changes in the outer part of the solid earth, in the waters, and in the air. Their remains, or fossils, provide a basis for the relative dating of sedimentary rocks and associated events, and, because of the close relation between organisms and their physical surroundings, also furnish data for deductions regarding the nature of environments both on the land surfaces and in the seas.

Earth science is customarily divided into several branches, most of

which are commonly included in the broad field of geology. Other
branches of earth science, such as meteorology, climatology, pedology,
and mathematical geography, constitute an important part of the field
of geography. The student of geology is concerned with the surface
forms, composition, and structure of the earth and the various agencies
which are continually altering it. Familiarity with present earth processes
and conditions enables one to reconstruct the sequence of past events
and interpret the history of the earth and its inhabitants from the
beginning of geological time. The ultimate aim of geological research is
geological history. The student of geography, on the other hand, is
interested primarily in the relation of life, especially the life of man, to
its environment. As the natural sciences of geology and geography are in
some phases intimately related and mutually overlapping, this book
does not propose to draw a boundary between the two subjects (see
Appendix A).

In brief, the content of earth science may be summarized as the study
of (1) the composition of the earth and the interrelations of its parts
both inorganic and living; (2) the causes and the results of changes; (3)
the arrangement of natural events in chronological sequence and areal
relationship.

METHODS OF INVESTIGATION

Field Work. Field work in earth science consists largely of the investigation of phenomena in their natural environment and in their natural
relationships to one another. Surveying and the making of maps is
obviously an important part of the work of an earth science field
investigator. In any region the nature of the survey, the features and
degree of detail to be included, depends on the purpose of the work and
the maps of the region already available. In unmapped regions the first
task is to construct some sort of base map which will show the general
boundaries, drainage, and some key locations. For most of the United
States excellent large-scale maps showing area, drainage, relief, and
culture, have been constructed by the United States Geological Survey
and are commonly used as base maps in further field work. On these,
the investigator can record the areal distribution of rocks, the structure,
the mineral deposits of economic value, the cultural patterns, and any
other desired features. Simple surveys may be carried out with only a
few instruments, such as a pocket compass, clinometer, aneroid barometer, hammer, pocket lens, and camera. In more ambitious projects,
however, a variety of highly technical instruments and men trained in
their use are required.

In addition to constructing maps, the worker in the field will keep a
notebook in which he records all his observations of natural and cul-

tural phenomena in as much detail as possible. Close observation and careful recording of facts form the basis on which safe and reasonable conclusions may be drawn.

Collecting of specimens is also an essential part of field work. The number and type collected will depend on the skill of the investigator in determining which ones are pertinent to his purpose. All specimens— minerals, rocks, fossils, and others—are carefully labeled as to locality and relationships at the time they are collected.

In recent years the exploration of the earth has grown tremendously. This has been the result, largely, of the combination of geology with physics in the science of geophysics. Now the ocean basins are being explored not by direct observation, but by such physical instruments as the seismograph, the gravimeter, and the echo sounder carried on ships. The thicknesses of the ice caps on Greenland and Antartica are determined by physical instruments. The use of geophysical exploration is becoming more and more important in locating deep structures that are favorable to the accumulation of oil.

Laboratory Work. The specimens and other data gathered in the field can be examined at greater length and in more detail in the laboratory than is convenient in the field. By the use of the microscope, the blowpipe, chemical reagents, and also by comparison with previously identified collections, the specimens are identified and their characteristics carefully tabulated. The actual construction of maps, charts and diagrams from data collected in the field takes place in the laboratory or map room, where the various instruments required are available. The geologist or geographer doing original work will probably spend three or four days in the laboratory for each day in the field. For this reason, a large part of the work of college and university departments of geology and geography consists of the training of students in laboratory techniques and methods.

HISTORICAL DEVELOPMENT

The beginnings of earth science are interwoven with the myths, legends, and vague speculations of antiquity. The first definite theories to affect the Western world were those evolved, or at least first expressed, by the Greeks. Naturally, one of the earliest problems to confront inquisitive man was that of the form of the earth. In the time of Homer (before 900 B.C.) the earth was considered a flat disc surrounded by the river Oceanus. Thales of Miletus, who lived in the seventh and sixth centuries, B.C., is claimed as the first exponent of the idea of a spherical earth. The Pythagorean philosophers adopted this theory, arguing that a sphere, being the most perfect solid figure, was the only one worthy to be the dwelling place of man. Aristotle (382-322

B.C.) demonstrated the sphericity of the earth by three arguments: (1) the tendency of matter to fall together toward a common center; (2) the circular shadow of the earth on the moon during an eclipse; and (3) the shifting of the horizon and the appearance of new stars as one travels north or south. These proofs formulated over 2,000 years ago are as valid now as they were in Aristotle's time, although others have since been added. (See pages 21 and 22.)

Herodotus and other early Greeks observed fossil shells, similar to the shells of organisms living in the sea, imbedded in rocks and correctly concluded that the localities where such remains occur had formerly been covered by the sea. Noting the great amount of silt brought down annually by the Nile, Herodotus aptly remarked, "Egypt is the gift of the river." Aristotle observed to a certain extent the dependence of plants and animals on their physical surroundings. He speculated on the difference in the character of races of man living in different climates and correlated the political forms of communities with their location on a seashore or in natural strongholds. On the other hand, Aristotle erroneously attributed earthquakes to wind within the earth, and volcanic eruptions to the escape of the wind that caused the earthquakes.

Probably the most prominent of the later Grecian contributors to earth science were Strabo and Ptolemy. Strabo traveled widely and made some critical observations. He recognized Vesuvius as a dormant volcano, although there was then no human record of an eruption from that mountain. He correctly described floodplains and deltas as the product of deposition by rivers. In some localities he noted evidence that the land had risen and in others that it had subsided in relation to sea level.

Ptolemy, who lived in Alexandria in the second century, is probably most widely known as the great exponent of the geocentric, or Ptolemaic system, of astronomy. He and others of his day believed that the earth was the center of the universe around which the other heavenly bodies revolved. In spite of this mistaken conception of the relations of the earth to its neighbors, Ptolemy contributed a great deal to the geographical knowledge of the earth itself. In his *Guide to Geography* he concentrated much of the Greek geographical lore, with descriptions and maps of what was then known of the habitable world. Ptolemy's work, preserved during the Middle Ages by the Arabs, strongly influenced Columbus centuries later in undertaking a westward voyage to India. Discoveries made by that and succeeding voyages, however, soon made Ptolemy's larger conceptions of earth relations obsolete.

The study of pure science was not popular with the Romans. They were much more interested in law and order, military power and expansion of the Empire. Some of them speculated on the phenomena of nature, but in most cases their speculations were founded on fancy rather than on carefully observed facts. They, like the Greeks, were prone to ascribe earth features and events to the acts of the gods or other supernatural influences.

In his *Natural History* (77 A.D.) Pliny the Elder gives us a detailed account of man's knowledge and understanding of natural phenomena at that time. According to him: "The nature of all things in this world . . . are here deciphered and declared." This voluminous work is a conglomeration of fact and fancy, of information and misinformation. Of the thirty-seven books in Pliny's *Natural History*, five deal with the mineral kingdom. Here he describes the minerals and other stones that were then known and used. Mingled with his descriptions of their physical properties he makes quaint and fanciful statements as to their origins and their magical and medicinal properties. A few examples will suffice. He says that rock crystal is nothing but frozen water, a very hard variety of ice, which, from its occurrence on high mountains, has become so permanently frozen that it is difficult to melt again. It has special medicinal value in the treatment of open wounds. After correctly stating that amber is hardened gum from certain trees, he goes on to say that a collar of amber beads around the neck of an infant is a preservation against poison as well as against the illusions and frights that drive folks out of their wits. The diamond is correctly described as the hardest of all known things. But hardness is confused with brittleness in the test that he describes. He says that if this stone is placed on an anvil and struck a mighty blow with a hammer, it will not only break the anvil but also cause the hammer to fly to pieces. If, however, the diamond is first steeped in blood freshly drawn from a goat and subjected to this test, it will be shattered.

On the subject of mountains Pliny says nothing of how they were formed, but he tells us why they were made. At the beginning of Book 36 in his *Natural History* we find this statement:

> All things else which we have handled heretofore even to this book may seem in some sort to have been made for man, but as for mountains, Nature framed them for her own self: partly to strengthen (as it were) certain joints within the veins and bowels of the earth; partly to tame the violence of great rivers and to break the force of surging waves and inundations of the sea and in one word by that substance and matter whereof they stand, which of all others is most hard, to restrain and keep within bounds that unruly element of water.

Although in other fields of intellectual effort the Classical period is marked by some of the greatest achievements of the human mind, the contributions of this period to earth science are not impressive. While some observations of value were made by Classical writers, in most instances their conclusions were not based on the patient collection and comparison of facts, but were mere speculations.

During the Dark Ages that followed the collapse of the Roman Empire, earth science made no progress in Christendom. All learning was confined to the church, and the strictly literal interpretation of Scripture led the ecclesiasts to denounce all contrary facts and theories as heretical. Even the scholastic philosophers were apparently not much interested in natural phenomena. Scholars, as well as others, believed that they were moving in a physical world governed not by invariable laws whose actions and results could be known, but in one in which a multitude of mysterious and unknown forces, influences, and virtues was everywhere at work and where anything might happen as a result of their intervention.

The Arabs, however, collected and translated some of the earlier works of the Greeks and Romans; they also contributed ideas of their own, and thus kept the lamp of learning alight during the Dark Ages. Foremost among the Arabs in this respect was Avicenna (979-1037) of Persia. Although known primarily as a great physician, Avicenna, in his *Kitab-al-Shifa,* expressed modern ideas on the origin of rocks, fossils, mountains, and valleys. He stated that the sea has gradually encroached upon the land and then ebbed away many times thus producing the rock strata, layer on top of layer. As additional evidence that the lands had formerly been covered by the sea, he cited the shells of aquatic animals enclosed in the rocks. He further stated that valleys which separate the mountains are formed by the erosion of wind and floods over many ages, and that most mountains are at the present time in the stage of decay and disintegration.

The understanding and interpretation of earth features involves the concept of slow changes over long periods of time. This concept developed slowly. People had observed violent aspects of nature, such as floods, tornadoes, and volcanic eruptions, which produce marked changes in a short period of time. They were inclined to believe that all changes were sudden and violent, that is, that all earth features were formed in a cataclysmic manner. It was not generally realized that a sense of time and patient observation, as well as logical reasoning, are necessary to recognize the nature and the effects of the slow changes.

With the revival of Classical studies in the Renaissance, the problems of earth science once more began to attract attention, especially in Italy and western Europe. Leonardo da Vinci (1452-1519) ridiculed the prevalent notion that fossils were produced by some mysterious influence of the stars. He correctly asserted that they were the remains of plants and animals that had become buried and preserved where they lived and died. Copernicus (1473-1543), by observation of the heavenly bodies with the scanty instrumental means available to him, came to the conclusion that the sun is the center of our system and thus established the Copernican or heliocentric system of astronomy. Apian revived and enlarged the geography of Ptolemy in his *Cosmographicus liber* (1524). Mercator (1512-1594) and other cartographers produced new maps to accommodate the rapidly growing store of facts accumulated by exploration which made Ptolemy's maps obsolete. Galileo (1564-1642) demonstrated that the earth rotates from west to east on its axis. He also invented the thermometer in 1597 and thus contributed greatly to the advancement of meteorology.

During the seventeenth and early part of the eighteenth centuries, progress in earth science was not rapid. Prominent in this period were the cosmogonists, who indulged in fanciful speculation and wildly extravagant theories of the origin of the earth, based mostly on imagination. At the same time, however, some progress was made in the patient accumulation of facts and in logical inferences from those facts. The thinkers and writers of this period were still under great handicaps. Education was limited to a few; printing was on a very small scale; communication of information and ideas between different countries and different parts of the same country was not easy; travel was slow and difficult; and the church still frowned upon unorthodox ideas. Nevertheless, the foundations of earth science were slowly being laid in various parts of Europe. To the growing mass of facts and their arrangement in systematic order based on cause and effect, many investigators made their contributions.

Perhaps the most notable of these men was Nicholas Steno (Stensen) (1631-1687) of Denmark and, later, Florence. He made important contributions to the knowledge of crystal forms and structures and also developed modern ideas on the past history of the earth as revealed in the rocks. For example, he discovered that the angles between similar pairs of faces of quartz crystals are always constant, which indicates that the crystals follow a definite pattern of growth. From his study of fossils and the rocks in which they are preserved, he concluded that large areas of the present lands had formerly been covered by the sea.

Not until about the year 1800, however, had the facts, principles, and methods become trustworthy enough to establish the modern science of geology. The works of James Hutton of Scotland in various phases of physical geology, of Abraham Gottlob Werner of Germany in mineralogy, Jean Baptiste de Lamarck of France in paleontology, and William "Strata" Smith of England in stratigraphy stand out above all others in establishing the principles and methods of modern geology. On the foundations established in western Europe, earth science has had a remarkable development, giving rise to many subdivisions and spreading to all parts of the world.

James Hutton (1726-1797) was educated in law and in medicine, but, on inheriting landed property, he turned to agriculture for a time. In 1768 he retired to Edinburgh and spent the rest of his life in travel, in

Fig. 1-1. James Hutton (1726-1797), usually considered the founder of modern geology. *(Williams and Wilkins Co., Baltimore)*

FIG. 1-2. Abraham Gottlob Werner (1750-1817), pioneer in mineralogy. *(Geological Society of London)*

FIG. 1-3. John Playfair (1748-1819), elucidated the Huttonian Theory of the Earth. *(Geological Society of London)*

observation, in reflection, and in writing on various aspects of the history of the earth. Hutton is generally known as the founder of modern geology. Considerable progress had been made in the classification and description of minerals and rocks before Hutton's time, but he conceived larger ideas. He wanted to trace back to their origins, not only the minerals and rocks, but also the surface features of the earth, such as mountains and valleys. He recognized that many of the present rocks have been formed from the waste materials of older rocks, such waste (sediment) being deposited in the sea and later uplifted. In his observations he recognized that some rock masses have come from deep sources as molten matter that was injected into the overlying rocks and, in some cases, expelled to the surface. Thus he distinguished between sedimentary and igneous rocks. He was convinced by his observations that most of the landscape features of the earth were formed over long periods of time by the slow processes of weathering and erosion. As to the length of time during which present earth processes have been active, Hutton says: "There is no sign of a beginning, no prospect of an end." In 1785 Hutton presented his views on the origins of many earth features to the Royal Society of Edinburgh in a paper entitled *Theory of the Earth, or an Investigation of the Laws Observable in the Composition, Dissolution, and Restoration of Land upon the Globe.*

Although a keen observer and a clear thinker, Hutton was not a lucid writer. Therefore his *Theory of the Earth* was not widely read. Fortunately, John Playfair (1748-1819), a Scottish mathematician and philosopher, was a close friend and frequent traveling companion of Hutton's. He was a lucid writer. In his *Illustrations of the Huttonian Theory of the Earth* (1802) he has clearly stated many of Hutton's views. The most oft-quoted of these is now known as *Playfair's Law*, or the law of accordant stream junctions. In this statement, or law, Playfair gives convincing evidence that most valleys are the results of the work of the streams that flow in them. (See p. 158 for a fuller statement on this point.)

Abraham Gottlob Werner (1750-1817) is often called the "Father of German Geology." Such a designation has little meaning, for "German geology," outside of local conditions, and applications, is the same as geology elsewhere. It would be more appropriate to say that he was the father of mineralogy. The science of geology has universal applications. Werner was a dynamic and an inspiring teacher in the School of Mines at Freiburg, Saxony. He did much to advance the determinative descriptions and the classification of the minerals, and to inspire his students to further observation. He also clearly demonstrated the chronological succession of strata, the younger on top of the older.

Werner did not travel widely and some of his broader theoretical conclusions have been found to be erroneous. He contended that all rocks, including basalt, consist of sediments that were deposited in a universal sea. Hutton had concluded that basalt was solidified from molten matter that rises from depths within the earth. Thus there arose the controversy on the origin of basalt. Those who followed Hutton's belief were called *Plutonists*, and the followers of Werner were termed *Neptunists*.

Leopold von Buch (1774-1853), one of Werner's former students, did much to decide the controversy on the origin of basalt in favor of the Plutonists. In his travels to volcanic regions, active and extinct, he became convinced of the igneous origin of basalt. Von Buch was also a forerunner of Louis Agassiz on the idea of former glaciation, for he recognized that many of the erratic boulders on the north German plain had come from Scandinavia.

Jean Baptiste de Lamarck (1744-1829), a native of Picardy, France, is generally recognized as the "Father of Invertebrate Paleontology." His *Histoire naturelle des animaux sans vertebres*, published in several volumes from 1815 to 1822, gives the results of his meticulous investigations of invertebrate animals, both living and fossil. Lamarck expounded the belief that animal species are not permanently fixed, or unalterable, and that more complex forms have developed from simpler ancestors. In this view of life development he was a forerunner of Darwin. Lamarck went further and stated the cause for changes in organisms. He said that new structures and new organs are developed because of want, or need, to survive in a changed environment, and that atrophy, or loss of function, results from the lack of need and, therefore, the lack of use. He also states his belief that changes which have been acquired by an individual in its lifetime are transmitted to the offspring. The veracity of this theory is still a subject of debate.

George Cuvier (1769-1832), of France, is regarded as the "Father of Vertebrate Paleontology." Cuvier followed soon after Lamarck and gave most of his attention to the vertebrates. While professor of natural history in the Collège de France he published in 1800 his *Leçons d' anatomie comparée*, a classical work in five volumes. In his *Regne animal disbritrie d'après son organisation* (5 vols., 1829-30) he includes the main results of his studies of living and fossil animals. In his larger generalities Cuvier was inclined toward the belief in catastrophism rather than uniformitarianism, probably because his collections of fossils were not complete enough. He favored the idea that the succession of different animals in time was due to successive creations rather than to the slow processes of evolution.

William (Strata) Smith (1769-1839) is generally known as the "Father of English Geology," but it would be more appropriate to name him as the "Father of Modern Stratigraphy." Smith was a surveyor, or civil engineer. In the course of his work in the fossiliferous strata of England

FIG. 1-4. Christian Leopold von Buch (1774-1853). Foremost among the early German geologists in recognizing the igneous origin of basalt. Forerunner of Louis Agassiz in recognizing the evidences of former continental glaciation of northern middle latitudes. *(Williams and Wilkins Co., Baltimore)*

FIG. 1-5. Jean Baptiste de Lamarck (1744-1829), father of invertebrate paleontology. *(American Museum of Natural History)*

FIG. 1-6. William "Strata" Smith (1769-1839), discoverer of the basic laws of stratigraphy. *(Geological Society of London)*

he learned that the different formations could be identified by the types of fossils that they contain. Over the years since then this idea has been tested in many different localities and with strata of different ages; and it is found to be true. Thus the principle that strata of different ages contain different assemblages of fossils has become one of the main bases for dating the relative ages of the strata in the crust of the earth. Smith collected and labeled many fossils and indicated the rock formation in which each was found. With this information, supplemented by other observations, he constructed the first geological map of England, Wales, and part of Scotland.

In the first comprehensive textbooks of geology in the English language Charles Lyell of Britain (1797-1875) did much to establish the science of geology along the lines of Hutton's earlier thinking. His *Principles of Geology* (3 vols., 1830-33) is considered one of the great books of the world. It went through 12 editions from 1830 to 1876. This classic of geology may still be read with profit. In addition to establishing many of the principles of geology, he gives a rather complete history of the development of the science during that interval. Lyell was a great champion of the doctrine of uniformitarianism, that the present earth features can best be explained as the result of present processes acting over a long period of time. He and Charles Darwin were contemporaneous for many years, with frequent exchanges of thought, and each was strongly influenced by the other. Lyell was knighted for his outstanding work in developing a new science.

The theory of evolution, as worked out by Charles Darwin (1809-1882) and others has become one of the great unifying principles in earth science. Darwin's concept of the development of the earth throughout long geological periods, the realization that both the organic and inorganic constituents of the world are constantly changing in accordance with definite laws of nature, the interrelations and interdependence of the various aspects of the earth, and the intimate relations between life and its physical environment is justly called the grandest generalization of the nineteenth century.

Darwin lived long enough for his greatness to be recognized by his contemporaries, and he was buried in Westminster Abbey. In an autobiographical chapter of *Life and Letters* (edited by his son, Francis Darwin, London, 1887) Darwin said that his success was chiefly due to "the love of science, unbounding patience in long reflecting over any subject, industry in observing and collecting facts, and a fair share of invention as well as of common sense." He also says: "I have steadily endeavoured to keep my mind free so as to give up any hypothesis, however much beloved, as soon as facts are shown to be opposed to it." These statements by Darwin well represent the attitude and the creed of any student of nature.

FIG. 1-7. Sir Charles Lyell (1797-1875). A champion of uniformatarianism as opposed to catastrophism. His writings did much to advance the young science of geology. *(Geological Society of London)*

FIG. 1-8. Charles Darwin (1809-1882), foremost in establishing the principle of evolution. *(American Museum of Natural History)*

FIG. 1-9. John Wesley Powell (1834-1902), Director of the U. S. Geological Survey from 1881 to 1894. Pioneer in the geological and geographical exploration of Western United States. Without benefit of his right arm, which he lost in the Battle of Shiloh, Powell led a boat journey through the Grand Canyon in 1869. His report of his observations on this journey, in addition to his other observations in the surrounding territories, establishes him as a great American geologist. *(Columbia University Department of Geology)*

Another of Darwin's interesting and instructive comments may be cited. In recounting one of his fossil collecting trips to Wales with Adam Sedgwick he says: "We tend to see only what we know." He goes on to say that glacial phenomena, such as erratic boulders, glacial striae, and grooves were abundant in the region; but neither he nor Sedgwick made any note of them. Louis Agassiz had not yet expounded his belief that temperate latitudes had formerly been glaciated. This incident illustrates the difficulty which the mind must overcome in order to recognize evidence that requires new concepts and new explanations for phenomena that are all around us.

By the nature of the subject the science of the earth is not an abstract science. In addition to its practical (economic) value it has philosophic dignity; it has poetic significance; it deals not only with the physical world, but also with the development of life. Those who espouse this study soon find themselves imbued with an inexorable urge to wander

> Into regions yet untrod;
> And read what is still unread
> In the manuscripts of God.

The principal divisions of earth science are listed in Appendix A. It is beyond the scope of this book to trace the development of each of these branches. In later chapters some of the outstanding leaders are mentioned at appropriate places.

As one delves more deeply into any branch of earth science he finds connections with other branches; also, he finds connections with other sciences that are not designated as earth sciences. The established fields of geophysics and geochemistry well illustrate the interrelationships of the various sciences. It seems that the distinctions and separations of the various categorized sciences that deal with natural phenomena are artificial and arbitrary, for nature has no such categories.

Suggestions for Further Reading

ADAMS, Frank Dawson, *The Birth and Development of the Geological Sciences* (Baltimore, Williams and Wilkins, 1938).

CLOOS, HANS, *Conversation with the Earth* (New York, Knopf, 1953).

FENTON, Carroll Lane, and FENTON, Mildred Adams, *The Story of the Great Geologists* (New York, Doubleday, 1945).

GEIKIE, Sir Archibald, *The Founders of Geology* (New York, Macmillan, 1905).

LYELL, Charles, *Principles of Geology* (London, 1876).

MATHER, K. F., and MASON, Shirley L., *Source Book in Geology* (New York, McGraw-Hill, 1939).

MERRILL, George P., *The First One Hundred Years of American Geology* (New Haven, Yale University Press, 1924).

PLAYFAIR, John, *Illustrations of the Huttonian Theory of the Earth* (Edinburgh, 1802). Facsimile Reprint, with an introduction by George W. White (Urbana, University of Illinois Press, 1956).

VON ZITTEL, Karl, *Geschichte der Geologie und Paleontologie* (Munich and Leipzig, 1899).

——— 2 ———

The Earth as a Planet

THE SOLAR SYSTEM

THE SOLAR SYSTEM, the only planetary system known to us at present, consists of the sun, which is one of the many stars, and all the bodies that revolve around it. Most of the mass of the solar system is concentrated in the sun; its diameter is 864,000 miles, and it has a density about one and a half times that of water. Its surface temperature is approximately 6000°C., and the temperature at the center is estimated to be about 50,000,000°. Because it is so much nearer to the earth than are the other stars, being distant only 93,000,000 miles on the average, it appears to us, not as a pinpoint of light, but as a fiery ball in the sky. From this glowing mass, energy is radiated in all directions into space. The small portion of this radiant energy which is intercepted by the earth provides our planet with the necessary light and heat to sustain life, raises the moisture that falls as rain and snow, sets the winds in motion, and thus impels the various processes of erosion.

The source of the sun's heat (and light) has been a subject of controversy. Some have contended that the heat is generated by atomic disintegration, such as the disintegration of heavy radioactive elements into lighter and simpler ones. Others have proposed that the building up of more complex atoms from simpler ones is the most probable cause of the sun's radiant energy. Based on recently acquired knowledge of nuclear physics, the latter process, that is, the building up of more complex atoms from simpler ones, is the more favored explanation.

According to this view the sun, and other stars, originated as masses of hydrogen, the simplest element, and have grown by gravitational accumulation from the cosmic cloud in which they were born. As the mass of each star grows the temperature in the interior increases. At a temperature of 5,000,000° four atoms of hydrogen combine to form an atom of helium. The conversion of the light hydrogen into the heavier

16

helium causes shrinkage of the volume and further rise in temperature. At a temperature of 150,000,000° three atoms of helium combine to form one atom of carbon. Combinations of helium with the carbon produce other elements.

These atomic combinations are now going on as they have in the past. Each star has its amount of fuel to use, depending on its mass. The greater the mass the more the heat in the interior, the faster the processes of atomic combination, and the greater the amount of radiant energy; also, the shorter its life, for a star is dead when its fuel is consumed and the atomic processes cease.

Compared with other stars, our sun is of less than average mass. It is burning its fuel at a modest rate. On the basis of color, temperature, and mass, astronomers tell us that our sun is approximately half way in its stellar evolution. It is now in the midst of the process of converting hydrogen to helium. This process has been going on for six billion years and will continue for another six billion, with a slight rise in temperature. The carbon stage following is supposed to be much shorter and to be accompanied by a great expansion of the diameter of the sun and an increase in radiation to the extent that it will prohibit life on the earth. After the exhaustion of its supply of hydrogen and helium the sun will slowly decline in brightness and eventually will die.

Nine known planets, of which the earth is one, revolve around the sun. Some of the planets, like Jupiter, are much larger than the earth; some, like Mercury, are smaller. Two, Mercury and Venus, are nearer to the sun than the earth; the others are farther away. The largest planet, Jupiter, comes in the middle of the sequence. All the planets revolve around the sun in a nearly common plane which is slightly inclined to the sun's equator, in a period of revolution that increases with distance from the sun. The planets are all of similar form—oblate spheroid—and probably of similar composition; all are rotating at different speeds about axes inclined at various angles to the plane in which they are revolving; and all but Mercury and Venus and probably Pluto have satellites corresponding to our moon.

In addition to the planets and their satellites, the solar system includes several hundred asteroids or planetoids, bodies apparently similar in behavior to the planets but much smaller, that occupy positions between the orbits of Mars and Jupiter. There are also some periodic comets which revolve around the sun in highly eccentric orbits. Numerous meteors and smaller particles called planetesimals, or cosmic dust, complete the list of known bodies in the solar system.

When they enter our atmosphere and are heated to incandescence by friction, meteors are commonly called shooting stars. Most of them are consumed and dissipated in the air, but some reach the ground in the

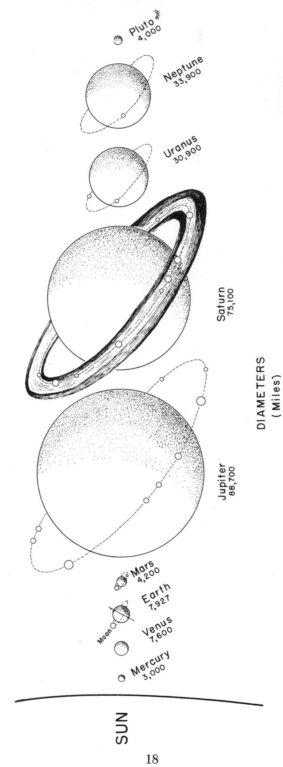

FIG. 2-1. The relative sizes of the nine planets in the solar system. The arc of the sun is drawn on the same scale as that of the planets.

18

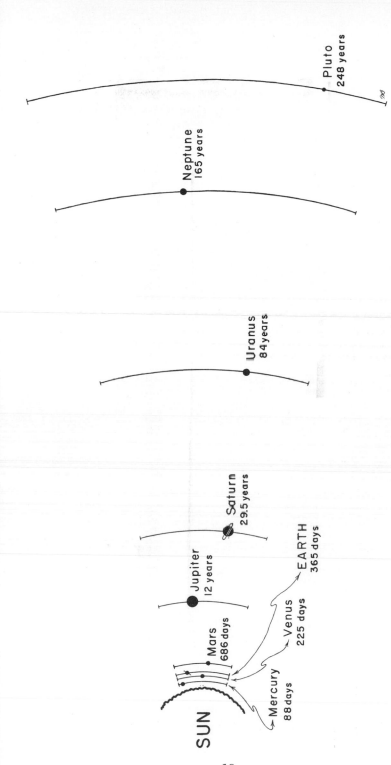

FIG. 2.2. Periods of revolution of the planets in the solar system. Distances from sun are roughly to scale.

solid state. These are known as meteorites, and range in size from small pellets up to masses of several tons. Some consist of stony matter, others are mainly iron and nickel. Large quantities of cosmic dust, calculated at several thousand tons annually, also fall through the earth's atmosphere. Thus the earth is still growing by the accretion, or infalling, of matter from without. These samples of cosmic matter may be the scattered fragments left over from the creation of our solar system and so give a clue to the probable composition of the earth's interior.

At an average distance of 240,000 miles the earth's satellite, the moon, revolves around the earth in a period of about 28 days. The moon's period of rotation is the same as that of its revolution; thus we always see only one and the same half of its surface. Because of its small mass (about one-eightieth that of the earth) the moon can retain neither an atmosphere nor a hydrosphere. It gives us only reflected light and a negligible quantity of heat.

The earth is a very insignificant fraction of the solar system and the solar system itself but an insignificant fraction of the universe. The

FIG. 2-3. Ahnighto—A large Cape York meteorite. *(American Museum of Natural History)*

sun is a modest star in a stellar system whose members are numbered in billions. Beyond our stellar system, or galaxy, are the galaxies which are other systems comparable to ours in size and number of stars. Thus, from the astronomical viewpoint, the earth is indeed small, unimportant and insignificant—except to us.

Table of Facts Concerning the Sun and Planets

Planets	Mean Distance from Sun, millions of miles	Period of Revolution	Rotation Period	Equatorial Diameter, miles	Density (water=1)
SUN			24.5 days (at equator)	864,000	1.41
MERCURY	36.0	87.96 days	88 days	3,000	3.73
VENUS	67.2	224.70 "	?	7,600	5.21
EARTH	92.9	365.25 "	23 hrs. 56 min.	7,927	5.52
MARS	141.5	1.88 yrs.	24 " 37 "	4,200	3.95
JUPITER	483.3	11.86 "	9 " 56 "	88,700	1.34
SATURN	886.1	29.45 "	10 " 38 "	75,100	0.69
URANUS	1,782.8	84.01 "	10 " 42 "	30,900	1.36
NEPTUNE	2,793.5	164.78 "	15 " 42 "	33,900	1.30
PLUTO	3,673.0	248.0 "	?	4,000	? 4.30

FORM, SIZE, AND DENSITY OF THE EARTH

The form of the earth is an oblate spheroid. This means it is not a perfect sphere, but is slightly flattened at the ends of its axis and bulged along the Equator by the centrifugal force of rotation. Proofs of the spherical form of the earth given by Aristotle long ago are: (1) the tendency of matter to fall together toward a common center; (2) the circular shadow of the earth on the moon during an eclipse; and (3) the shifting of the horizon and the appearance of new stars as one travels from north to south. To these ancient proofs we may add: (4) the weight of a body is very nearly the same at all places on the earth's surface. Since the same body grows heavier as it approaches the center of the earth, this could not be the case if the earth were not nearly spherical. (5) The curvature of the earth may be actually seen on high air photographs and by observing ships at sea, and the amount of curvature can be measured by sighting at targets of equal height placed in line along the seashore. (6) Finally, the earth has been circumnavigated in many directions, and the uniform length of the circumference in these various directions is characteristic only of a spherical body.

The circumference of the earth is almost 25,000 miles, and its diameter about 8,000 miles. Because the earth is not a perfect sphere, its diameter varies from about 7,900 miles through the poles to about 7,927 miles through the Equator. Its surface area is nearly 197 million square miles, almost three-fourths of which is water.

The mass or weight of the earth is found by comparing its gravitational attraction on a small sphere at the surface with that of a large sphere of known mass on the same small sphere. In this manner it is found that the mass of the earth as a whole is 5.52 times as much as a body of water with a volume or size equal to that of the earth. Thus the relative weight or average density of the earth is 5.52. By weighing thousands of samples of rocks it is found that the surface materials have an average density of 2.7. Assuming a uniform rate of increase inward, the material at the center must be about 11 times as heavy as water.

EARTH MOTIONS AND THEIR RESULTS

Rotation. The earth rotates on its shortest diameter, called its axis, and revolves around the sun. Both these motions were recognized by Copernicus in 1543. Later, Galileo demonstrated that the earth rotates from west to east. He discovered that objects falling through the air always fell a little to the east of a point directly below that from which they were dropped. At the Leaning Tower of Pisa, for example, the rotation of the earth, Galileo reasoned, causes an object at the top of the tower to move faster than one at its base. The proof of the earth's rotation by Foucault's pendulum was first carried out in 1851 by a heavy weight suspended from the dome of the Pantheon in Paris. Once set in motion, a pendulum will continue to swing in the same plane. Except at the Equator, a line on the floor parallel to the plane of a vibrating pendulum will gradually swing around to a position at right angles and continue on around until it is again parallel to the vibrating plane. The pendulum appears to change its plane of vibration. Actually, the building turns around the pendulum as the earth rotates.

Perhaps the most obvious result of the earth's rotation is the alternation of daylight and darkness. In most places this succession affords convenient intervals for man to work and rest. As the earth rotates from west to east, sunrise and high noon move from east to west; thus, solar time varies in an east-west direction. In order to avoid the many difficulties that would result from keeping solar time, the earth has been divided into 24 standard time zones, each comprising 15° of the earth's circumference. Throughout each zone, clock time is taken from solar time at a central meridian. In passing from one zone to the next the traveler must set his watch back one hour if traveling westward, and forward one hour if traveling eastward. Because of the preference of the inhabitants and for the convenience of railroad terminals the boundaries between the time zones are irregular in many places.

Rotation also causes the deflection of winds, currents and other moving bodies on the earth's surface to the right (clockwise) in the Northern Hemisphere and to the left (counterclockwise) in the Southern Hemisphere. This principle, called Ferrel's Law, will be discussed further in connection with winds and ocean currents.

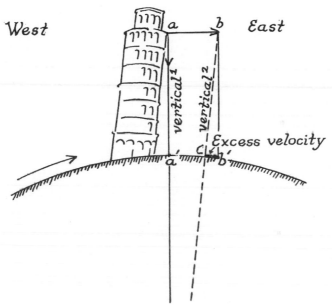

FIG. 2-4. Illustration of Galileo's demonstration at the Tower of Pisa. Because of the earth's rotation, the falling object, deflected to the east, will land at b' rather than at the point a' directly above which it was dropped.

The tides of the ocean and seas, although generated by the gravitational pull of the moon and sun on the earth, owe their westward direction of travel and regularity of occurrence to the rotation of the earth and the revolution of the moon around the earth. The moon's gravitation is able to distort the surface of the ocean into a slightly elliptical form, with the long axis parallel to the direction of pull. As the direction of the moon's force keeps changing, because of the earth's rotation as well as the moon's own revolution around the earth, the

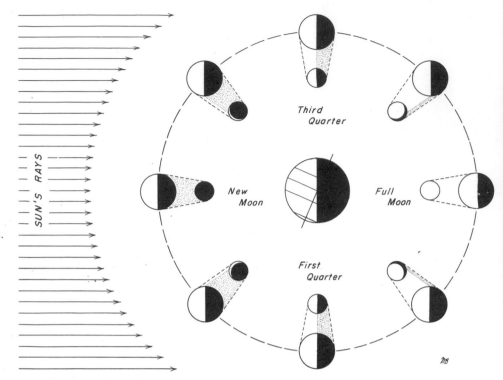

FIG. 2-5. Phases of the moon. From the outer ring of drawings it can be seen that one-half of the moon is always directly illuminated by the sun; the inner ring shows the portion of the moon made visible, by reflected light, to an observer on earth.

tides follow the moon in its passage through the heavens. The tidal forces of the sun and moon not only displace the water on the surface, but also cause strains in the solid earth and pull it somewhat out of shape. A fuller discussion of tides is given in Chapter 16.

Revolution and Inclination of the Axis. The earth revolves around the sun in a fixed path, or orbit, which is slightly elliptical, so that the distance of the earth from the sun varies during the year from 91,500,000 miles in the early part of the winter of the Northern Hemisphere to 94,500,000 miles in the early part of the summer. The period of this revolution, a little more than 365 days, determines the length of the year.

The succession of seasons also depends, in part, on the earth's revolution around the sun. If the earth's axis were perpendicular to the plane of its orbit there would be no seasons. But the axis on which the earth rotates is inclined, or tilted, 23½° from the perpendicular, that is, 66½° from the plane of the orbit. Thus, as the earth travels around the sun, the vertical rays of the sun migrate from 23½° south to 23½° north of the Equator. The warm season, with its long days and short nights, and the cold season, with its short days and long nights, occur alter-

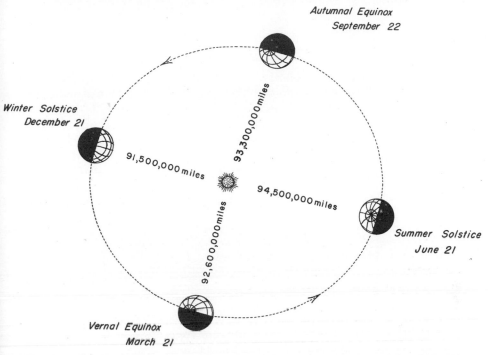

FIG. 2-6. Seasons of the year. This plan view of the earth in its orbit illustrates the annual northward and southward migration of the sun's vertical rays. Note especially the position of the North Pole in the circle of illumination.

nately in the Southern and Northern hemispheres. Near the Equator, where the noonday sun is never far from the zenith, the difference in temperature from season to season is not great.

LATITUDE AND LONGITUDE

Latitude. A circle around the earth which bisects the distance between the North and South poles is called the Equator; circles parallel to the Equator are parallels. The length of these parallels becomes shorter from the Equator toward the poles. Distance north or south of the Equator is called latitude, and is expressed in terms of degrees, the Equator being latitude 0°, the poles 90° north and south. The Tropic of Cancer—23½°N., the Tropic of Capricorn—23½°S., the Arctic Circle—66½°N., and the Antarctic Circle—66½°S., are definitely related to the inclination of the earth's axis. Vertical rays of the sun migrate between the Tropic of Cancer, at the time of the June solstice, and the Tropic of Capricorn, at the time of the December solstice, as the earth revolves on its inclined axis around the sun. North of the Tropic of Cancer and south of the Tropic of Capricorn the sun's rays are never vertical. The parallels just touched by the circle of illumination at the time of the solstices are

25

the polar circles. Inside the Arctic and Antarctic circles the sun's rays are always at a low angle, and the length of the longest day and longest night varies from 24 hours at the circles to 6 months at the poles.

Longitude. North-south lines on the earth's surface perpendicular to the Equator and converging at the poles are called meridians. Position on a parallel is denoted by means of the meridians which cross it. The meridian which passes through Greenwich, England, where the British Royal Observatory was established in 1675, is usually chosen as that meridian from which distances east and west are reckoned, and is called the prime or zero meridian. Distance east or west of this prime meridian is known as longitude and is measured from 0° to 180°.

Although latitude and longitude are angular distances they can be readily converted into distances in miles provided the size of the globe is known; and, conversely, the size of the globe can be calculated if the length of a degree of latitude is known. The length of a degree of latitude is everywhere about 69 miles. Near the Equator it is slightly less and near the poles slightly more because of polar flattening. A degree of longitude has about the same length as a degree of latitude at the Equator, but decreases steadily until it becomes nothing at the poles, where the meridians meet. The poles are the only places which have latitude but no longitude. At the North Pole the only direction is south, and at the South Pole the only direction is north.

International Date Line. On a journey around the world the time changes 24 hours, and the traveler loses a day if he travels with the sun and gains a day if he travels in the opposite direction. On returning to Seville after their trip around the world, Magellan's men were puzzled by the fact that they had lost a day. Of course, the round-the-world traveler does not really live 24 hours more or less; in traveling eastward his days are shortened, one hour for each 15°, and his watch must be set ahead. When the traveler gets back to his starting point his reckoning will be one day ahead of that of the people who stayed at home; he must, therefore, set his calendar back and repeat a day. Whichever way one travels around the world the date must be changed somewhere. The most convenient place to do this is at the 180th meridian, which lies near the middle of the Pacific Ocean and which comparatively few people cross. This meridian, with some modifications to include the Aleutian Islands with Alaska and the Fiji and Chatham Islands with New Zealand, has become the International Date Line.

Location. Wherever one may be, the number of degrees from the zenith to the noonday sun is equal to the number of degrees of latitude between the observer's position and that part of the earth where the sun's rays are then vertical. The position of the sun for each day in the year has been calculated and is given in the *Nautical Almanac*, which is carried by mariners and explorers. Thus the latitude may be determined

by measuring with a sextant the number of degrees in the angle between the noonday sun and the zenith of the observer, and adding or
subtracting the number of degrees by which the sun is north or south
of the Equator. If an observer notes that the noonday sun is 20°
south of his zenith on June 21, his latitude is 20° plus 23½°, or
43½° North. Latitude may also be obtained by instrumental observation
upon the North Star and other stars.

Longitude is determined by comparing local time with Greenwich
time which is kept on ships by accurate marine clocks called chronom-
eters. Before the perfection of the chronometer (about 1760) navigators
were uncertain as to their longitudinal position. Since any place on the
earth's surface rotates through 15° in one hour, there is a difference of
15° of longitude for every hour of difference between local time and
Greenwich time. If local noon occurs when the chronometer reads 2 P.M.
the observer is 30° west of the Greenwich meridian. Any point on the
earth's surface may be located accurately by determining that it lies at
the intersection of a certain parallel with a certain meridian.

TERRESTRIAL MAGNETISM

The earth is a great magnet. Like other magnets it has two poles.
These magnetic poles do not coincide with the rotational or true North
and South poles. According to observations by Amundsen from 1903
to 1906 the North Magnetic Pole was in latitude 71°N. and longitude
96°W.; from data obtained on the *Discovery* the South Magnetic Pole
was latitude 72° 50'S. and longitude 156° 20'E. The positions of the magnetic poles shift a little from year to year, but the change is not known
to be great.

Since one end of a magnetic needle points to the North Magnetic
Pole, there are many places where the compass does not indicate true
north and south. The departure of the magnetic needle from true north
and south is the magnetic declination. As the locations of the magnetic
poles shift slightly, the declination of a given place does not remain
quite constant. If the compass is to be used for determining directions
accurately, it is necessary to know the magnetic declination of a region.
The declination being known, the compass is of great value to surveyors,
explorers, navigators, and others. Indeed, before its invention men could
not venture out of sight of land in ships with confidence of being able
to return.

Aurora and Magnetic Storms. The Aurora Borealis, or Northern
Lights, and the similar phenomenon in the Southern Hemisphere, the
Aurora Australis, are thought to be in some way related to terrestrial
magnetism. Brilliant displays of auroras occur at the same time as
magnetic storms, which disturb, and sometimes put out of commission

FIG. 2-7. Aurora Borealis, as seen from Alaska. *(American Museum of Natural History)*

for hours, telegraph, cable, and radio communication. A clue to the origin of the aurora has been suggested by information gained from the artificial satellites, rockets, and lunar probes launched during the International Geophysical Year. The phenomenon has been attributed to the superheating of the upper atmosphere above the Arctic and Antarctic polar zones by countless collisions of charged solar particles with the atoms and molecules of the earth's atmosphere. The particles emitted by the sun are attracted by the earth's magnetic field and are funneled toward the polar regions. The position of the earth's geomagnetic axis in relation to the sun is most favorable for attracting the solar particles during the spring and fall equinoxes and it is during these periods that auroral displays are most common.[1]

[1] Robert Jastrow: "Artificial Satellites and the Earth's Atmosphere" in *Scientific American*, August, 1959.

Suggestions for Further Reading

SANDAGE, *Allan*, "Birth and Death of a Star," *American Journal of Physics*, Vol. 25, No. 8, Nov. 1957.

WHIPPLE, Fred L., *Earth, Moon and Planets* (Philadelphia and Toronto, Blakiston, 1946).

The Planet Earth, A Scientific American Book (New York, Simon and Schuster, 1957).

— 3 —

Origin and Age of the Earth

ORIGIN OF THE EARTH

$\mathbf{F}$ROM TIME IMMEMORIAL, man has speculated as to the origin of the earth. Although early explanations were mainly poetic or fanciful, in the last century or two the problem has been attacked in a scientific way. But the obstacles to its solution are many. The time of origin was long ago, and the record is obscure and difficult to interpret. The earth is one of a family of planets in the solar system; and any explanation of its origin should also account for the other planets. In the present state of our knowledge we cannot be entirely certain that any one of the current hypotheses is correct. All that can be done is to outline a scheme that will best conform to the conditions and laws of nature as we know them. With the increase of knowledge, old hypotheses may be discarded as unsatisfactory and new ones devised. The principal modern hypotheses agree that the sun is the mother of the planets.

The Nebular Hypothesis. The Nebular, or "Ring," or "Hot Earth," Hypothesis of Laplace, formulated near the end of the eighteenth century, assumed that the sun and all other members of the solar system once composed a rotating, glowing-hot gaseous mass, discoid in shape, and somewhat larger than the present orbit of Pluto. Cooling caused shrinking, shrinking quickened rotation, and rotation bulged the equatorial part of the nebular mass until the main body of the rotating gases shrank away from the equatorial bulge, leaving it outside as a ring. Once separated, the ring disintegrated and its materials coalesced into a sphere, making a planet. Thus the nine planets were formed from nine successive rings, the outermost (Pluto) being the first and the earth seventh. The sun is the remainder of the original mass and still a hot

30

FIG. 3-1. Pierre Simon, Marquis de Laplace (1749-1827), mathematician and astronomer who developed the Nebular (Ring) Hypothesis of the origin of the earth. *(University Society, New York City)*

FIG 3-2. Thomas Chrowder Chamberlin (1843-1928), American geologist who, with Moulton, formulated the Planetesimal Hypothesis of the origin of the earth. *(Geological Society of America)*

FIG. 3-3. Chamberlin and Moulton's conception of the disrupted sun from which the solar system was formed. *(American Museum of Natural History)*

rotating body that may give birth to additional planets. In turn, some of the planets imitated the parent body and developed rings which became satellites. According to Laplace, the earth at its beginning was a ring of hot gas which became a spheroidal body and later gave birth to the moon. By cooling, the greater part of the original gases of the earth have become liquid or solid, forming the hydrosphere and the lithosphere, respectively, while the atmosphere consists of uncondensed original gases. Further cooling will condense and finally solidify the remaining gases.

For more than a hundred years this hypothesis was accepted, but progress in the knowledge of earth history, astronomy, and physics has raised strong arguments against it. If the earth has been cooling since its origin and will continue to cool until there is complete solidification of all its liquid and gaseous material, geological evidences of past climates should show uniform cooling. But, on the contrary, known data indicate the occurrence of widespread glacial periods alternating with widespread warm periods since early geological time. The interior heat of the earth, which under the Nebular Hypothesis is considered original heat, can be satisfactorily explained as resulting from processes of radioactivity and chemical reorganization at present going on within the earth. Furthermore, physicists and astronomers now believe it highly improbable that intermittent planetary rings would separate from the rotating parent mass. Had the centrifugal force of rotation become stronger than gravity, the gaseous matter would more probably have been thrown off particle by particle in a continuous stream; and even if such rings were to form, it cannot be demonstrated how they would coalesce into globular planets. Also, the retrograde motion, that is, revolution in the direction opposite to that in which their planets rotate, of two of the satellites of Jupiter and one of those of Saturn is not in accordance with this hypothesis. These and other objections have caused the Nebular Hypothesis to lose favor among most scientists.

The Planetesimal Hypothesis. Early in the present century Chamberlin, a geologist, and Moulton, an astronomer, both of the University of Chicago, formulated the Planetesimal, or "Cold Earth," Hypothesis. According to this hypothesis the substance of the planets was torn from the sun in a series of bolts by the tidal pull of a passing larger star acting in conjunction with explosive forces within the sun. Some of the bolts left the sun from the side facing the passing star and others from the opposite side. On leaving the sun the expelled matter cooled rapidly and much of it condensed into solid particles called planetesimals. After cooling each bolt consisted of a solid nucleus, or else a nuclear swarm of planetesimals, surrounded by more scattered solid particles and cool gases. The gravitational pull of the passing star twisted the series of bolts into two spiral arms extending from the sun and started the whole solar system revolving, each separate particle in its own orbit. The sun with its surrounding spires of planetesimals thus had the appearance of a spiral nebula.

The planets, their satellites, and the asteroids have grown by the accretion of the planetesimals around the nuclei, or denser portions of the spirals. Intersection of the orbits, causing collisions of the particles, is believed to have been the main cause of growth. At first, when the amount of scattered material was great, the growth of the nuclei was probably rapid, but as the surrounding material grew scarcer accretion became increasingly slow. The larger nuclei resulted in the planets, while the smaller ones formed the satellites and asteroids.

After it was pulled from the sun, the earth material cooled rapidly. This hypothesis, in fact, does not find it necessary to assume that the earth as a whole was ever in a molten condition. Heat was and still is being developed, by the friction of impact of incoming material, by compression, and by chemical reorganization and radioactivity in the interior. When heat becomes excessive molten pockets form and are forced outward in volcanic action. The atmosphere has grown with the rest of the earth by the attraction of outside tenuous matter and by the volcanic expulsion of gases from the interior. The hydrosphere has developed largely by the condensation of erupted water vapor.

Among the objections to the Planetesimal Hypothesis is the evidence that the earth has passed through a molten stage. It seems likely that the earth has a heavy metallic core surrounded by more or less concentric layers of less and less dense material. This zonal arrangement according to density would be a natural result in the cooling of molten matter, but is difficult to explain on the assumption that the earth remained solid throughout its growth. Another objection to the Cold Earth Hypothesis is the fact that the densities of the major planets are so low as to indicate that they are largely gaseous. Furthermore, it now seems that the eruptive force of the sun is not powerful enough to eject material effectively in the form of bolts.

Although serious arguments such as those above have been brought against the Planetesimal Hypothesis, it is to many people today the most acceptable explanation of the earth's origin. Among the important points in its favor is the fact that most of the processes on which it is based, such as the accretion of meteors and cosmic dust to the earth, the generation of heat by radioactivity, and the eruption of liquids and gases from the interior, can now be observed in operation, though presumably at a slower rate than in the past.

Stages of Growth under the Planetesimal Hypothesis. Nuclear stage. According to the Planetesimal Hypothesis the earth material solidified soon after separation from the parent sun, and the earth grew to its present size by the accumulation of planetesimals around a nucleus.

The nuclear stage started, it is believed, with the condensation and solidification into a solid earth core of a portion of the disrupted gaseous matter containing a large proportion of heavy metallic elements, such as iron and nickel.

Initial volcanic stage. As the earth grew, the compression of gravity and the decomposition of radioactive substances developed high temperatures in the central parts. This heat crept outward and reached rocks at pressures low enough to permit liquefaction. With the movement of the molten matter outward and to the surface, volcanic processes were inaugurated.

Initial atmospheric stage. The initial nucleus of the earth was probably too small to hold an atmosphere, but as it became larger, its increased gravitation enabled it to attract gaseous molecules. Some of these molecules were probably gathered in like other planetesimals; others may have been liberated by the heat of impact as the solid planetesimals struck the earth; but probably the greatest quantities of gases were erupted from volcanoes, which are still contributing additions to the atmosphere.

Initial hydrospheric stage. When the earth had attained sufficient size, water vapor, the source of which was the same as that of the other atmospheric gases, accumulated in the atmosphere. When the saturation point was reached, the water vapor, condensed to liquid moisture, was precipitated and initiated the hydrosphere. The growth of the hydrosphere, like that of the atmosphere, has resulted mainly from volcanic action and still continues.

Initial life stage. After partial development of the atmosphere and the hydrosphere, conditions on the growing earth became suitable for the existence of life. How life actually started on the globe is not known, but it might be assumed that its inception in simple form took place as soon as physical conditions on the earth were favorable.

The Gaseous Hypothesis. The Gaseous or Tidal Hypothesis was developed in 1919 by two British scientists, Jeans and Jeffreys. Like the Planetesimal Hypothesis, the Gaseous Hypothesis postulates the disruption of the sun by a passing star and the formation of the planets from the disrupted material.

Important points in which the scheme proposed by Jeans and Jeffreys differs from that of Chamberlin and Moulton are: (1) No importance is assigned to the explosive forces of the sun in ejecting material. (2) The material disrupted from the sun was pulled out by the passing star in a long spindle-shaped body of hot gas, called a filament. (3) The filament rapidly became segmented and its parts were shaped into spheres (planets). (4) The earth maintained the hot gaseous state for a considerable time, gradually cooling through a molten stage to a solid lithosphere. (5) The atmosphere and the hydrosphere consist largely of primordial matter not yet consolidated. (6) The satellites were formed by tidal disruption of the planets in the same manner as the sun was disrupted by another star.

Stages of Growth under the Gaseous Hypothesis. According to this hypothesis the earth in its first stage was a gaseous, hot and self-luminous mass which cooled gradually through a rather long molten stage to a solid lithosphere. During the molten stage the materials became more or less zonally arranged according to density. On cooling to approximately the present temperature, the ordinary processes of weathering, erosion, and rock formation began, life originated and geological time was inaugurated.

The Dust Cloud Hypothesis. Among the more recent hypotheses of earth origin the Dust Cloud Hypothesis has received considerable attention. In the volume titled *Nuclear Geology,* listed at the end of this chapter H. C. Urey has modified and extended this hypothesis. In this view the sun and other stars originated from the accumulation of the widely dispersed material in cosmic dust clouds. The earth and the other planets originated from such dust clouds by some process incidental to the formation of the sun. In this hypothesis the planets were not torn from the sun by violent tidal or explosive forces. Instead, they represent the local accumulation of cosmic matter that was not drawn completely into the sun. Also, the satellites represent still more local accumulations that have not been captured by the planets.

It should be noted that the foregoing accounts of the origin and early history, or stages of *growth* of the earth are more or less hypothetical because the record of those times is extremely obscure. The record of the earth's later history, or stages of *maturity* is, of course, better preserved and fairly well known in broad outline. Some parts of this later history can even be read in considerable detail, and more data are being constantly added.

AGE OF THE EARTH

Most of the early speculations on the age of the earth were purely imaginative and of little scientific value. The growth of the physical sciences after the Renaissance provided means for a scientific attack on the problem. Even then, there were strong deterrents to scientific investigation. For example, Archbishop Ussher of Ireland declared (1654) that from his study of the Scriptures the Creation had taken place in the year 4004 B.C. This statement was unfortunately inserted as a marginal note in the King James version of the Bible and tended to discourage research on this problem.

The rift between scientists and churchmen was slowly narrowed. In the last 160 years, notable attempts have been made to calculate the

FIG. 3-4. The American Falls of the Niagara with Honeymoon Bridge spanning the gorge below. The length of the gorge is a measure of the duration of the Falls. *(Chamber of Commerce, Niagara Falls, N. Y.)*

age of the earth on a scientific basis. A standing committee of the National Research Council is now actively engaged in furthering investigation and correlating the results of the various methods of computing geologic time.

Estimates of geologic time are based on activities that have produced known effects in a known interval of time. Measurements of the rates of various natural processes have been made for a limited number of years. The retreat of Niagara Falls has averaged 5 feet a year in the last few years; downcutting by the Nile at the Cataracts has been 25 feet in 4,500 years; wind erosion at a certain place in the Gobi Desert was 5 feet in 156 years; certain glaciers deepen their cirques 0.57 millimeters a year; the bluffs of till along the shore of Cape Cod are receding 1 to 3 feet a year; on fresh lava in Hawaii, 2 feet of soil formed in 45 years; in the marshes at Lynn, Massachusetts, 3 to 4 inches of peat accumulated in 50 years; movement along the Buena Vista thrust fault is 1 inch a year; and annual varves of clay representing 20,000 years or more, have been counted in many lake beds.

From these and many other data, the ages of various earth features are calculated. Processes of the present are projected into the past. The length of time required to excavate the Grand Canyon is computed on the basis of present downcutting by the river; the rate of lowering

FIG. 3-5. **Varved clay.** Each pair of layers, one light and one dark in color, represents a year's deposition. Darker bands are stiff winter clay; lighter bands are summer silt. *(Photo by F. J. Pettijohn. Geological Society of America)*

of the whole drainage basin of the Mississippi is measured by the amount of material the river annually discharges into the sea; the time required for the accumulation of all known sedimentary rock, a thickness of 70 miles, is estimated from the rate of recent accumulation; the age of the ocean is figured from the amount of sodium and chlorine it contains, assuming that these elements have always been carried by streams at the present rate; and, finally, the ages of various radioactive minerals and the rocks in which they are contained, are based on the present rates of atomic disintegration of the minerals.

Because of imperfections in the records of most of the natural processes, time estimates based on them are regarded as minima. As new information and discoveries are brought to light, estimates of geologic time have become longer. In 1778, Buffon estimated 75,000 years; in 1860, Phillips placed the age of the earth at about 60 million years; in 1900, most geologists accepted 100 million years as the probable figure. Since the discovery of radium in 1902 and the knowledge that some of the so-called elements break down into others, the figure has been multiplied many times.

Radioactive Methods of Age Determination. Age determinations by radioactive decay are based on the premise that a parent element decays at a constant rate into a daughter element, or series of daughter elements. For example, potassium decays to argon directly, that is, in one step, whereas, uranium 238 passes through a radioactive chain to the stable daughter, lead 206. Neither heat, pressure, nor any other known condition affects the rate of change. Consequently, estimates of time based on this activity are deemed most nearly accurate. Thus, the ratio now present between the parent element and the daughter element gives the data for calculating the length of time that the parent element has been decaying. The figure obtained is the age in years of the rock in which the parent and daughter elements are found.

The rates at which the different radioactive elements decay differ greatly. The rate for any element is designated as its half-life. This means that in a certain length of time one-half of the original atoms will remain, the others having been changed.

Uranium, thorium, rubidium, and potassium have long half-lives. They are used for measuring great ages. By these methods the absolute ages of some rocks at several localities on different continents have been determined to be more than 3,000 million years old. The localities and ages in millions of years of some of the oldest rocks so far dated are: Manitoba, 3,360; Witwatersrand, 3,712; Southern Rhodesia, 3,740; and the Transvaal, 3,850.

Carbon 14, which is radioactive, is formed in the atmosphere from nitrogen and the neutrons of cosmic rays. Living plants absorb and contain a certain percentage of this radioactive carbon in relation to ordinary Carbon 12. When a plant dies its radioactive carbon gradually is lost. The rate of loss has been determined. Thus, the radioactivity of dead plants and of the materials derived from them is a measure of the time since the plants died.

Inasmuch as the half-life of radioactive carbon is relatively short, it can be used for age determinations only up to about 40,000 years. Even so, it is quite useful in dating many archeological objects and also geological events of recent times.

In general, the use of radioactivity in dating events has tended to lengthen our concept of the ages of the old rocks and hence the total length of geologic time. On the other hand, the more recent dates derived from radiocarbon have shortened our conception of the length of time since the last glaciation.

The determination of dates from radioactive samples involves a series of highly skillful operations. The sample had best be collected by a geologist, who observes the geological relationships and judges whether or not the sample has been contaminated by more recent material. Absolute age determinations are made in the laboratory by physicists and chemists, or geophysicists and geochemists, where the samples are carefully prepared and weighed and where such highly technical instruments as the radiometer and the mass-spectrometer are used.

Summary. In calculating the ages of objects and events the value of any one criterion can best be judged if it can be checked with numerous other criteria. By thoroughly understanding even the simplest geologic process and carefully observing and recording its rate of progress, many of us have the opportunity to contribute something to this important field of research. "The present is the key to the past."

In the study of earth science it is essential that the student realize the vastness of geological time. As the astronomer must think in terms of magnificent distances so the student of the earth must think in terms of long vistas of time. Without an appreciation of the time element the work accomplished by the various earth processes cannot be understood. Most of the processes of change operate slowly, and man's span of life is short. In fact, the whole length of the time of human habitation of the globe comprises an insignificant fraction of geological time. If we let twelve hours on the clock represent the length of geological time, the existence of the human race on the earth would occupy less than half a minute, and the length of recorded human history only a small fraction of a second.

Suggestions for Further Reading

CHAMBERLIN, T. C., *The Origin of the Earth* (Chicago, University of Chicago Press, 1927).

FAUL, Henry (Editor), *Nuclear Geology* (New York, Wiley, 1954).

JEFFRIES, Harold, *The Earth: Its Origin, History and Physical Constitution* (New York, Macmillan, 1929).

KNOPF, Adolph, "Measurement of Geologic Time," *Scientific Monthly*, November, 1957.

RUSSELL, H. N., DUGAN, R. S., and STEWART, J. Q., *Astronomy I* (*The Solar System*) (New York, Ginn, 1945).

UREY, Harold C., *The Planets: Their Origin and Development* (New Haven, Yale University Press, 1952).

ZUENER, F. E., *Dating the Past* (London, Methuen, 1953).

— 4 —

Structure and Processes of the Earth[1]

MAJOR DIVISIONS OF THE EARTH

THE FORM OF THE EARTH as a whole is spheroidal, and its major divisions are zonally arranged with the densest material on the inside and the lightest on the outside. This zonal arrangement is not perfect, and we shall see later that important earth processes arise from this imperfection.

As stated in Chapter 1, we find at the outermost part of the spheroidal earth a complete gaseous envelope, the atmosphere; next is a partial covering of water, the hydrosphere; beneath the hydrosphere and in places projecting above it is the outer rocky zone, the crust. Exploration of the earth beneath the crust is done entirely by geophysical methods, mainly by the recording of the behavior of seismic waves. From these data the interior of the earth is zonally divided into mantle,[2] outer core, and inner core. To complete the general picture we may add the living world of plants and animals, which constitute the *biosphere*.

These divisions of the earth are not mutually exclusive nor independent. The atmosphere contains water and solid particles; the hydrosphere absorbs air, dissolves solid matter, and carries rock particles as sediment; the lithosphere absorbs both air and water which react with and change the rocks; and the biosphere depends on land, air and water for its existence.

[1] This chapter is a brief summary of the material in the following chapters. It should be read now as a preview and again at the end of the book as a final summary.

[2] The term "mantle," as used by geophysicists, is not to be confused with the term "mantle rock," which geologists have long used to designate the unconsolidated surficial material, soil, etc., on top of the crust.

The Atmosphere. The atmosphere is an intimate mixture of gases carrying variable amounts of dust and minute organisms. An analysis of dry air shows about 78 per cent of nitrogen, 21 per cent of oxygen, 0.93 per cent argon, 0.03 per cent of carbon dioxide, and small amounts of hydrogen, neon, helium, krypton, xenon, ozone, ammonia and sulphurous gases. Natural air, furthermore, is never absolutely dry; water vapor, in highly variable amounts, is always present. From the geological standpoint, the oxygen, carbon dioxide, water vapor and dust are the most important constituents of the air.

The atmosphere is known to extend 1,000 miles above sea level and probably continues much farther. At an average elevation of about 8 miles a well-defined change in the condition of the atmosphere marks the boundary between the *troposphere* below and the *stratosphere* above. In the stratosphere, the convection currents, water vapor, clouds, and differences in temperature prevalent in the troposphere are almost absent. The upper boundary of the troposphere, the *tropopause*, varies in elevation from 4 miles at the poles to 11 miles at the Equator.

Since gases are highly compressible, the air is densest at the bottom and becomes rarer as altitude increases. At sea level the pressure is nearly 15 pounds to the square inch; at 72,395 feet over South Dakota the balloon *Explorer* II in 1935 found the pressure to be 0.6 pound to the square inch. Thus 95 per cent of the atmosphere is below 13 miles in altitude.

Temperature in the troposphere decreases with increasing altitude at the rate of about 6°C. for each kilometer, or 3°F. for each 1,000 feet. Sounding balloons have recorded essential uniformity of temperature in the stratosphere as far up as 20 miles.

Unequal heating of different portions of the surface of the lithosphere and hydrosphere causes differences of temperature in the overlying air. As warm air expands and becomes lighter and cold air contracts and becomes heavier, areal differences in pressure develop. Lateral movement of air from regions of higher pressure to those of lower pressure is called wind. The greater the difference in atmospheric pressure at any one level, the stronger the wind.

The significance of the mantle of air as an integral part of the earth is often not fully appreciated. In the process of weathering, air reacts chemically with the rocks, forming new compounds, and changes in its temperature cause disintegration of the exposed lithosphere. Moving as wind, air transports rock material, and creates waves and certain ocean currents. Everywhere water is evaporated into the vast reservoir of air and subsequently is precipitated, often far from the source, as rain or snow. In addition, this gaseous film serves as a thermal blanket which retains and distributes the heat of the sun, and carries dust particles which aid in the diffusion of sunlight. It protects us from violent bombardment by meteorites, most of which are vaporized by the heat of friction as they travel through the air. The oxygen, carbon dioxide, and moisture of the atmosphere are necessary for the respiration of plants and animals which inhabit the globe. Also, carbon dioxide and moisture (water) are necessary for photosynthesis.

The Hydrosphere. The hydrosphere includes the ocean, seas, lakes, streams and ground water and covers about 72 per cent of the surface of the lithosphere. The greater part of the hydrosphere is found in the ocean, which has a maximum depth of about 6 miles and an average depth of about 2½ miles. If the surface of the lithosphere were even so that the ocean would cover it uniformly, the universal depth of water would be about 2 miles.

The ocean is not all water. Nearly 2 per cent of its volume consists of nitrogen, oxygen, and other gases dissolved from the atmosphere; and about 3.5 per cent of its weight consists of various soluble solids, chiefly sodium chloride, derived from the lands. Organisms living in the ocean derive their food ultimately from these dissolved salts and gases. In addition, a considerable quantity of sediment is held in suspension.

Unequal heating, wind currents, differences in salinity, earth rotation, and other factors produce a complicated circulation system in the ocean. This circulation, which has an important influence on climate, will be discussed later.

Streams, wind, and other agents annually carry countless tons of sediment from the lands and deposit it in the ocean, seas and lakes. This sediment, together with the remains of organisms living in the water, is deposited on the bottom where it is eventually consolidated into sedimentary rocks of various kinds. Thus the process of construction of new rock layers goes on simultaneously with the destruction of the land by erosion. By the nature and organic content of the rocks composing them, many parts of the present lands show that they have formerly been covered by water. The relative positions of the rocks and the kinds of organic remains buried in them enable one to determine the relative ages of the rocks and reconstruct important events in the histories of the various regions. Thus the beds of lakes, seas and the shallow portions of the ocean record and preserve the history of the earth.

The Lithosphere. The lithosphere is the term that has long been used for that part of the earth that lies beneath the atmosphere and the hydrosphere. It is also designated as the solid earth, to distinguish it from the liquid hydrosphere and the gaseous atmosphere. The surface of the lithosphere has an area of about 197 million square miles, 72 per cent of which is covered by water. Irregularities on the surface are of various degrees of magnitude. The top of the highest mountain, Mt. Everest in the Himalayas north of India, is 29,140 feet above sea level; and the greatest known ocean depth, reported from the Mariana

Trench in 1960, is 37,800 feet. Thus the total relief on the surface of a globe 8,000 miles in diameter is a mere 12.7 miles.

Continents and ocean basins are the largest, or first-order, relief features of the lithosphere. These great elevated and depressed portions of the surface are sharply separated from each other by the steep continental slopes. Water fills the ocean basins to overflowing and encroaches on the continents as shallow epicontinental seas. On the continents, plains, plateaus, mountains, and volcanoes in various stages of erosion make up the landscapes. The larger features of the ocean basins are probably comparable to those of the continents; but they are not modified by the subaerial processes of erosion. Submarine erosional processes are now being studied, but, as yet, they are not as well understood as those that operate on the lands. Throughout the long past there has been a tendency for heavy-rock areas to subside and light-rock areas to rise. The ocean basins, therefore, are underlain by heavier rocks than the continental masses.

The observable part of the lithosphere is composed of rocks, arranged in layers and other forms of various shapes and sizes. Nearly everywhere the surface of the rock is weathered and otherwise broken down into incoherent particles and mixed with decayed organic matter. This thin veneer is the soil. Downward the soil passes into the subsoil, which is less weathered and contains less organic matter. Beneath the soil and subsoil which constitute the mantle rock is the bedrock, extending down as far as man has been able to penetrate. Although solid, the bedrock is not impervious, for joints, pores, and other openings contain ground water and air.

Below the depth of a few miles one passes from the region of direct observation to the realm of indirect observation and speculation. It is known that the interior is hot, for hot materials are expelled from it, and temperature measurements in mines and wells show an increase downward at an average rate of about 1°C. per 100 feet. If this increase continued to a depth of 40 miles the temperature would be above the melting point of ordinary rocks at the surface. Pressure, caused by the weight of overlying rocks, also increases with depth and is calculated to be more than 3 million atmospheres at the center of the earth. Pressure raises the melting point. On the basis of temperature alone it is difficult to imagine a solid interior; on the basis of the enormous pressures it is difficult to conceive of any other than the solid state.

Earthquake (seismic) waves give us important information on the nature of the earth's interior. Shocks are transmitted from their points of origin around the earth and also through the earth. The waves that travel through the earth are of two kinds, transverse, or S wave, and longitudinal, or P wave, and the rates at which they travel depend on the elasticity of the material through which they pass—the more elastic the rocks the greater the speed. The transverse wave does not pass through liquids or gases. Seismic waves are discussed further in Chapter 23.

Zones of the Lithosphere. According to the best information now available the "solid" earth consists of *crust, mantle, outer core,* and *inner core.*

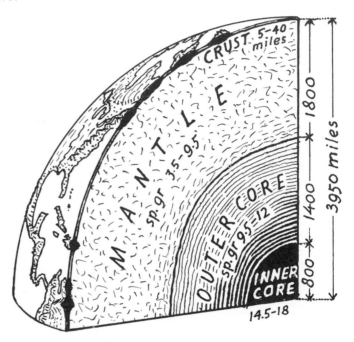

FIG. 4-1. Diagram showing the arrangement of earth materials according to weight. Figures on the diagram indicate densities of the inner zones. The specific gravity of the crust ranges from 2.5 to 3.4.

The crust is the outermost zone. It consists of solid rock and ranges in thickness from 5 to 40 miles. The crust is thicker in the continental areas than in the ocean basins. Also, the nature (composition) of the rock in the continents is different from that which underlies the ocean basins. In the continents the acidic, or sialic, or granitic type of rock, rich in aluminum, predominates. Beneath the ocean basins the rock is heavier (more dense), consisting mainly of the basaltic type, or sima, rich in iron and magnesium. The specific gravity of the crust ranges from 2.5 to 3.4.

Beneath the crust is nearly 1,800 miles of material known as the mantle. The behavior of earth waves indicates that this zone is essentially solid and increases in density with depth. Its specific gravity is judged to range from 3.5 at the top to 9.5 at the bottom. Although the mantle has a high rigidity for small stresses of short duration, there is geological evidence that the upper part at least yields to prolonged stress by slow flow, as if it were in a plastic state. It is also believed that in localized areas in this zone the rocks melt to form magmas which provide the materials and the energy for igneous intrusions that rise into the overlying crust and for volcanoes that break forth at the surface.

The core of the earth is the inner portion which has a radius of about 2,200 miles. Records from earthquakes indicate that the core consists of an *outer core* of 1,400 miles radius and an *inner core* of 800 miles radius.

The outer core is thought to be liquid because the S wave does not pass through it and the P wave travels with reduced velocity. Once the P wave gets through the outer core its velocity through the inner core shows a marked increase, indicating that the inner core is solid. From calculations based on the specific gravity of the earth as a whole and on the composition of meteorites, the inner core of the earth is thought to be composed mainly of iron and nickel with some cobalt.

The Biosphere. Our general picture of the constitution of the earth would not be complete without including the living organisms—plants, animals and man. Temperature, pressure, food supply, and respiration place rigid restrictions on the habitat of living things. Great numbers and kinds of plants and animals live in the ocean, seas and fresh-water bodies, many others live on the land, and a few spend much of the time in the air. Practically all are limited to a thin zone where land and air, land and water, or water and air meet. Man is, of course, a land-living animal who can control his environment sufficiently to take short excursions into the water and air.

The systematic study of organisms properly belongs to the field of biology; however, certain aspects of the relationship between plants and animals and their physical environment are so important to the study of earth science that we cannot omit them from consideration. These relationships will be discussed in later chapters.

EARTH PROCESSES

From the foregoing brief statement of the composition of the earth we now turn to a similar brief discussion of earth processes.

Gradation. Gradation includes all those processes by which the atmosphere, hydrosphere, and biosphere change the surface of the lithosphere. It consists of wearing down, or degradation, and building up, or aggradation. The processes of gradation are usually slow, but continuous, and over long periods of time produce very great changes. They may be classified as follows:

FIG. 4-2. The etching of a landscape by erosion. Bryce Canyon, from Inspiration Point. *(National Park Service)*

I. *Degradation, or erosion*—the wearing down of the lands by air, water and ice

   A. Weathering—the breaking down of rocks by the atmosphere
      1. Decomposition, or chemical weathering by oxidization, hydration, carbonation, solution, and so forth
      2. Disintegration, or physical weathering by temperature changes, wedgework of ice, wetting and drying
      3. Mass movement by creep, landslides, and solifluction
   B. Wind abrasion and transportation of sediment
   C. Stream corrasion, corrosion, and transportation
   D. Grinding and transportation of sediment by waves and currents
   E. Plucking, scouring and transportation of rock material by glaciers
   F. Work of plant roots and burrowing animals

II. *Aggradation, or deposition*—the building up of rock formations by deposition of eroded material and by accumulation of organic remains

   A. Deposition of sand and dust by the wind, forming sand dunes and loess beds
   B. Deposition of sediment by streams, forming alluvial fans, floodplains and deltas
   C. Deposition of sediment by waves and currents along shorelines and in the ocean, seas and lakes

D. Deposition of material by melting glaciers

E. Accumulation of organic matter, such as peat and coal from swamp plants and limestone from corals and other marine organisms

Diastrophism. Diastrophism is the term applied to all movements of solid parts of the earth with respect to each other. These movements are generally slow, so that accurate observations must be made to see the results of a short period of time. Abundant evidence is at hand, however, to show the results of diastrophic forces acting over periods of thousands and millions of years. The elevation of former sea bottoms to form lofty mountains and high plateaus and the subsidence of areas so that they are covered by thousands of feet of sediment require millions of years. Rapid displacements on a small scale, such as those involved in earthquakes, do take place; but the magnitude of such movements is measured in tens of feet or less for any one disturbance and must be repeated thousands of times over millions of years to account for the major displacements in the lithosphere.

The diastrophic processes may be classified as follows:

1. *Uplift*—the elevation of portions of the lithosphere with respect to adjacent areas
2. *Subsidence*—the relative depression of portions of the lithosphere
3. *Warping*—tilting on a fulcrum so that one side rises and the other subsides
4. *Folding*—the buckling of strata into corrugations by lateral compression
5. *Faulting*—the breaking and displacement of rock masses along fractures
6. *Jointing*—the fracturing of rock without noticeable displacement

Volcanism. Volcanism includes all the phenomena of the formation, movement, and solidification of molten rock matter. Any mass of molten rock within the body of the earth is commonly called a *magma*. The formation of such a magma probably takes place in any portion of the earth's interior where the temperature is high enough to liquefy the rocks. The molten material rises toward the surface along fissures and other weak structures, dissolving, fusing, and distending its passageway. By loss of heat as it rises, the greater part of the molten matter solidifies before reaching the surface, assuming various intrusive forms. Sometimes, on the other hand, a magma retains its fluidity and is impelled by sufficient pressure to burst forth at the surface as volcanoes or as fissure eruptions. Such rock material poured out on the surface is known as *lava*.

Volcanic processes may be simply classified as:

1. *Extrusive*—surface eruptions of lava and associated solids, liquids and gases

2. *Intrusive,* or *plutonic*—movement and solidification of molten matter
   below the surface

Metamorphism. Metamorphism includes all those processes, except
weathering and erosion, which change the texture, structure, or mineral
composition of previously existing rocks. Most sedimentary and igneous
rocks have been changed more or less since they were formed, and the
degree of change considered necessary to produce a metamorphic rock
is somewhat arbitrary. The fundamental cause for change in rocks is
change in environment. Processes of gradation, diastrophism, and vol-

FIG. 4-3. An elevated shoreline. The flat terrace of an uplifted wave-cut bench extends
inland from the modern cliffed shore, Laguna Beach, Calif. *(Fairchild Aerial Surveys, Inc.)*

canism bring rocks into new environments. At places rocks are becoming more deeply buried; at other places they are being exhumed by erosion; at some places they are invaded by igneous matter. Rocks and minerals that are stable under one set of conditions are unstable under other conditions, and they change to meet the new conditions.

The chief agents of metamorphism are solutions, heat, pressure, and movement. The principal kinds of metamorphism may be classified thus:

1. *Hydrometamorphism*—the changes brought about by water and vapor solutions of various temperatures which add new material to the rocks.

FIG. 4-4. **Uneven coastline due to glaciation and drowning.** Boston Bay. *(U. S. Geological Survey)*

Some of these solutions consist of ordinary ground water, while the hotter ones arise from igneous masses.

2. *Contact metamorphism*—the changes produced where an igneous mass invades older rock and alters it along the contact by heat and injections of molten matter

3. *Static metamorphism*—the changes produced in deeply buried rocks by the pressure of the overlying load

4. *Dynamic metamorphism*—the rearrangement of the constituents of rocks brought about by movement as a result of prolonged directed pressure

There is usually some overlapping of these various processes of metamorphism; in some regions one can see the results of all four kinds.

ISOSTASY

The interrelations of gradation, diastrophism, and volcanism may be elucidated by a brief discussion of isostasy. Literally translated from the Greek, *isostasy* means "equal standing." As applied to the earth it is conceived that there is equilibrium of pressure in a zone at a depth of 100 kilometers or less below sea level. This implies that the relief of the surface is balanced by differences in density; those portions of the lithosphere beneath the higher areas have lower specific gravities than those portions beneath the lower areas. The continental masses are composed

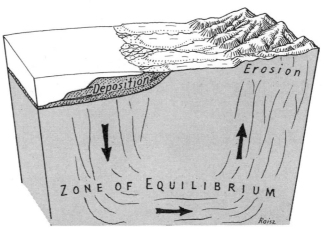

FIG. 4-5. **Diagram illustrating isostasy.** As gradation removes material from the continental mass to the ocean basin, the latter sinks beneath the increasing weight of debris at the same time that the continent, relieved of its load, rises. It is thought that, in the zone of equilibrium, rock matter flows, much like a highly viscous liquid, from one segment to the other.

FIG. 4-6. Daytona Beach, Fla., an offshore bar. *(Daytona Beach Resort Area Photos)*

FIG. 4-7. Brown's Mountain Anticline, W. Va., known locally as the Devil's Backbone. An example of an upfolding rock. *(U. S. Forest Service)*

of lighter materials than the oceanic segments; within the continents the highlands are underlain by lighter materials than the lowlands. Because of differences in density of materials, light segments rise and heavy segments sink until the pressure in a subsurface zone becomes balanced. The depth below sea level of this zone of equal pressure is usually estimated as somewhat less than 100 kilometers.

Now consider the various segments of the earth in perfect balance, some standing higher than others because of lighter specific gravity. Such an earth would be in perfect isostatic adjustment. But this condition cannot long endure. Gradation removes material from the higher regions and deposits it in the low places, thereby upsetting the balance of equal weight. Movement, or diastrophism, takes place to regain the balance. Thus gradation and diastrophism are closely dependent on each other. Further, consider the movement of igneous material. It may happen, and probably often does happen, that molten matter will move laterally from one segment of the earth to an adjacent one, thus reducing the weight of one segment and increasing that of the other. The lighter segment will rise and the heavier will subside—diastrophism. We see now that both diastrophism and volcanism will cause gradation, for the rising of portions of the lithosphere or the pouring out of lava on the surface sets the stage for erosion and deposition. In fact, each of the great earth processes—gradation, diastrophism, and volcanism—is a cause for the operation of the others; and each is also the result of the others.

The interdependence of the earth processes is strikingly portrayed by Joseph Barrell, one of America's great geologists, as follows:[3]

There comes to us from ancient times the myth of the Titans and their wars against the powers of heaven. They were the twelve lawless giant children of Uranus—the lord of heaven and ruler of earth—and of Gaea—the personification of earth, the primal mother and first-born of Chaos. Because of the menace of their growing strength they were imprisoned by their father in Tartarus, but from these abysses of darkness they were released by their mother, incensed at the fate of her children. They piled mountains on mountains till they climbed to heaven. In wild battle they overthrew and abased their father; and Cronus, the youngest of the Titans, sat upon the throne. But the curse of Uranus against his sons was fulfilled. The reign of Cronus came to an end, overthrown in turn by his own son Zeus. He was then compelled to disgorge the children which he had swallowed in vain effort to thwart his father's curse. The rebellious Titans were again imprisoned; guards were set to watch them forever, and the gods of sun and sea and rain, the children of the Titans, ruled in their stead.

Into this ancient myth we, in this latter day, may read more than the early

[3] Joseph Barrell, "Central Connecticut in the Geological Past," *Connecticut Geological and Natural History Survey, Bulletin* No. 23 (1915), pp. 40-44.

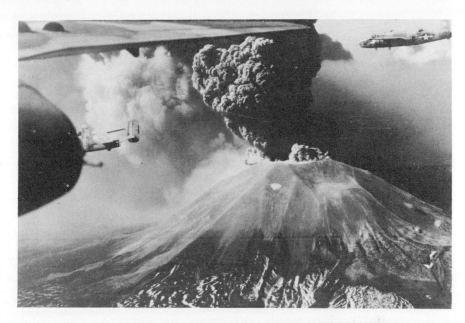

FIG. 4-8. Vesuvius in eruption, 1942.

FIG. 4-9. Contorted micaceous gneiss. (*American Museum of Natural History*)

narrators of it knew. Previous to the age of science, the earth was looked upon as changeless since the first creative day. But geology, by interpreting the meaning of ceaselessly moving air and water, and by studying the record of the crust, has opened to the mental vision the warfare of the resistless powers which shape and reshape the surface of the world.

Solar heat maintains the earth's water largely in fluid, and the atmosphere in gaseous, form. But the concentration of solar energy upon certain parts of the earth produces circulation systems in these mobile envelopes which work to spread out this energy, and lead to its dissipation. The air, most easily moved by changes of temperature, carries with it from the ocean the vapor of water, to be condensed in cloud and precipitated in rain, and thus extends the beneficent water circulation over the surface of the lands. The air sweeps along desert dust and sand; the flowing waters carry away rock detritus and hold also rock substance in solution. The exposed portions of the crust are thus impelled to sluggish changes, recorded through geologic time by erosion and deposition. Movements in the four Greek elements—fire, air, water, and earth—form a mutually dependent chain. These elements become interwoven and the energy which flows through them from sun to earth drags all into circulation. These surface energies of the world are sunborn forces, working to level the uplifted lands and extend the dominion of the sea, and their control of the earth's surface is recorded by the sediments piled up through geologic time.

The earth, however, possesses forces of her own. From time to time the eroded lands rise again. More locally new mountain ranges are reared above the clouds, and re-invade the home of Zeus. The crust of the ocean sinks lower, draws from the lands the flooding waters, and restricts the rule of Poseidon to his proper realm. The energies of the mysterious interior overflow, and lava fields or volcanic cones add to the rocky crust above the level of the sea. Thus the earth-born Titans chafe against their subjugation. They are never completely conquered; and here and there for a brief space of time their rebellion, as they again claim dominion, spreads ruin on the earth.

But there are disgorged from the molten rocks, which break into or through the outer crust, great quantities of water vapor and carbon gases with smaller quantities of other gases. Freed from the pressure of the depths the gases expand to many times the volume of the parent rock. Judged by the amount of the igneous rocks which have invaded the outer crust through geologic time, the emanations seem possibly sufficient to have given rise to the entire atmosphere and ocean without necessarily invoking primal or cosmic source. But the enrichment of the atmosphere gives the rain increased power to destroy the rocks. The ocean probably has increased in volume through the ages, fed by steam exhaled from the underworld, and thus thereby gained in power to invade the rain-eroded lands. This result, however, has been counteracted by a more than corresponding increase in the volume of the ocean basins. So it is seen that the upward struggles of the inner earth, by increasing the air and water at the surface, have added in the end to the power of the opposing agents and insured the more speedy ruin of those structures which the earth-born forces build.

Thus the surface of the earth is the battle ground of forces born of the sun and working through the earth's gaseous and liquid mantles against those other forces born of the earth's interior which mold the crust with giant power. Geologic history is the record of this never-ending and ever-shifting warfare between the powers of light and the powers of darkness. Progress is born of conflict not only in the human world, but in the material world as well. . . .

But it is only because of this eternal conflict that all life of the land has found existence. The currents of air and water tend to make equable the climates of the zones, and, as rain, the water sustains the life of the lands. Air and water break down the rocks into soil, the life-nourishing mantle of Earth. As it becomes impoverished of soluble matters, it is with equal pace worn away from above and rejuvenated from the rocks below. The forces of uplift and of igneous activity widen the land areas and renew their elevations. The escaping gases enrich the atmosphere with carbon dioxide and thus provide the gaseous food of plants. Let the sun-born forces resign their rule, and a speedy death would sweep over the surface of the world. Let the fettered Titans cease their striving, and in a few short geological ages the wasted lands would be invaded by the sea. The water would have widened like the air into a universal envelope; at last would be stilled through nature the reverberations of the ever-sounding sea, and Poseidon, another child of Cronus, would have come to share with Zeus supreme dominion of the world.

Land life, as shown, only finds existence because of the world conflict, and in its midst. But beyond mere existence there has prevailed the law of progress which has built up flower, beast, bird, and man from the same primal germ. This law too rests upon the same eternal struggle, because life tends always to become adjusted to its surroundings. That which does not change becomes extinct, and the world is inherited by the changed and best adapted. No sooner, however, has adjustment come in a time of geologic quiet than an epoch of earth unrest starts again the turning wheel of change. New migrations begin, and new conflicts arise between the forces of earth and her living forms: only the best of each kind is spared to carry forward the web of life. Thus it is that the changing environments resulting from the shifting vicissitudes of the battle between the forces of earth and sun, as marked by the advancing and retreating strandlines, and the fall and rise of mountains, have made for progress and have stimulated the evolution of all that higher life which dwells upon the lands, and of that highest life which has begun to look with understanding into the depths of space and time.

— 5 —

Maps, Diagrams, and Photographs

MAPS

THE SHAPE and movements of the earth and its relation to the sun are of primary importance in the making of maps. Since any point on a sphere is exactly like any other point, it would be impossible to locate points by observations of latitude and longitude if there were no rotation, no poles, and no Equator. The only way to make maps would be by direct, accurate, long-distance measurements from some center, a process that would be very costly on land and practically impossible on sea. The earth sphere, however, rotates on its axis once a day, and this axis is therefore different from every other diameter. The two poles, which are the ends of the axis diameter, are definite points; and the Equator is a definite line midway between the poles. Latitude, therefore, can be accurately portrayed with reference to these fixed positions. For computing longitude there is no natural point or line at which to begin the count. In this case an arbitrary place must be chosen, and, as indicated earlier, most countries have adopted the meridian of Greenwich, England, as the zero meridian for reckoning longitude.

Maps can be used to show the location and distribution of a great many features on the surface of the earth, both natural and cultural, and their relation to each other in distance and direction. In the study of earth science, maps are indispensable as instruments of investigation and as a means of recording and portraying facts. Because all maps are conventionalized, not literal pictures of the earth's surface, students must understand three fundamental aspects that apply to all maps in order to interpret them properly, namely: (1) the scale, (2) the projection, and (3) the symbols.

Map Scales. The scale of a map shows the relation between distance on the map and actual distance on the surface of the earth and is expressed on each map in one or more ways. It may be stated as an arithmetical ratio or fraction, for example, 1:1,000,000. In this case one inch on the map represents one million inches, about 16 miles, on the earth's surface. Scale may also be shown graphically by a linear bar divided into units representing miles or kilometers, on which actual distances on the map may be measured directly. On some maps the scale is expressed verbally as, "an inch to the mile," or "one inch equals 50 miles." The scale chosen for a map determines the scope of the map and fixes the amount of detail that may profitably be entered on it. In order to understand the space relations involved, the scale of every map studied must be noted. The larger the scale of a map, the more nearly it approaches the actual size of the area portrayed and the greater the amount of detail that can be included on it. A map on the scale of two miles to the inch includes an area four times as large as a map of the same size on the scale of one mile to the inch; therefore, the features appear larger and in much more detail on the latter.

Map Projection. A globe of the same shape as the earth is the only method by which the earth's surface can be portrayed without distortion. Because of the inconveniences of handling, storing, displaying, and using globes and segments of globes it is desirable to represent the curved surface of the earth on flat sheets, or maps. From these maps our ideas about the appearance of the earth's surface are commonly derived, and the mental images we have of the shapes and relative areas of land masses and their positions with respect to each other depend in large measure on the kinds of maps with which we become familiar.

The various methods devised for representing the meridians and parallels of a globe on a plane surface are known as map projections. Some projections are true perspective projections, while others are devised by mathematical computations. Because it is impossible to show the curved surface of the earth on a flat surface without sacrificing some element of truth, all of the various map projections involve distortion of one or more of the following qualities: area, shape, scale, and direction. No map that includes a considerable portion of the earth can be correct in both shape and area. Some projections are constructed so as to show the *shapes* of earth features correctly. They are called *conformal* projections. Other projections, called *equal-area* projections, show *areas* in the proper ratio. Still others, the *azimuthal*, preserve the correct *directions* of all lines drawn from the center of the map. A few of the more commonly used map projections are here briefly explained and illustrated.

Mercator's projection, developed in 1569, is a conformal cylindrical

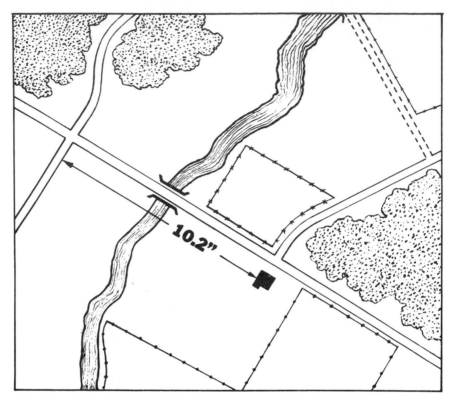

MAP A   RF = 1:20.000

**MAP B
RF = ?**

FIG. 5-1. Map scales. RF means representative fraction, that is the relation between distance on the map and distance on the ground. Maps A and B cover the same area on the earth. The scale of Map B (1:60,000) is one-third that of Map A (1:20,000), the map space it requires is only one-ninth. The indicated map distances between two points on the maps are relative only. *(U. S. Department of Defense)*

projection still used for almost all sailing charts and many other maps of the entire world. The principle involved in this projection may be understood by imagining a cylinder wrapped around the globe touching it everywhere at the Equator. Straight lines are drawn from points in the equatorial plane of the globe through various points on its parallels and meridians and projected until they touch the cylinder. The points in the equatorial plane are spaced so as to exaggerate the latitude in the same ratio as the longitude and thus preserve the conformal shape. When the cylinder is cut down the side and opened out flat, there is revealed a network of horizontal parallels and vertical meridians. Features of any kind may now be put on this map grid according to their known latitude and longitude.

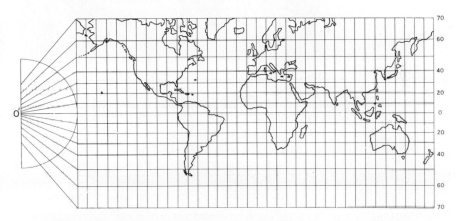

FIG. 5-2. Mercator projection. *(U. S. Coast and Geodetic Survey)*

At the Equator, where the cylinder touches the globe, this projection shows the earth's features without distortion, but the scale is progressively enlarged and areas are exaggerated more and more as the poles are approached. As the meridians are represented as parallel lines, the poles cannot possibly be shown on the Mercator projection.

In spite of its distortion of area outside the equatorial region and the change of scale with latitude, the Mercator projection is very useful to navigators. The meridians and parallels are straight rectangular . lines, and any straight line which crosses them makes constant angles. On this projection the navigator can draw a straight line between any two points, read the angle between this line of constant bearing, or *rhumb* line, and the meridian, set his compass to this angle and go directly to his destination without change of compass.

Mollweide's Homolographic equal-area projection (1805) shows the entire surface of the earth inside an ellipse, the major, or equatorial, axis is twice as long as the minor axis. Parallels are straight lines and trend with the Equator; meridians are equally spaced and all except the middle one are ellipses. Shapes are good near the middle meridian, but are more and more distorted toward the margins.

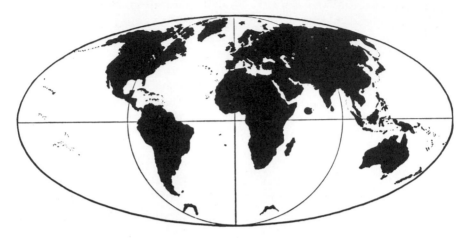

FIG. 5-3. Mollweide's homolographic projection of the sphere. *(U. S. Coast and Geodetic Survey)*

Goode's Homolosine (1923) is a modification of the homolographic projection which uses several mid-meridians and, also, interruptions in the grid. It is an equal-area projection which minimizes distortion of shapes. By placing the mid-meridians in the continents and the grid interruptions in the ocean, the continents are of good shape. The grid interruptions and mid-meridians may also be placed so as to split the continents and give unity to the oceans. Renner (1946) has devised a somewhat similar projection for the oceans (See Fig. 7-3).

Lambert's Azimuthal equal-area projection (1772) is often used for hemispheres and sometimes for continents, and is especially good for polar hemispheres. In this case the meridians are represented by straight lines radiating from the pole in their proper angular relations, the parallels by concentric circles around the pole. In order to maintain equal area the parallels are progressively closer together away from the pole. Angular directions are correct all ways from the center of the map. Shapes are very good near the center but become considerably distorted near the margin.

In the *Gnomonic* projection, or great-circle chart, the eye, imagined to be at the center of the globe, projects the parallels and meridians of the surface onto a tangent plane. This plane may be tangent at the Equator, at one of the poles, or at any other convenient point, depending on the location of the region to be mapped. Distortion of area increases away from the point of tangency and becomes extreme if the

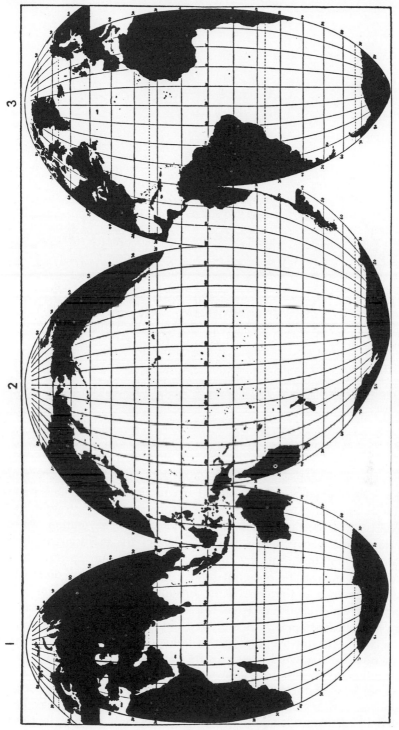

FIG. 5-4. Homolographic projection, interrupted for ocean units. (*U. S. Coast and Geodetic Survey*)

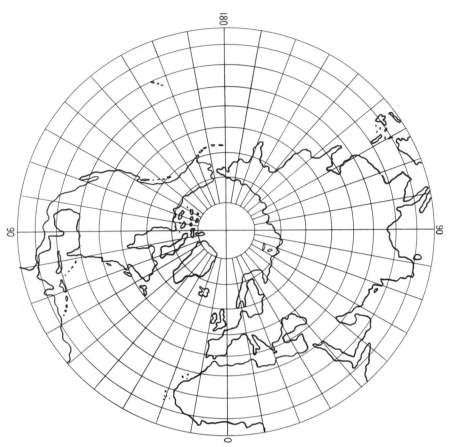

FIG. 5-5. Gnomonic polar projection. *(U. S. Coast and Geodetic Survey)*

projection is extended to include more than one-fourth of the globe.

On the Gnomonic projection all great circles, or planes that pass through the center of the sphere, are represented by straight lines—a property of importance in both air and surface navigation. Since the shortest route between two points is that of the great circle, the navigator can plot this route by drawing a straight line on the Gnomonic chart. But, such a line does not have a constant compass direction. For use on the voyage, therefore, it is customary for the navigator to transfer the great-circle route from the Gnomonic to a Mercator or other map, on which it appears as a curved line. The difficulty is not removed by this transfer, for a curve on the Mercator map is not a line of constant bearing. To avoid the necessity of continually changing the compass directions the route is drawn as a series of chords of the curve.

Some form of the *conic* projection is commonly used for continents, countries, and smaller areas. The *Simple Conic* projection may be illustrated by placing a conic map sheet so that it is tangent to the globe

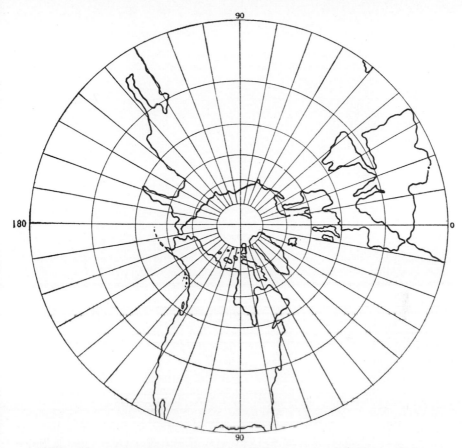

FIG. 5-6. Lambert's azimuthal equal-area polar projection. *(U. S. Coast and Geodetic Survey)*

along a standard parallel passing through the center of the area to be mapped. Lines are drawn from the center of the globe through numerous points on its parallels and meridians and extended until they intersect the cone. When the cone is opened the parallels are found to be arcs of concentric circles and the meridians are radiating straight lines. At the central, or standard parallel where the sheet was tangent to the globe, all elements of the map are true—angles, distances, shapes, areas; away from the standard parallel, shapes and areas become distorted. It is therefore not suitable for areas that cover a wide range of latitude.

In the *Lambert Conformal Conic* the surface of the earth is projected onto a secant cone so that there are two standard parallels. A greater range of latitude can thus be covered without marked distortion of scale and area. Between the standard parallels the scale is reduced, while outside of them it is enlarged. With standard parallels at 33° and 45°N.,

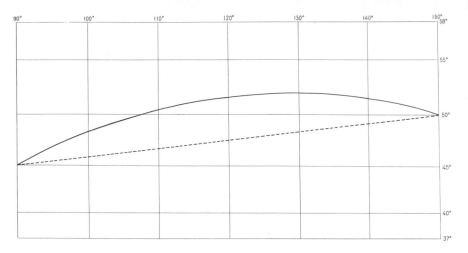

FIG. 5-7A. Rhumb line and great circle on the Mercator projection.
Dotted line is rhumb line, solid line is great circle. *(U. S. Coast and Geodetic Survey)*

the map of the United States on this projection has a maximum scale error of less than 2.5 per cent. For this reason, most of the aeronautical charts of the United States are drawn on the Lambert Conformal Conic projection.

In the *Polyconic* projection each parallel is taken as standard, as if the surface of the globe had been projected onto a series of tangent cones. On each map the central meridian is a straight line, intersected at equal distances by the parallels. The other meridians are curves which become more concave toward the mid-meridian with distance away from it. Since the parallels are arcs of nonconcentric circles, they diverge away from the central meridian.

The Polyconic projection, neither truly conformal nor equal-area, is an example of a good compromise of both. Furthermore, the tables for its construction are easily worked out and are applicable to all longitudes. It is well suited to large-scale maps that are prepared in separate sheets and consequently is used by the United States Geological Survey for its topographic map series.

We have seen that the curved surface of the earth cannot be represented on a map without distortion of some kind. The choice of projection is, therefore, largely a matter of selection for particular purposes. It is necessary to decide what purpose the map is to serve and then select the projection that comes nearest to fulfilling the needs of that purpose. Many of the maps commonly used, as the Polyconic, are the result of compromise between correct shapes, correct areas, and correct directions; no one condition is strictly fulfilled or greatly exaggerated.

Symbols. To show the areal distribution and degree of intensity of many types of information, map symbols must be used. The kinds of

64

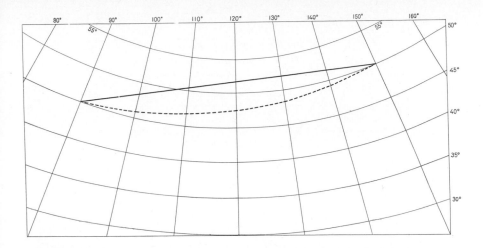

FIG. 5-7B. Rhumb line and great circle on the Gnomonic projection.
Dotted line is rhumb line, solid line is great circle. *(U. S. Coast and Geodetic Survey)*

devices used depend on the scale of the map, the types of features shown, and the purpose and preference of the map-maker. As a rule an explanation of the symbols used, or legend, is given with the map. Some symbols are so widely used that they have become more or less standardized.

Color. In map-making, color is exceedingly important. It is used to distinguish land from water, lowland from highland, the various rock formations, soil types, political divisions and much other information. On physical wall and atlas maps it is common to represent the ocean and other bodies of water in blue, different shades indicating different depths of water, the deeper shades for the greater depths. Frequently the shallow water over the continental shelves is left white to accentuate the contrast between land and water. Land below 500 feet in elevation is usually shown in deep green; from 500 feet up to 1,000 feet a lighter shade of green is used; yellow indicates land between 1,000 and 2,000 feet; light brown from 2,000 to 5,000 feet, dark brown from 5,000 to 10,000 feet, and red shows areas above 10,000 feet. If one understands the color scheme on this type of map the general physical features of a region can be grasped at a glance.

On the geological maps of the United States Geological Survey a definite scheme of colors is used, so that a certain color always represents the rocks of a given period, and patterns of lines and letter symbols designate the formations within a period. Most of the state geological surveys have adopted the color scheme of the federal survey. The number of colors and the variety of pattern and letter symbols used on geological maps are too great for detailed explanation here. The general scheme is explained on the inside of the cover of the folios of

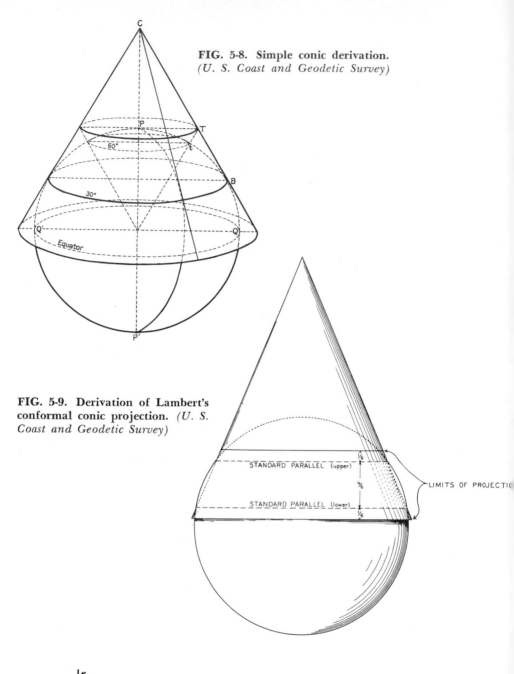

FIG. 5-8. Simple conic derivation.
(U. S. Coast and Geodetic Survey)

FIG. 5-9. Derivation of Lambert's
conformal conic projection. (U. S.
Coast and Geodetic Survey)

STANDARD PARALLEL (upper)

STANDARD PARALLEL (lower)

LIMITS OF PROJECTIO

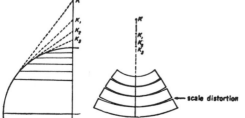

scale distortion

FIG. 5-10. Derivation of and scale
distortion in the polyconic projection. (U. S. Coast and Geodetic
Survey)

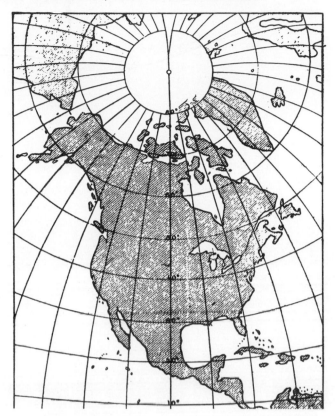

FIG. 5-11. Polyconic projection of North America.
(U. S. Coast and Geodetic Survey)

the United States Geological Survey and is illustrated in detail in the legends printed alongside the maps.

Political maps, soil maps, climatic maps and other maps showing distribution often make use of color. On temperature maps it is customary to use red for warm and blue for cold regions. In some cases there may be no standardization of color usage, each map-maker selecting his own colors. The principal aims are to bring out the appropriate degree of contrast between the different units shown and to produce a pleasing effect. Line patterns or letter symbols are usually printed over or under the color. Indeed, anything that can be shown by colors can also be shown by line patterns in black and white, though not so strikingly.

Circles and Dots. On small-scale maps cities are shown with circles, the size of the circle being somewhat proportional to the size of the city. Dots represent the smaller towns. Circles in proportionate sizes are also used as symbols on many commodity maps such as those

Tabular Summary of Map Projections

Projection	Parallels	Meridians	Merits	Disadvantages	Use
Mercator	Straight, horizontal, spaced closer near Equator	Straight, vertical, spaced equally	Conformal; straight rhumb lines	Scale distortion increases with latitude; poles cannot be shown	Navigation charts; world maps
Mollweide's Homolographic ..	Straight, horizontal, spaced closer near poles	Ellipses, spaced equally on any one parallel	Equal area	Shapes distorted in far quadrants	World maps, hemispheres
Goode's Homolosine	Straight, horizontal, spaced closer near poles	Irregular curves; straight mid-meridian for each continent, or for each ocean	Equal area; Interruption of grid in oceans gives good shape to continents	Interruptions break continuity of oceans or of continents	World maps
Lambert's Azimuthal Polar ..	Concentric circles, spaced closer away from pole	Radiating straight lines, spaced equally	Equal area; angular directions are correct all ways from center	Shapes distorted away from center	Polar regions, continents

Projection	Parallels	Meridians	Merits	Disadvantages	Use
Gnomonic Polar	Concentric circles, spaced closer near pole	Radiating straight lines, spaced equally	All great circles are straight lines	Both shape and area are greatly distorted away from center	Planning air and sea routes
Simple Conic	Concentric circles, spaced farther apart away from standard parallel	Radiating straight lines, spaced equally on any one parallel	Small distortion near standard parallel	Great distortion of scale away from standard parallel	Middle-latitude areas of narrow latitudinal dimensions
Lambert Conformal Conic	Concentric circles, spaced wider away from standard parallels	Radiating straight lines, spaced equally on any one parallel	Conformal	Small distortion of scale away from standard parallels	Areas in middle latitudes with greater dimensions from east to west than from north to south, such as the U.S.
Polyconic	Nonconcentric circles, spaced wider away from the mid-meridian	Curves, spaced equally on any one parallel	Good compromise between conformal and equal area; easy to construct	Adjacent map sheets do not match exactly along eastern and western borders	Series maps, such as the U.S. Topographic sheets

showing the production of minerals, lumber and corn, whereas dot maps are very effective in showing density of distribution of people, water power, and coal mining, each dot representing a given number of persons, horse power, or tons.

Topographic Maps. In addition to showing length and width it is often important to show the third dimension, or relief of the land. Some maps, as we have seen, show relief by the use of different colors for different elevations. There is also the *shaded relief* map which shows general relief by shading so as to give the impression of sunshine and shadows. Another method is by the use of *hachures,* or lines drawn in the direction of slope. Where the slope is steep the lines are made short and heavy; where the slope is gentle, the lines are longer and lighter. Some hachure and shaded maps are skillfully made and give a very clear picture of the form of the land. Most of them, however, give only a general idea of the landscape and are of little value to the surveyor or engineer in planning the location of railroads, dams and irrigation canals, nor do they give much help to the student in the appreciation and understanding of landforms. Furthermore, hachuring and shading so fill up a map that there is little room to include other features than the relief.

The most exact method yet devised for showing relief is the contour-line map. A *contour* line, or simply a contour, is a line drawn through points of the same elevation above, or below, sea level. The shoreline, drawn at mean sea level, is the zero contour line. If the land were to sink or sea level rise 20 feet the new shore line would be a contour 20 feet above the first. In making contour maps, numerous altitude measurements are made with the spirit level and lines are drawn to connect points of the same elevation.

The vertical distance between contour lines is the contour interval. This varies on different maps: if the region is a plain with low relief, contours may be drawn at intervals of 5 or 10 feet; if it is mountainous or cut by deep canyons, the interval may be 100 feet or more. The scale of the map is also important in determining the contour interval used—the smaller the scale the larger the contour interval. Obviously, the larger the scale and the smaller the interval the more accurate is the map.

Much of the United States has now been mapped by the United States Geological Survey. The majority of these maps are issued in sheets covering 15 minutes of latitude and longitude on a scale of about 1 mile to the inch and with a contour interval of 20 feet. Large-scale maps are becoming more popular and numerous. Other scales are 2 miles to the inch and one-half mile to the inch. These topographic maps are of great value to the surveyor, the engineer, the geographer, the geologist and others who know how to use them. On a map with a 20-

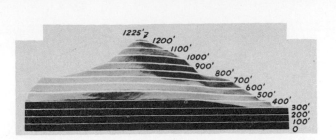

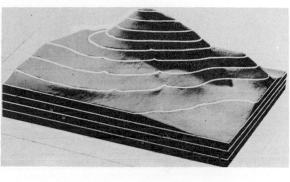

FIG. 5-12. Horizontal and two oblique views of a contour model. *(U. S. Department of Defense)*

FIG. 5-13. Contour map of the model shown in Fig. 5-12. *(U. S. Department of Defense)*

71

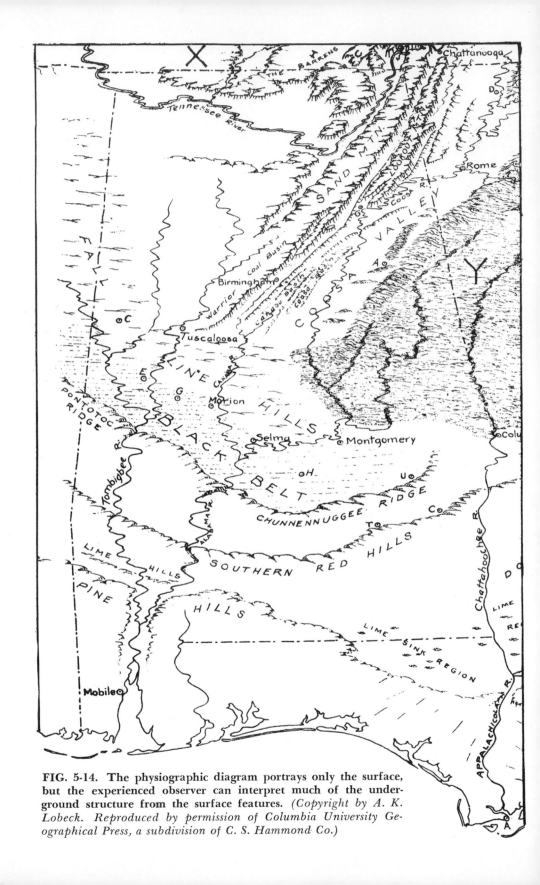

FIG. 5-14. The physiographic diagram portrays only the surface, but the experienced observer can interpret much of the underground structure from the surface features. *(Copyright by A. K. Lobeck. Reproduced by permission of Columbia University Geographical Press, a subdivision of C. S. Hammond Co.)*

foot contour interval the altitude of a point can be ascertained with a limit of error of less than 20 feet. The large-scale and the Polyconic projection allow very little distortion of shape and area. In all, one has a very exact three-dimensional representation of the landscape.

In addition to relief, which is shown with brown contour lines, the United States topographic maps show water in blue and cultural features in black. Some also have a green overprint to indicate woods. The student of earth science would do well to become acquainted with topographic maps early in his studies, and as that acquaintance grows into familiarity his rewards become greater.

DIAGRAMS

In addition to maps, there are various types of diagrams and charts that are effective in illustrating a limited amount of specialized or detailed information that cannot be adequately shown in the dimensions of the ordinary map based on some projection of parallels and meridians.

The Physiographic Diagram. The physiographic diagram is a means of showing types of landscapes as they appear from oblique airplane views by the use of more or less pictorial symbols. Designed primarily for use on a small scale, this method has been skillfully developed by A. K. Lobeck and by Erwin Raisz. The physiographic diagram presents a bird's-eye view with such clearness and simplicity that the observer immediately grasps the main elements in the landscape of a region, but as it gives no information on actual slopes and elevations it cannot be used for exact morphological calculations.

Structure Sections. The arrangement of rock formations beneath the surface is shown by means of structure sections, which represent rocks as they would appear if revealed by a vertical slash downward from the surface. Data for drawing a structure section are obtained by careful measurement of the thickness and attitude of the rock formations at the surface. Where additional information is desired, the underground conditions may be learned from well logs, mine shafts, tunnels, and testborings, and by geophysical methods. If one understands the habits of rocks, their positions underground can be reasonably inferred from the data available, where they cannot be directly measured.

Block Diagrams. A block diagram is a combination of physiographic diagram and structure section, representing in perspective both the surface and the structure at the same time. The top of the block gives a bird's-eye view of the surface of a region, and the sides of the block show the underlying structure of the rocks. A block diagram thus gives a three-dimensional picture, and shows graphically the relationship between the surface and the underlying structure.

Columnar Sections. The thicknesses and succession of rock formations

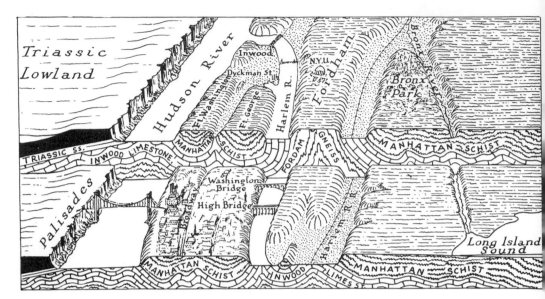

FIG. 5-15. Combination of structure sections with the physiographic diagram. This figure gives views in a vertical plane as well as in the horizontal. *(Copyright by A. K. Lobeck. Reproduced by permission of Columbia University Geographical Press, a subdivision of C. S. Hammond Co.)*

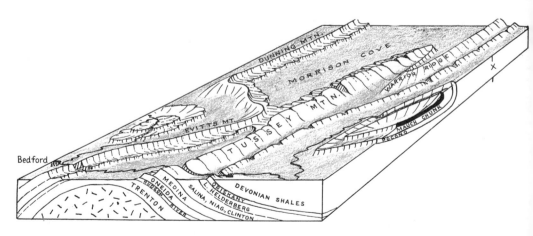

FIG. 5-16. With the block diagram one can present views of landforms in three planes. *(Copyright by A. K. Lobeck. Reproduced by permission of Columbia University Geographical Press, a subdivision of C. S. Hammond Co.)*

in any region may be shown by a geologic columnar section. Each formation, represented by an appropriate pattern or color symbol, is allotted space to correspond with its average thickness in the region. Sedimentary beds are depicted in their proper age relations, the oldest formation at the bottom, and igneous intrusions, regardless of the fact that they are younger, are included with the formations they penetrate. The columnar section gives a graphic, generalized view of the physical character, average thicknesses, and relative ages of the rocks in a given region, but their structural relationships can best be shown in the geologic cross-section or block diagram.

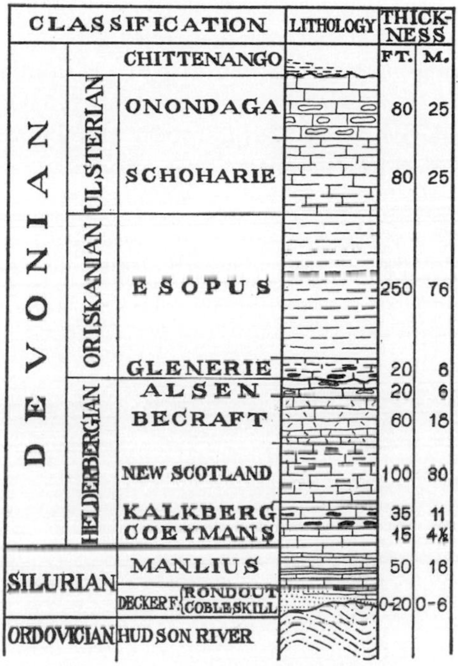

CLASSIFICATION			LITHOLOGY	THICK-NESS	
		CHITTENANGO		FT.	M.
D E V O N I A N	ULSTERIAN	ONONDAGA		80	25
		SCHOHARIE		80	25
	ORISKANIAN	ESOPUS		250	76
		GLENERIE		20	6
	HELDERBERGIAN	ALSEN		20	6
		BECRAFT		60	18
		NEW SCOTLAND		100	30
		KALKBERG		35	11
		COEYMANS		15	4½
SILURIAN		MANLIUS		50	18
	DECKER F.	RONDOUT / COBLESKILL		0-20	0-6
ORDOVICIAN		HUDSON RIVER			

FIG. 5-17. This columnar section shows the sequence, lithology (in symbols), and thickness of sedimentary rocks in the vicinity of Catskill, New York. After Chadwick and Kay, *XVI International Geologic Congress Guidebook, No. 9A)*

Hypsographic Charts. Percentages of the land surface at various altitudes and also the area of the sea floor at various depths are commonly shown by hypsometric, or hypsographic, charts. For these purposes a line graph, in which area is plotted against altitude, is usually employed.

Small-scale charts of this kind have long been used to portray in a generalized way the major relief features of the earth. In more recent years this method has been used in detailed studies of small areas. Data for these detailed hypsographic charts are obtained by measuring with a planimeter the area enclosed by each successive contour line on the topographic map and expressing this area as a percentage of the total area of the region.

Climatic Charts. Although various types and combinations of climatic data may be shown in graphic form, the most commonly used charts are those showing average monthly temperature and precipitation for representative stations. Data entered on these climatic charts are the results of weather observations averaged over a period of several years. A line graph running across the chart rises or falls according to the average temperature for each successive month from January to December, and a vertical bar graph, rising from the bottom of the chart, represents precipitation for each month.

PHOTOGRAPHS

Photographs differ from maps and diagrams in that they are not selective. They show in greater or less detail all features that are visible from the point of view and do not differentiate between the important and the unimportant.

Kinds of Photographs. *Ground* photographs are taken at the surface of the earth, usually with the optical axis of the camera in an approximately horizontal position. *Aerial,* or air, photographs are of two main types—the *vertical* and the *oblique.* In making vertical photographs the camera is generally mounted in an airplane so that the lens projects through a hole in the bottom of the plane and the optical axis is in a vertical position, whereas obliques are made with the optical axis of the camera at some angle to the vertical. In this latter case the camera may be mounted in the bottom of the plane or it may simply be held over the side of the cockpit. *Composite* photographs are made with multi-lens cameras, usually with one lens in a vertical position and two or more in oblique positions. A *mosaic* consists of a matched assemblage of either verticals or composites and covers an area too large to be covered by a single photograph.

Characteristics of Photographs. Ordinary ground photographs, more or less familiar to everyone, are valuable for profile and one-sided views. Since the area covered by a ground photograph is triangular in shape the scale is greatly distorted, decreasing rapidly from the foreground to background. Furthermore, objects near the camera obstruct the view beyond.

An oblique air photograph presents a pictorial perspective view of the landscape. It covers a trapezoidal area and the scale decreases from

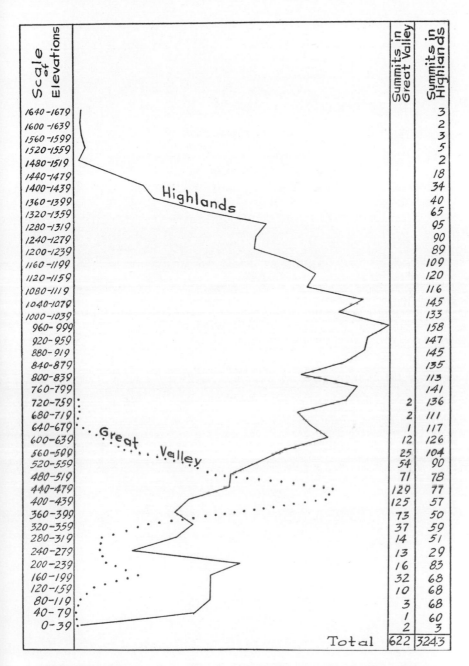

Scale of Elevations	Summits in Great Valley	Summits in Highlands
1640-1679		3
1600-1639		2
1560-1599		3
1520-1559		5
1480-1519		2
1440-1479		18
1400-1439		34
1360-1399		40
1320-1359		65
1280-1319		95
1240-1279		90
1200-1239		89
1160-1199		109
1120-1159		120
1080-1119		116
1040-1079		145
1000-1039		133
960-999		158
920-959		147
880-919		145
840-879		135
800-839		113
760-799		141
720-759	2	136
680-719	2	111
640-679	1	117
600-639	12	126
560-599	25	104
520-559	54	90
480-519	71	78
440-479	129	77
400-439	125	57
360-399	73	50
320-359	37	59
280-319	14	51
240-279	13	29
200-239	16	83
160-199	32	68
120-159	10	68
80-119	3	68
40-79	1	60
0-39	2	3
Total	622	3243

FIG. 5-18. **Chart and graphs of summit elevations in the West Point and Schunemunk quadrangles.** The figures at the right give the number of summits at each elevation in 40-foot intervals. About one-sixth of the area of the two quadrangles is in the Great Valley.

FIG. 5-19. Ground photograph. In this view of a series of low waterfalls with small potholes in the foreground the ground photograph is most effective. *(New York State Museum, Albany)*

FIG. 5-20. This ground view of the Grand Canyon, taken from the high Yavapai Point, is effective in showing the horizontal structure of the rock beds and the alternating cliffs and slopes. *(National Park Service)*

foreground to background, but not as rapidly as in a ground photograph. Slopes facing away from the camera are shortened and low features are obstructed by intervening high features.

Since a landscape seen from directly above has a markedly different aspect from that of the same landscape seen from the ground, vertical photographs give a picture that is unfamiliar to most of us. All surfaces look flat, unless shadows accentuate the relief. If, however, overlapping verticals are viewed with a stereoscope or by one who has developed natural stereoscopic vision, the relief of the surface can be seen clearly. While low features in the background are hidden from view in ground and oblique air photographs, the vertical view gives us a complete and unobstructed picture.

The area covered by a vertical photograph is rectangular like the photograph itself, and, if the ground is flat, the scale is approximately the same throughout the picture. Where the focal length of the camera and the height of the plane above ground are known the scale of the photograph, or representative fraction, can be found by placing the former over the latter in fractional form.

Example:

Focal length of camera $= 1$ foot
Height of plane above ground $= 20,000$ feet

$$\frac{1}{20,000} = \text{R.F.}$$

Like the Azimuthal map projection, vertical photographs show true directions along all lines radiating from the center. Relief of the ground, however, distorts distances, the high points being thrown outward and the low points inward with respect to the center of the photograph. Tilt of the plane also causes distortion. For these reasons vertical photographs must be rectified before they are used for making accurate maps.

Uses of Photographs. Although photographs are widely used in many fields, their applications in earth science are especially important. With the rapid development of aerial photography in recent years this importance has increased and probably will continue to expand. Photographs are useful in earth science primarily as illustrations of natural features and processes, as a method of geographical, geological and engineering surveying, and as source material for making maps.

Photographic pictures are often more effective and more economical than word pictures in conveying true impressions of natural features. By reaching the mind through the visual sense, they quickly and effectively bring to life the printed or spoken word. The photographs in this book, for example, are fully as important as the written text and should be studied assiduously by the student.

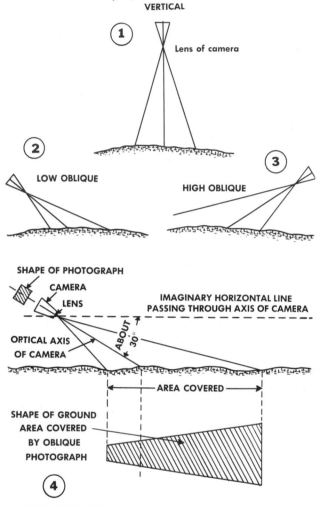

FIG. 5-21. Shape and size of territory covered by oblique and vertical photographs. (*U. S. Department of Defense*)

In nearly all kinds of geographical, geological, and engineering surveys, photographs are great savers of time and expense. By the study of air photographs the geographer can classify and describe geographic units; the geologist can recognize topographic forms, determine the distribution and structure of rock types and often discover mineral deposits and fossil-bearing strata; the engineer can locate dam sites and select the best routes for highways, railroads, and power lines.

More than three-fourths of this country has now been photographed from the air for the United States Department of Agriculture, and air photographs are increasingly valuable in the programs of land utilization, soil mapping, erosion control, and various other phases of conservation.

For map-making purposes, too, air photographs record information more rapidly and with less expense than can be done by ground survey methods. Furthermore, regions that are not accessible on the ground can now be photographed from the air. Since the photograph records all visible features, the map-maker may select and transfer to the map those that are important for his particular purpose. In order to use air

FIGURE 5-22. Where color and tone contrasts are marked, the single vertical photo is effective in showing land and water, woods, cultivated land, roads and railroads, and other natural and cultural features. An important advantage of the vertical over the oblique is that the scale on the former is more nearly uniform throughout.

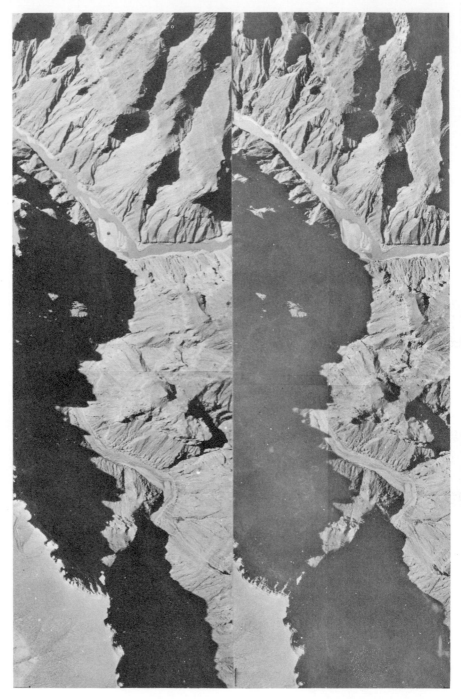

FIG. 5-23. Stereopair of a portion of the Navajo Reservation in the Colorado Plateau. The relief is brought out most effectively by the use of a stereoscope with an eye base of 2½ to 3 inches.

photographs for making accurate maps, scale distortions must be rectified and the relief of the ground plotted—functions that are performed by the new science of photogrammetry.

Suggestions for Further Reading

DEETS, Charles H., and ADAMS, Oscar S., *Elements of Map Projection* (U. S. Coast and Geodetic Survey Special Publication No. 68, 5th Ed., Rev., 1944).

EARDLEY, A. J., *Aerial Photographs: Their Use and Interpretation* (New York and London, Harper, 1942).

LOBECK, A. K., and TELLINGTON, Wentworth J., *Military Maps and Air Photographs* (New York and London, McGraw-Hill, 1944).

PUTNAM, William C., *Map Interpretation with Military Applications* (New York and London, McGraw-Hill, 1943).

RAISZ, Erwin, *General Cartography* (New York, McGraw-Hill, 1948).

SMITH, H. T. U., *Aerial Photographs and Their Applications* (New York, Appleton-Century-Crofts, 1943).

—— 6 ——

The Elements of
Weather and Climate

$\mathbf{M}$AN LIVES in a sea of air. As a consequence, he is much affected by the changes that take place in the gaseous medium that surrounds him. The influence of the atmosphere on man is not only direct, but also indirect, through its effect on the natural vegetation, soil, and topography. Of all the elements in man's natural environment, climate is the most important. Large portions of the earth are inhospitable to man because of unfavorable climate, while other portions provide optimum climatic conditions for man's well-being. A knowledge of climate is important not only because of its great influence on man now, but also for a fuller understanding of the history of the earth. There is abundant evidence that the climates of many parts of the earth have changed in the past, for reasons not now clear. Probably continued study will clarify this important problem.

WEATHER AND CLIMATE DEFINED

Weather is the physical condition or state of the atmosphere at any one time. As these conditions change, so does the weather change. Climate is the composite of weather conditions over a considerable period of time. A bare statement of the average climate of a locality is of slight value unless it is accompanied by a statement of the types of weather which compose it. Victoria, Canada, and Omaha, Nebraska have nearly the same average annual temperature and rainfall, but the types of weather of which the averages are made differ markedly at the two stations. At Victoria the temperature never rises far above nor drops far below the average; rainfall is heaviest in the winter months; long droughts never occur. At Omaha, on the other hand, extremely cold winters and hot summers are common and the rainfall is heaviest in the

FIG. 6-1. Eskimo hut. At one climatic extreme is this inhospitable area — ice-bound much of the year. Here most of man's necessities are wrested from the sea. *(Ewing Galloway)*

FIG. 6-2. At another extreme are conditions as represented by this group of **Medje porters, Gamagui, Belgian Congo.** *(American Museum of Natural History)*

summer months; prolonged droughts are not uncommon. If one wishes to gain an accurate picture of the weather and climate of any station he should look beyond the annual averages, and even beyond the monthly averages. He should know the day-to-day extremes. "It is not the averages, but the extremes that kill."

ELEMENTS OF WEATHER AND CLIMATE

The principal elements of weather and climate are (1) temperature, (2) pressure and winds, and (3) moisture and precipitation. Temperature is the term used to express the intensity or degree of heat. Practically all of the heat energy on the earth is the result of insolation, or radiation from the sun. Air in more or less horizontal motion is known as wind. Unequal distribution of temperature over the earth's surface causes differences in atmospheric pressure which give rise to winds. Air moves from regions of higher to regions of lower pressure. Moisture is present in all the atmosphere as water vapor, often condensed into clouds; it may be precipitated in the form of rain, hail, sleet, or snow. The capacity of air to gather and retain water vapor is largely dependent on its temperature, the higher the temperature the greater the capacity for moisture. On sufficient cooling, the air will not be able to retain all the moisture it gathered while warm, and condensation and precipitation result. That the operations of the elements of weather and climate are closely interdependent will be shown in the following paragraphs.

Temperature. *How Temperature Is Measured.* Temperature, (or the degree of heat), is measured by a *thermometer*. The most common thermometer is a sealed glass tube evacuated of air and partly filled with mercury, although other liquids, such as alcohol, are used when instruments are exposed to temperatures lower than the freezing point of mercury. As the temperature changes, the liquid in the tube expands and contracts; its upper surface rises or falls, and the position of this surface is read from a graduated scale on the tube. The Fahrenheit scale is the one most commonly used in America and England. On this scale the boiling point of water is placed at 212° and its freezing point at 32°. The simpler Centigrade scale, on which the freezing point of water is placed at 0° and the boiling point at 100°, is commonly used in Europe and South America. Centigrade may be converted to Fahrenheit by multiplying by 1.8 and adding 32. Thus 20°C. equals 68°F.

$$20 \times 1.8 + 32 = 68$$

Thermometers are sometimes constructed of a flat, curved metal tube filled with a liquid. Differential expansion and contraction of the metal and the liquid change the curvature of the tube. This working element may be connected with a hand, or pointer, that moves over a dial scale as the temperature changes. Such thermometers may also be connected with an arm bearing a stylus, or pen, so placed as to rest on a paper chart wrapped around a drum turned by clockwork. The pen rises and falls with the temperature and writes a record on the uniformly revolving drum. Such a self-recording thermometer is called a *thermograph.*

In order to obtain the correct temperature of the air a thermometer must be properly exposed. It must be placed in the shade; if set in the sun, it will absorb direct *insolation* and, therefore, will not show the correct air temperature. It must also be placed so that it will not be affected by direct radiation from the ground and buildings.

How the Atmosphere Is Heated. Absorption of solar radiation. The atmosphere gets practically all of its heat directly or indirectly from the sun. Radiant energy from the sun, which we commonly call heat and light, is transmitted mainly in the form of short waves which travel at the rate of about 186,000 miles a second. The energy that comes from the sun is generally called *insolation.* Certain substances, such as glass and most of the gases of the atmosphere, allow this radiant energy to pass through them so freely that they are said to be transparent to the light and diathermanous to the heat. Some of the lesser constituents of the atmosphere, however, mainly water vapor, carbon dioxide, ozone, and dust, absorb about 10 to 15 per cent of the direct solar radiation intercepted by the earth. In addition, some of the radiation which is not absorbed directly is reflected, especially from snow and water surfaces, back into the atmosphere where a small additional portion is absorbed.

Absorption of radiation from the lithosphere and hydrosphere. Much of the solar radiation that passes through the atmosphere is absorbed by the lithosphere and the hydrosphere and they become radiating bodies. The short-wave solar radiation absorbed by the lithosphere and hydrosphere is converted into long-wave terrestrial radiation. While the atmosphere will absorb only a small percentage of the incoming solar radiation it will absorb probably 90 per cent of the outgoing terrestrial radiation. This aspect of the effect of the atmosphere on the lithosphere and the hydrosphere is analagous to that of the glass roof of a greenhouse; it allows the short-wave solar radiation to pass freely but greatly retards the outgoing long-wave radiation. In this way the surface temperature is kept higher and more uniform than it would otherwise be.

Conduction and convection from the lithosphere and hydrosphere. Heat will pass by conduction from a warmer to a colder body if the bodies are in contact with each other. Thus an iron placed on a hot stove is also heated. Although air, water, and the ground are rather poor conductors, some transfer of heat by conduction takes place between them. Because they are better absorbers of solar radiation, the ground and water often become warmer than the air. The layer of air resting on the warmer bodies therefore is heated by conduction. On a hot summer day the surface of an asphalt road appears wet in the distance. This is a mirage effect produced by the difference in the refraction of light between the warm layer of air next to the hot surface of the road and cooler air above.

The principle of convection is illustrated by the hot-air heating system. In such a system air, heated by a burner, rises and is replaced by cold air, which in turn is heated and rises. In the same manner the lower portion of the atmosphere is heated by radiation and conduction from the warm areas of the ground and water. The warm air expands, becomes light, and rises; cooler air then flows in to displace it and is in turn heated. In this way large masses of air are heated by being brought into contact with warm surfaces.

Compression. A descending current or mass of air is subjected to compression because it is moving from an area of lower to one of higher atmospheric pressure. Compression of a gas produces heat, as the molecules are crowded together. In the case of wind blowing over a mountain and sweeping down into the lowlands beyond, the compression of the air as it descends raises its temperature, so that it becomes a warm wind, like the *foehn* of the Alps and the dry *chinook* of Montana. Why is the air that has moved over a mountain warmer at the leeward foot than it was at the windward foot? It is because of the latent heat of condensation, gained when clouds and rain and snow form high up on the windward side.

How the Atmosphere Is Cooled. Radiation. Whenever the air is warmer than the land and water beneath, it loses heat to them by conduction. This condition prevails during the night, especially the long winter nights, when there is no incoming solar radiation. The space above the atmosphere is constantly colder than the air itself; consequently there is a continuous process of radiation from the atmosphere to outer space. As a rule the lower layers of air are warmer than those above and radiation proceeds upward from the warmer to the colder and so into the space beyond.

Conduction. Warm air resting on cold land or water will lose some of its heat to the colder bodies by conduction. Presumably there is no conduction of heat from the atmosphere to outer space.

Expansion. Air cools when it expands. A rising current of air expands as it moves to higher altitudes where pressure is less. The work done by the expanding air in pushing aside other air to make room for itself consumes energy. The loss of this energy from the expanding air in the form of heat results in a lower temperature.

Vertical Distribution of Temperature. Under normal conditions there is a fairly uniform decrease in temperature with increase in altitude up to the top of the troposphere. The average rate of temperature decrease is about 3.5°F. for each 1,000 feet of altitude. This rate is called the *normal vertical temperature gradient*. At any given altitude cold air is denser or heavier than warm air, but with increasing altitude the air becomes lighter, because it is rarer, while the temperature becomes lower. The lower air is warmer for two main reasons: (1) it is closer to the ground, which is its principal source of heat; (2) the lower air is denser because it is compressed by the overlying air, and contains more of the constituents that absorb heat than does the higher air.

Inversions of Temperature. On clear cold nights in fall and winter, when terrestrial radiation is especially rapid, it frequently happens that the air close to the surface becomes colder than that at higher altitudes.

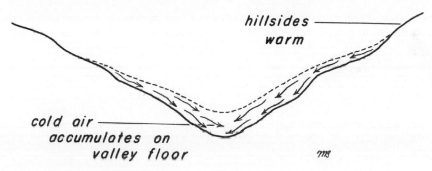

FIG. 6-3. Local inversion of temperature in a valley at night.

This condition is known as a temperature inversion. Local inversions may be caused by air drainage, whereby cold heavy air flows down slope into a valley or other depression and forces the warmer lighter air to move aloft. Recognizing the value of this air drainage, fruit growers usually set their orchards on hillsides rather than on valley floors. Another type of inversion occurs when a cold wind from a high-pressure area forces itself under a warm, light air mass.

Daily and Yearly Temperature Changes. The warmest period of the day is usually two or three hours after noon and the coldest period is just before sunrise. This daily change in temperature reflects the balance between the incoming solar radiation and the outgoing terrestrial radiation. From sunrise until about 3 P.M. the earth receives heat faster than it is radiated away. By about 3 P.M. the sun has sunk so low that incoming solar radiation is less than the outgoing terrestrial radiation. This imbalance increases until sunrise next morning.

The normal daily range in temperature is sometimes modified or even upset by certain conditions. Cloudy skies, which interfere with radiation, may prevent the temperature from rising after noon; a cold air mass from higher latitude may arrive in the daytime and cause the temperature to drop lower than that of the preceding night; or south winds may cause temperature to rise throughout the night.

The yearly cycle of temperature is similar to the daily cycle. It reflects the balance and imbalance between insolation and terrestrial radiation throughout the year. In the Northern Hemisphere there is a steady average rise from March to July or August and then a gradual decline until January or February. The period of highest temperature lags 30 to 40 days after the time of highest sun and longest day, and the period of coldest weather lags the same amount after the time of lowest sun and shortest day. In winter the excess of outgoing over incoming radiation continues to cool the ground and air until the days are long enough and the sun high enough to turn the balance in the other direction. Likewise, in summer the excess of insolation over outgoing radiation continues for some time after the period of highest sun.

The annual range of temperature, which is the difference between the mean average temperatures of the warmest and coldest months, varies greatly throughout the world. The greatest annual ranges are found in the interiors of the continents in the Northern Hemisphere, where the summers are very hot and the winters very cold. Over the ocean the range is far less than over the land, and near the Equator, where insolation varies little, the annual range of temperature is also small.

The distribution of temperature according to latitude and altitude, as well as the transfer of heat and cold by the great wind systems, will be discussed later.

Atmospheric Pressure. *Measurement of Air Pressure.* Although scarcely noticeable to our senses, air has weight. A column of air 1 inch square extending from sea level to the outermost limit of the atmosphere weighs nearly 15 pounds. This is equal to the weight of an inch-square column of mercury 30 inches high or of water 34 feet high. This weight of the air, or atmospheric pressure, will push a liquid up into a tube having a vacuum at the top until the height of the column of liquid is sufficient for its weight to equal the weight of the column of air pushing on it. Such a tube with the open lower end resting in an open container of mercury is a *mercurial barometer.* As the atmospheric pressure increases, the column of mercury in the tube rises; as the pressure decreases, the mercury falls.

The height of the mercury, or relative atmospheric pressure, can be read directly from a scale marked on the tube in inches, millimeters or millibars. Since inches and millimeters are, of course, units of length, atmospheric pressure is more logically and accurately expressed in terms of bars and millibars, a bar (1,000 millibars) being a unit of pressure equal to one megadyne [1] per square centimeter.

[1] Megadyne = 1 million dynes—approximately the force exerted by 1 kilogram weight under the influence of gravity.

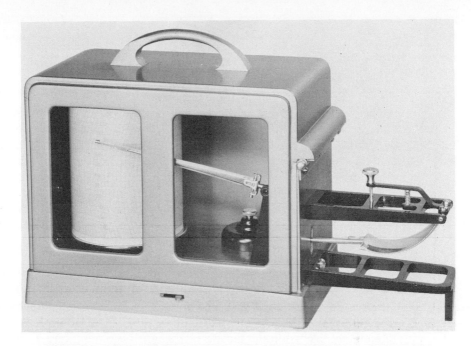

FIG. 6-4. Thermograph. The curved element outside the box consists of a metal tube filled with a liquid. *(Julien P. Friez and Sons, Inc., Baltimore)*

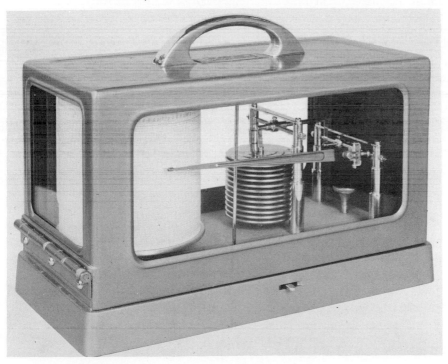

FIG. 6-5. Barograph. The discs are vacuum chambers. *(Julien P. Friez and Sons, Inc., Baltimore)*

Though somewhat less accurate, the *aneroid barometer* is more compact and less easily injured than the mercurial barometer. The essential element of an aneroid barometer is a flat vacuum box or series of boxes, each connected with a thin, flexible metal diaphragm cover. Differences in air pressure cause the diaphragms to move inward or outward. These movements are controlled by a spring and are in turn magnified and communicated to a hand which moves over a dial graduated in inches or millibars. Some aneroids, called *altimeters,* have a scale of feet on the dial and are used for measuring elevations, because of the relationship between air pressure and altitude. In the self-recording aneroid barometer, or *barograph,* the dial hand is replaced by a long pen lever, which traces the record on a weekly chart mounted on a clock-driven, regularly revolving drum.

Vertical Distribution of Pressure. Atmospheric pressure varies according to temperature and also according to altitude. Since the air is very compressible, it follows that the lowest part is most compressed and therefore densest; about one half of the mass of the atmosphere is below 17,500 feet. As altitude increases the air becomes more rarefied and pressure therefore decreases at the rate of about 1 inch of mercury for each 1,000 feet for the first few thousand feet above sea level. The following table gives approximate average pressures for various altitudes. These figures vary to some extent with temperature.

Altitude, above Sea Level in Feet	Pressure, in Inches of Mercury	Pressure, in Millibars
0	29.92	1,013.2
1,000	28.86	977.3
5,000	24.90	843.2
10,000	20.58	696.9
20,000	13.75	465.6
30,000	8.89	301.0
40,000	5.54	187.6
50,000	3.42	115.8

Relation of Pressure to Temperature and Moisture. Temperature is an important control of pressure. Since air expands when heated and contracts when cooled, warm air is consequently lighter than cold air. Over a warm region the air becomes heated, expands, rises and overflows to adjacent colder regions in the upper atmosphere. This transfer reduces the weight of air in the warm region and increases that of the adjacent colder region. Thus, as a rule, regions of high temperatures have lower atmospheric pressures than regions of lower temperatures.

The amount of moisture in the air also has an influence on atmospheric pressure. A cubic foot of water vapor weighs less than a cubic foot of dry air at the same temperature. Therefore, moist air is lighter than dry air of the same temperature.

At any given place the atmospheric pressure changes from day to day and from hour to hour because of changes in the temperature and water vapor content of the air that are largely the result of the passage of different air masses. At sea level the pressure usually fluctuates between 28 and 31 inches of mercury, the normal being 29.92 inches, (about 1.013 bars) or one atmosphere. A bar is equivalent to 29.53 inches of mercury and is the normal pressure at an altitude of 350 feet above sea level.

Isobars and Pressure Gradients. Isobars, or lines connecting points of equal pressure, are used to show the regional distribution of pressure. On the United States Weather Bureau maps they are drawn with an interval of 4 millibars. Pressures are indicated as they would be if reduced to sea level. Changes in pressure from day to day can be clearly seen by examination of a series of these daily maps.

Pressure gradient, or barometric slope, refers to the direction and rate of changes in pressure. The direction of the gradient is at right angles to the isobars, just as the slope of a land surface is at right angles to the contour lines, and the rate of change, or steepness of the gradient, is shown by the spacing of the isobars, closely spaced isobars, for example, indicating a steep pressure gradient.

Winds. *Nature and Cause of Winds.* Air moving essentially parallel with the ground is called wind; more or less vertical air movements are currents. Initiated by differences in atmospheric pressure, wind moves from a region of higher pressure to one of lower pressure, that is, down the barometric slope. The steeper this barometric slope, or pressure gradient, the greater is the velocity of the wind. The air flowing down the pressure gradient follows the law of gravitation in the same manner as water flowing down hill. This statement may, at first, seem anomalous, for water on the land always flows downhill, whereas air may rise and move over a mountain, yet they both obey the law of gravitation.

Direction and Velocity. Wind is named by the direction from which it comes. A west wind blows from west to east; a breeze blowing from the sea is a sea breeze. Windward is the direction from which the wind comes, leeward the direction toward which it blows. A windward coast is one along which winds continually move onshore. Wind direction is determined by means of an *anemoscope*, or wind vane, so constructed as to point to the direction from which the wind blows. When connected to a self-recording apparatus, it makes a continuous record of wind directions. In many localities the wind blows from one direction more often than from any other and is referred to as the *prevailing wind.*

Because of the retarding action of friction on the uneven surface of the ground, wind velocity is usually greater over water than over land,

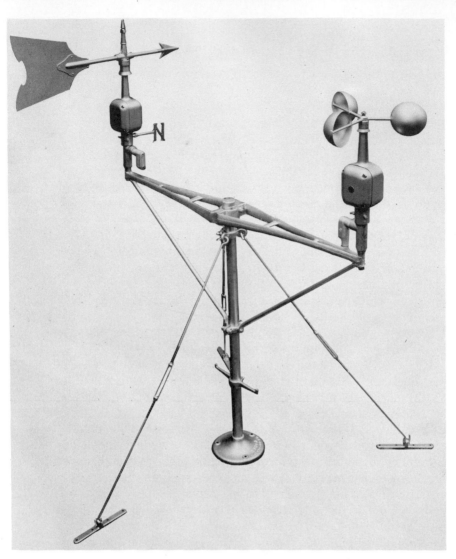

FIG. 6-6. Three-cup anemometer and anemoscope, or wind vane.
(Julien P. Friez and Sons, Inc., Baltimore)

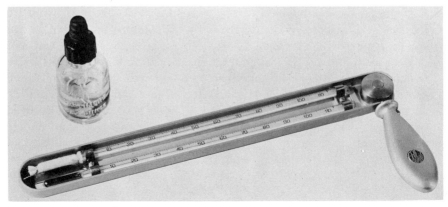

FIG. 6-7. Sling psychrometer for determining relative humidity.
(Julien P. Friez and Sons, Inc., Baltimore)

and greater aloft than near the surface. Wind velocity is measured in miles per hour by the *anemometer*. This instrument consists of three or more metal cups attached by horizontal arms to a vertical shaft. When the cups are revolved by the wind striking their hollow insides, this revolution may be communicated mechanically to the vertical shaft by a system of cog wheels. The rotation of the shaft may in turn be communicated to a hand which moves over a dial or electrically to an *anemograph* to make a continuous record of wind velocity.

Winds moving at different velocities are given different names. A simple classification follows in the table below.

Name of Wind	Miles per Hour
Calm	0 to 2
Light breeze	2 to 12
Moderate wind	13 to 23
Strong wind	24 to 37
Gale	38 to 55
Storm	56 to 75
Hurricane	75 plus

Moisture and Precipitation. *Source and Distribution of Water Vapor.* The surface of the ocean is the greatest source of atmospheric moisture. Lesser bodies of water, vegetation, and damp land surfaces also contribute significant amounts. The atmosphere gathers moisture by the process of evaporation and loses it by condensation and precipitation. Much of the water vapor evaporated from the ocean is carried by winds to the land where it is precipitated and delivered back to the ocean by streams and glaciers. The amount of water vapor in the atmosphere is highly variable from place to place and from time to time in any one place, ranging from almost zero up to nearly 5 per cent by weight. The water-vapor content of the air decreases rather rapidly with increase of altitude, the amount at 6,500 feet being on the average only one-half that at sea level.

Absolute and Relative Humidity. Humidity refers to the condition of the air as regards water vapor. The capacity of air to gather and retain moisture depends only on its temperature—the higher the temperature of air the greater its capacity for moisture. *Absolute* humidity refers to the actual amount of water vapor present per unit volume of air and is usually expressed in grains per cubic foot. It is usually greater near the Equator than in the polar regions, greater in summer than in winter, and greater during the day than at night. Since distance from the sources of moisture also exercises an important control over the amount of water vapor in the air, absolute humidity is commonly greater over the ocean than over the interiors of continents.

Relative humidity refers to the amount of water vapor in the air compared with the amount that would be present if the air were saturated at that temperature, and is expressed in percentages determined by dividing the absolute humidity by the water-vapor capacity of the air. If the air is saturated its relative humidity is 100 per cent; if only half saturated, 50 per cent. Since the capacity of air for absorbing and retaining moisture varies with its temperature, the relative humidity of an air mass can be altered by merely changing its temperature, without changing the actual amount of moisture present in it. Relative humidity is important in determining the amount and rate of evaporation and also in predicting whether there can be any precipitation.

Measurement of Relative Humidity. Moisture will evaporate more quickly in dry than in relatively humid air, and more freely in circulating than in stagnant air. Furthermore, the lowering of temperature attendant upon evaporation is proportional to the amount of moisture vaporized. Upon these principles is based the determination of relative humidity by means of a *sling psychrometer.* This instrument consists of two thermometers, one with a wick of wet muslin around the bulb, the other dry, and the whole attached to a frame equipped with a handle by which it can be whirled. Unless the air is completely saturated, the wet-bulb thermometer will register a lower temperature than the dry, because heat is taken from the air around the wet bulb in the process of evaporation. The amount of difference in temperature between the two bulbs is inversely proportional to the humidity of the air. Psychrometric tables have been mathematically worked out, from which relative humidity may be read directly, once the difference in the reading of the two thermometers is known.

Condensation of Water Vapor. As stated above, the capacity of the air to hold moisture depends on its temperature. If unsaturated air is sufficiently cooled, a temperature is reached at which the air is saturated. This temperature is called the *dew point.* On further cooling, the capacity of the air for moisture is further reduced and condensation and precipitation take place, the excess water vapor appearing as clouds, fog or rain, or, if the temperature is below 32°F., as snow, hail or sleet. When the relative humidity of air is high, only a small amount of cooling is necessary to start condensation; when it is low, on the other hand, a large amount of cooling is necessary to reach the dew point. As a rule warm air has greater moisture content and therefore greater potentialities for condensation than cold air.

Dew and Frost. On cool nights in autumn, when radiation from the ground is relatively rapid, the air in contact with the ground may be chilled to the dew point and moisture will condense on the leaves and grass. If the dew point is at or below the freezing point, the condensation takes the form of tiny ice crystals, or frost. Dew and frost form on grass quite readily, because grass is a good radiator and therefore cools quickly; furthermore, grass and other plants give off moisture which is not readily evaporated at night when the air is cool. The formation of dew or frost is impeded by dry air, which must be greatly cooled to reach the dew point; by winds, which mix the air and prevent the lower portion from reaching the dew point; and by clouds, which slow up terrestrial radiation. Because low ground is moister and also because cold air from the uplands flows down slope into valleys, dew and frost are more likely to occur on low flat ground than on slopes.

Clouds and Fog. Clouds are formed by the condensation of water vapor around nuclei of minute dust particles in the air. In most cases, clouds consist of tiny droplets of water, but those formed where the moisture is below freezing are composed of ice particles. Most clouds are formed by the rising of warm, moist air, the ascending air expanding and cooling until the dew point is reached and some of the moisture condenses into clouds. Other clouds result from mixing along the contact between two air masses of different temperatures. Clouds at and near the earth's surface are known as fog.

There are three principal cloud types, distinguishable partly by form and partly by height above the ground. *Cumulus* clouds resembling great bunches of cotton with flat bases and cauliflower domes result from the rising of localized masses of air on warm sunny days. Ordinarily they indicate fair weather, but on very hot summer days, when convection is well developed, they may extend to great height and develop into towering, flat-topped thunderheads, which may produce local thunder showers. *Cirrus* clouds are thin clouds that occur at high altitude and are normally composed of minute ice particles. They vary in form from thin, scattered, wispy strands to an unbroken veil of fibrous texture covering the whole sky. Seen through cirrus clouds the sun and moon often have rings, or halos. Because they are often the first indication of an approaching front, cirrus clouds are frequently the forerunners of an approaching storm. *Stratus* clouds are low-lying and have the appearance of layers, or strata. They are often formed by the meeting of two air masses of different temperatures and are common during stormy weather. Gradations between the three principal types of clouds are given compound names, such as strato-cumulus, cumulo-cirrus and cumulo-stratus. The term *nimbus* is given to any dark cloud which is a source of precipitation.

Fog is a cloud in contact with the ground. It is often formed in lowlands at night when the air is chilled to the dew point, and also when a warm, moist mass of air meets and mixes with a cold one. The dense fogs in the Atlantic south of Newfoundland are formed by the meeting of the winds from the warm Gulf Stream and those from the cold Labrador Current.

FIG. 6-8. Cirrus clouds, often the first indication of an approaching storm.
(U. S. Weather Bureau, F. Ellerman)

FIG. 6-9. Cumulus clouds of fair weather. *(U. S. Weather Bureau)*

FIG. 6-10. Stratus Clouds: low stratus with altostratus overcast, during the passage of a slow-moving cold front. Such clouds do not make spectacular pictures. *(U. S. Weather Bureau)*

FIG. 6-11. Cumulonimbus clouds, sometimes called thunderheads. Rain is falling from the center of the cloud mass. *(U. S. Navy and U. S. Weather Bureau)*

Forms of Precipitation. Precipitation results from the continued condensation and growth of the moisture particles until they become too large to remain suspended in the air. If condensation takes place at a temperature above 32°F. the resulting precipitation is in the form of *rain.* If rain passes through a layer of colder air on the way down it may freeze and fall as *sleet.* In the strong, turbulent currents of thunderstorms water drops may be carried upward into freezing temperatures and eventually fall as *hail.* In fact, violent air currents may keep hailstones shuttling up and down until they grow to enormous sizes. *Snow* is not frozen rain, but forms when moisture crystallizes directly from vapor at a temperature below freezing. If snowflakes grow without interference they form beautifully symmetrical, six-sided crystals. *Ice storms* result when rain already near the freezing point falls on the colder ground and vegetation and freezes upon contact.

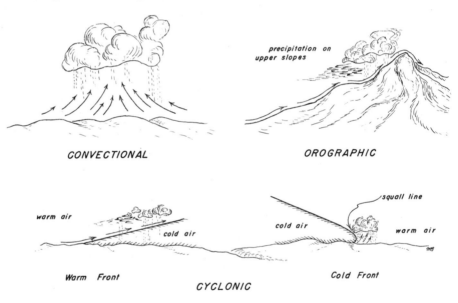

FIG. 6-12. **Types of precipitation.** Precipitation generally results from the rising and cooling of warm, moist air. In the convectional type, the air rises because it has been made warm and light by long contact with the heated ground. Orographic precipitation takes place where warm, moisture-bearing winds are forced to rise over highlands. Cyclonic precipitation is of two kinds. As a warm air mass encroaches on a cold one, it must rise over the cold, heavier air. A warm-front passage is, therefore, often accompanied by gently falling precipitation which may continue for days. But when the cold air mass is the encroaching one, it noses the warm air violently upward and initiates a series of wind and rain storms of short duration—making a squall line along the cold front.

Types of Precipitation. It is now apparent that precipitation is caused by the cooling of relatively warm, moist air. The most effective method of cooling large masses of air is to cause them to ascend to a higher altitude. Three types of rising air masses produce most of the earth's precipitation. (1) *Convectional* precipitation occurs when moist air over heated ground becomes warmer than the surrounding air and is forced to rise, expand, cool, and yield some of its moisture. Convectional rain is common in low latitudes and on hot summer days in middle latitudes, and usually comes in the form of short heavy showers just after the hottest part of the day. Thunder and lightning generally accompany the showers and, if the convection currents are especially strong and

FIG. 6-13. Tipping bucket rain gauge. *(Julien P. Friez and Sons, Inc., Baltimore)*

turbulent, hail is formed. (2) *Orographic* precipitation occurs when moist wind is forced to rise over a mountain or other elevation athwart its path. Thus the windward sides of many mountain ranges receive heavy precipitation, whereas the leeward sides, on which the air moves down, are dry. (3) *Cyclonic* precipitation often occurs in low-pressure areas, or cyclones, where winds from various directions converge and force large volumes of light air to rise. Cyclones and cyclonic weather will be discussed more fully later.

Measurement of Precipitation. Precipitation is measured in the number of inches, tenths and hundredths of inches of rain, or its equivalent in melted snow, that falls on a given exposed surface. Any straight-sided bucket or can may be used to catch the rain, the depth of which is then measured with a ruler. The standard United States Weather Bureau rain gauge consists of a cylindrical tank eight inches in diameter. A funnel fits over the open end of this cylinder and leads into a smaller inner cylinder, the cross-section area of which is one-tenth that of the top of the funnel. Thus the accumulation of water in the inner cylinder is ten times the depth of the actual rainfall. In this manner slight rainfall can be measured quite accurately. Some rain gauges are equipped with a tipping hopper or bucket which is electrically connected with a recording apparatus. The weight of each one-hundredth of an inch of rain tips the hopper and closes the electric circuit which operates a counter on the recording apparatus.

Suggestions for Further Reading

BLAIR, T. A., *Weather Elements*, revised by R. C. FITE (Englewood Cliffs, N. J., Prentice-Hall, 1957).

CAVE, C. J. P., *Clouds and Weather Phenomena* (New York, Macmillan, 1944).

GRANT, Hugh Duncan, *Cloud and Weather Atlas* (New York, Coward-McCann, 1944).

KOEPPE, C. E., and DELONG, George C., *Weather and Climate* (New York, McGraw-Hill, 1958).

PETTERSSEN, Sverre, *Introduction to Meteorology* (New York, McGraw-Hill, 1958).

TREWARTHA, Glenn T., *Introduction to Climate*, 3rd Ed. (New York, McGraw-Hill, 1954).

U. S. NAVY, *Aerology for Pilots* (New York, McGraw-Hill, 1943).

—— 7 ——

Climatic Controls

THE CLIMATE of any given place depends on its location with respect to (1) latitude, (2) the main pressure and wind belts, (3) ocean currents, (4) land and water, (5) altitude, (6) mountain barriers and (7) cyclonic and other storms. If we gain a clear understanding of the effects of these climatic controls, we can form a fairly correct estimate of the climate of a place merely by looking at the map.

LATITUDE

The primary factor in the variation and distribution of the climates of the earth is the unequal heating of the earth's surface. Latitude is the principal cause of this inequality. It exercises its control by determining (1) the intensity of solar radiation and (2) the length of daylight.

Intensity of Solar Radiation. The average altitude of the sun decreases from the Equator to the poles. At the Equator the noonday sun is never more than 23¼° from the vertical. At the tropics of Cancer and Capricorn the average altitude of the sun at noon is 66½° above the horizon; at the Arctic and Antarctic circles the average is 23½°; at the poles the sun is never more than 23½° above the horizon and is below the horizon for half the year. The more nearly perpendicular the sun's rays are when they strike the earth the greater is the insolation per unit area, because the heat of a given amount of sunshine is concentrated on a relatively small area. Slanting rays, on the other hand, spread out over a large surface and deliver less energy per unit area.

The intensity of solar radiation received at the surface (insolation) also depends on the amount of atmosphere the sun's rays must penetrate. When the sun is low its rays must travel through the atmosphere a greater distance than when it is high. At the times of the equinoxes the path of the sun's rays through the atmosphere is twice as long in latitude 60° as it is at the Equator. The more oblique the rays are, the greater the distance through the atmosphere, and the greater the absorption, scattering and reflection of the insolation. A part of the energy that is scattered and reflected is sent back into space and lost to the earth.

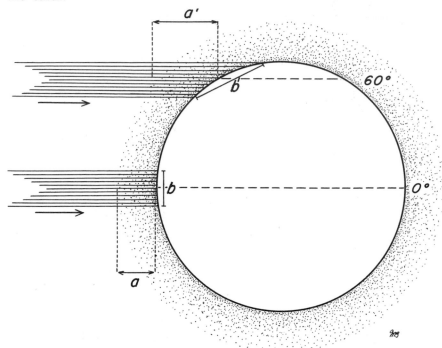

FIG. 7-1. Variation of insolation with latitude. With increasing latitude a given amount of solar radiation must pass through a greater thickness of atmosphere (*a* cf. *a'*) and must furthermore be spread over a larger surface on the earth. (*b* cf. *b'*)

Altitude of the Sun's Rays at Noon Above the Horizon

Latitude		Maximum		Minimum		Average
90°	N.—North Pole ..	23½°	June 21	−23½°	(below horizon) Dec. 22	0°
66½°	N.—Arctic Circle..	47°	June 21	0°	Dec. 22 (just at horizon)	23½°
23½°	N.—Cancer	90°	June 21	43°	Dec. 22	66½°
0°	—Equator	90°	March 21 Sept. 23	66½°	June 21 Dec. 22	78.3°
23½°	S.—Capricorn	90°	Dec. 22	43°	June 21	66½°
66½°	S.—Antarctic Circle	47°	Dec. 22	0°	June 21	23½°
90°	S.—South Pole ..	23½°	Dec. 22	−23½°	(below horizon) June 21	0°

Length of Day. At the Equator the days and nights are each twelve hours long throughout the year. Away from the Equator the days and nights are equal only at the times of the equinoxes; in summer the days are more and in winter less than twelve hours long. The length of summer days and winter nights increases directly with distance from the Equator, the rate of increase becoming very much accelerated in high latitudes, until each is six months long at the poles. That is to say that at the poles the sun is continuously above the horizon for six months and below the horizon for the other six months of the year. At first thought the unequal length of day and night would seemingly not affect the average yearly effectiveness of the sun, the long nights of winter being offset by the long days of summer. But, the long winter nights and short days of high latitudes allow snow and ice to accumulate for several months. When the long summer days do come, a great deal of their heat must be expended in melting the winter's accumulation of snow and ice before the land can be warmed. Seasonal variation in the length of day also plays a large part in producing the markedly contrasting cold and warm seasons of middle and higher latitudes. The longer days together with the higher altitude of the sun in summer make it understandable why summer temperatures are so much higher than those of winter in these latitudes.

Extremes in the Lengths of Day in Different Latitudes

Latitude	Longest Day, Hours and Minutes	Shortest Day, Hours and Minutes
0°	12:00	12:00
10°	12:35	11:25
23½°	13:26	10:34
40°	14:51	9.09
66½°	24:00	0.00

Distribution of Temperature. Latitude is the greatest single control of the distribution of temperature on the earth. All parts of the world in the same latitude have the same length of day and receive the sun's rays at the same angle. If latitude were the only control of the distribution of temperature, there would be a uniform decrease everywhere from Equator to poles, and *isotherms* (lines of equal temperature) would coincide with the parallels. Isotherms do have a general east-west trend, but factors other than latitude cause them to depart notably from the parallels. Foremost among the processes of temperature distribution are the *planetary winds* and the *ocean currents*.

The great circulations of air and water on the earth are mainly due to the imbalance between insolation and terrestrial radiation in different latitudes. In low latitudes insolation is greater than terrestrial radiation; in high latitudes insolation is less than terrestrial radiation. The movement of air in the planetary winds and of water in the ocean currents are attempts of the mobile parts of the earth to equalize the latitudinal distribution of heat.

In addition to the major processes of heat distribution, named above, there are other factors, more or less related to these processes, which have local influence on the latitudinal distribution of heat. The most important of these local factors are the relation of land and water, altitude, mountain barriers, and storms of various kinds and origins.

It should be realized that the above processes and factors have influences not only on the temperature, but also on the other elements of weather and climate. These are discussed blow.

MAIN PRESSURE AND WIND BELTS

Decrease in average annual insolation in relation to terrestrial radiation from the Equator toward the poles and the rotation of the earth from west to east together set up the circulation of the main wind belts, or planetary winds, which prevail over most of the earth. In the equatorial region, where annual insolation is greatest, an irregular belt 15° to 20° wide of low pressure with ascending air encircles the earth. This belt is known as the equatorial low-pressure belt, or the *doldrums,* or the *intertropical convergence zone.* As the air rises it expands and cools, finally reaching the dew point, with resultant clouds and precipitation. The heavy rain and thundershowers of the equatorial regions come in the middle or late afternoon after the daily temperature maximum.

On the poleward sides of the tropics in latitude about 30°N. and S. lie two belts, one in each hemisphere, where the atmospheric pressure is relatively high. These are the subtropical highs, or *horse latitudes.* The air that rises in the equatorial low-pressure belt moves northward and southward at high altitude. After remaining aloft for a while it is sufficiently cooled to settle in the subtropical highs. The descending air is contracting and becoming warmer; conditions are therefore not favorable for precipitation. Calm, light winds and aridity are typical.

Along the surface the air moves from the subtropical belts of high pressure to the equatorial low. Rotation of the earth deflects these winds to the right in the Northern Hemisphere and to the left in the Southern Hemisphere. Blowing from the northeast in the Northern Hemisphere and the southeast in the Southern Hemisphere, they are known as the northeast and the southeast *trade winds,* respectively. The trade winds, unless forced to rise over mountains, have no tendency to become cool and generally do not bring rainfall.

Only a portion of the air descending in the horse latitudes moves toward the Equator; the remainder moves toward the poles. This poleward moving air, deflected to the east by the rotation of the earth, gives rise to the two great belts of prevailing *westerly winds,* one from

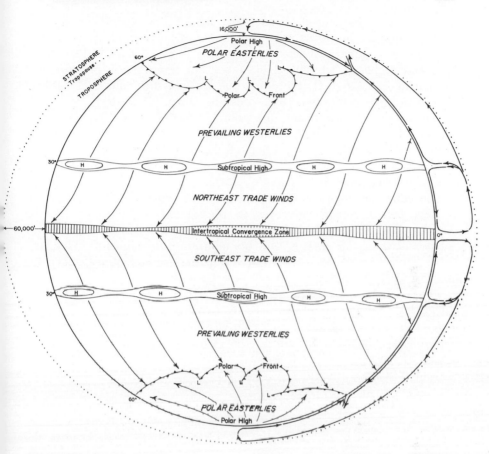

FIG. 7-2. Diagram of the planetary pressure and wind belts, including the intertropical convergence zone and the polar fronts. The thickness of the troposphere and the vertical circulation of air are also shown.

about 35°N. to 60°N. latitude, the other from about 35°S. to 60°S. latitude. These westerly winds are much interrupted by the variable winds of cyclonic storms which give rise to variable weather in all seasons.

Near the Arctic and Antarctic circles the pressure is somewhat lower than it is either poleward or Equatorward. Prominent centers of low pressure within this belt of the Northern Hemisphere are the Aleutian and Icelandic *lows,* toward which move many of the cyclonic storms of the westerly wind belt.

In the polar regions the atmospheric pressure tends to be permanently high because of low temperature. From these *polar highs* the air moves toward the Equator to the subpolar low-pressure belts. The southward and northward moving air masses are deflected westward by rotation, giving rise to the *northeast polar* and *southeast polar* winds, respectively.

Thus, on a globe unaffected by contrasts between land and sea, lowland and highland, we should have belts of atmospheric pressure and movement as follows: (1) the equatorial low-pressure calms, (2) easterly trade winds, (3) subtropical high-pressure calms, (4) westerly winds, (5) subpolar low-pressure calms, (6) polar easterlies, and (7) polar high-pressure calms. These belts shift position by some 20° from season to season with the changing position of the sun. Hence, there are many localities, such as southern California, which belong to one belt in one season and to another belt in another season.

The subpolar low-pressure belt is not well defined. There are more or less persistent low pressures in the regions of Iceland and the Aleutians. At most places, however, this subpolar belt is an area of lobate, clashing air masses, the boundaries of which shift back and forth. Outbursts of polar air from this boundary sometimes sweep far into the lower latitudes.

The irregular, lobate boundary between the polar air sweeping into lower latitudes and the warmer air moving poleward is called the *polar front*. Much of our changeable weather in the middle latitudes is due to the changes of fortune in the contest along the polar front between air masses of different origins.

OCEAN CURRENTS

In each ocean there is a great gyral-shaped current of complex origin, those in the Northern Hemisphere moving clockwise and those in the Southern Hemisphere counterclockwise. The direction of prevailing winds, the shapes of the water bodies, temperature differences, and the rotation of the earth all contribute to the production of these currents. In the North Atlantic the *Gulf Stream* moves from the Caribbean Sea and the Gulf of Mexico northeastward to the westerly wind belt, which it follows eastward across the Atlantic where it is called the *West Wind Drift,* or the *North Atlantic Drift.* This current carries middle-latitude temperatures to subpolar Iceland. On approaching Europe the current divides, one part going by northwestern Europe to temper the climate of the British Isles and the coastal region of Scandinavia. The other part turns southward to skirt northwest Africa, where it is called the *Canaries Current.* When it reaches the trade-wind belt, the Canaries current flows westward across the Atlantic again as the *North Equatorial Current.* In the South Atlantic the *Brazilian Current* moves southward along the coast of Brazil to the westerly wind belt, which it follows eastward as the West Wind Drift. On approaching South Africa the greater part of the current turns northward past southwest Africa as the *Benguela Current* and then westward in the trade-wind belt as the *South Equatorial Current.* Each of the other oceans has a great circulation system similar to those in the North and South Atlantic.

Ocean currents affect climate by carrying warm water into colder regions and cold water into warmer regions. Onshore winds in turn carry these temperatures to the adjacent lands. Winds blowing over warm water gather much moisture, and if cooled on reaching land, cause heavy rainfall. Because of the warm currents in the North Atlantic and the North Pacific, northwestern Europe and northwestern North America have milder and wetter winters than would otherwise be the case. On the other hand, winds blowing from cold waters tend to cause aridity and lower the temperature of adjacent lands. The Peruvian and Chilean coastal desert results in part from the drying westerly winds blowing from the cold *Humboldt,* or *Peru, Current.*

In the Northern Hemisphere the eastward-moving currents in the westerly wind belt carry warm water far to the east and carry warmth and moisture to the lands on which they impinge, because the North Atlantic and the North Pacific do not have broad communication with the cold water of the Arctic. On the other hand, the eastward-moving currents of the Southern Hemisphere are much colder, because of the broad access to the cold water of the Antarctic region. Southern South America is the only land area of the Southern Hemisphere that extends into latitudes that are high enough to be affected by the cold, dry air from the eastward-moving ocean current.

RELATION OF LAND AND WATER

Water bodies become warm more slowly and also cool more slowly than do adjacent land surfaces. This is due in part to the greater specific heat[1] of water, in part to the fact that the sun's rays penetrate water to a greater depth than they do the land, thus distributing their heat to a thicker layer of material, and in part to the mobility of water which allows convection currents to distribute the temperature. Land areas are, therefore, usually warmer in summer and colder in winter than are adjacent oceans. In the middle latitudes of the Northern Hemisphere, where land areas are largest, the difference in temperature between land and water is most pronounced.

Monsoons. Since the continents are relatively warm in summer and cold in winter, the pressure over them is generally lower in summer and higher in winter than over the oceans in the same latitudes. Therefore winds, resulting from the difference in pressure, tend to blow

[1] Specific heat of a substance is the number of calories required to raise the temperature of one gram one degree C.

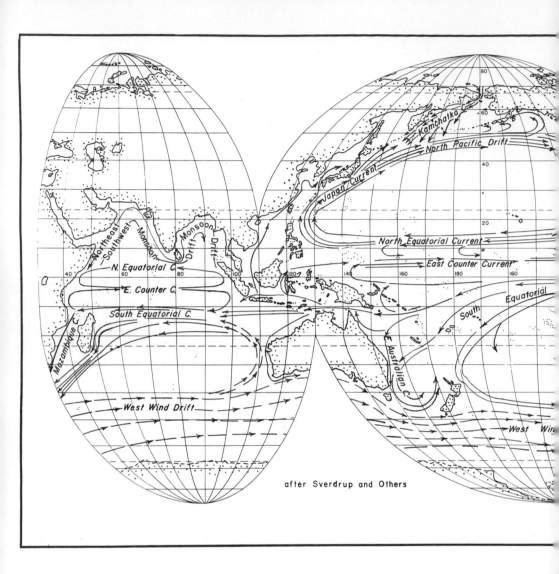

FIG. 7-3. Ocean curren

110

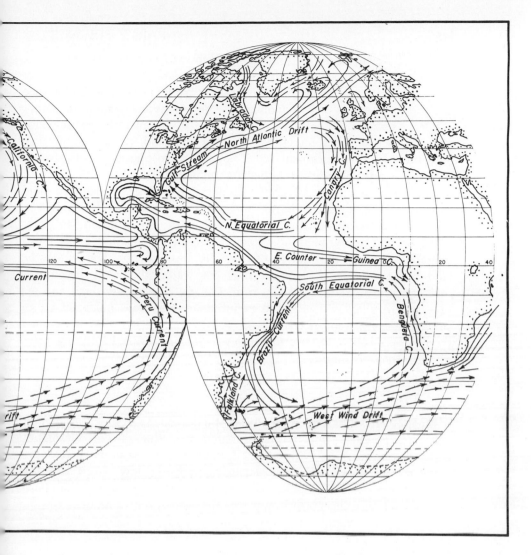

111

toward the continents in summer and toward the oceans in winter. These seasonal winds, known as *monsoons,* are best developed over Southern India and the Indian Ocean and are of noticeable importance in North America. So pronounced is the monsoon system in southeastern Asia that it dominates the climate. In summer the moist winds from the ocean, when forced to rise over the land, cause heavy rains; in winter the cold continent with its high atmospheric pressure sends cold, dry winds toward the relatively warm ocean.

Land and Sea Breezes. Daily temperature contrasts between land and water produce small diurnal monsoons called land and sea breezes. Along coasts there is often a drift of cool, heavy air from land to water at night and early morning, when the land has cooled to a lower temperature than the water. During the heat of the day, when the land becomes warmer than the adjacent water, the wind direction is reversed and a breeze comes in from the sea. These daily land and sea breezes are shallow winds and penetrate only a few miles inland or seaward. Along tropical coasts and also in middle latitudes in summer the cool sea breeze is very important in making coastal locations more pleasant than the interiors.

ALTITUDE

Increase in altitude is normally characterized by a decrease in temperature, pressure, and absolute humidity. Although both insolation and radiation increase with elevation, the fact that the latter increases at a faster rate than the former partly explains the low temperatures of lands at high altitudes. Exposed to the direct rays of the sun parts of highlands may become quite warm at midday, but at night, when the sun disappears, rapid radiation in the thin dry air causes the surface to cool off quickly. A wide diurnal range in temperature is usually typical of high lands.

Although absolute humidity decreases with increasing altitude, the relative humidity does not change much because of the decrease in temperature. Precipitation usually increases with increasing altitude, reaching a maximum at about 4,000 to 7,000 feet. Above 7,000 feet the lower temperature and lower absolute humidity cause the amount of precipitation to decline.

MOUNTAIN BARRIERS

Mountains athwart the path of prevailing winds greatly affect the distribution of rainfall. As air rises over such mountains it is cooled by expansion, and most of its moisture is precipitated on the windward side. On descending the leeward side, however, the air becomes dry and clear because it is being compressed and warmed. The dry leeward side of the mountain and the adjacent lowland constitute a *rain shadow*. From the Sierra Nevada-Cascade ranges eastward to the 100th meridian most of the United States is arid; and even farther east, in the Mississippi Valley, there are sometimes droughts. In western Europe, on the other hand, where the north-south mountains are not very high or continuous the winds that have picked up warmth and moisture from the Gulf Stream are able to penetrate far inland, and that half of Europe is well watered.

Mountain barriers also greatly influence the distribution of temperature. The subtropical climate of southern Europe is partly due to the fact that the Alps shut out the cold north winds. In this region oranges and palms grow in the latitude of New York and Boston. In the United States, however, there are no lofty east-west mountains, and cold waves from the north cause destructive frosts as far south as New Orleans and northern Florida. The orientation of any given locality also affects its climate; slopes facing south and southwestward receive more insolation than others.

STORMS

Importance of Storms. Storms are important in producing various types of weather, but perhaps they are of greatest significance as generators of precipitation. With the exception of orographic rain, nearly all of the earth's precipitation is produced by storms. As indicated earlier, most precipitation results from the condensation of moisture contained in rising and expanding masses of warm, moist air. Storms provide effective mechanisms for raising large quantities of air aloft.

Middle Latitude Cyclones and Anticyclones. *Nature and Distribution.* A low-pressure area, or mass of light air, with its associated weather phenomena is known as a *cyclone,* or a low. The *anticyclone,* or high, is an area of high atmospheric pressure, or a mass of heavy air, with its associated weather. These lows and highs vary from a few to several hundred miles in diameter. In cyclones the temperature is relatively high, winds converge toward the center from various directions, and quantities of warm air are forced to rise aloft where condensation and precipitation are likely to occur. In anticyclones, on the other hand, cold air slowly settles from aloft and winds move outward from the high center, giving clear cool weather. Cyclones and anticyclones are typical of the westerly wind belts of both the Northern and Southern hemispheres. In other regions they are scarcely noticeable. As a rule they are more pronounced and move faster in winter than in summer.

Origin and Movement. Differences of opinion exist as to the origin of cyclones and anticyclones. The most widely accepted hypothesis is the Polar Front Theory which was advanced by Bjerknes, a Norwegian meterologist. According to this viewpoint the highs and lows of the westerly wind belts result from the interactions and alternation of two contrasting types of air masses, one originating in the polar regions and the other in the subtropics. Cold air from the polar highs moves Equatorward and is deflected westward, forming the northeast and the southeast polar winds. Warmer air from the subtropical highs moves poleward and, by eastward deflection, forms the westerly winds. The contact between these contrasting air masses is the *polar front*. Eddies, or waves,

FIG. 7-4. Diagram showing the different types of air masses and fronts in the middle latitudes and the types of precipitation that accompany the passage of cyclones.

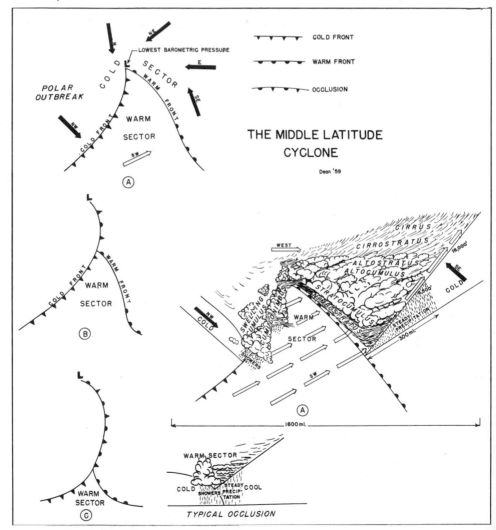

develop along this contact and the front becomes highly irregular, consisting of interlocking tongues of the two types of air masses. The tongues of subtropical air form the cyclones, while the polar tongues produce the anticyclones.

Both the cyclones and the anticyclones almost always move from west to east. They might be considered as eddies in the westerly winds, and their path across the United States depends largely on where the storm first enters the country. As a rule the cyclones pass over the northeastern United States and Gulf of St. Lawrence and move toward the Icelandic low-pressure area over the North Atlantic. Anticyclones have a tendency to move southeastward toward the Azores high in the horse latitudes.

FIG. 7-5. Types and directions of movement of the air masses that affect North America.

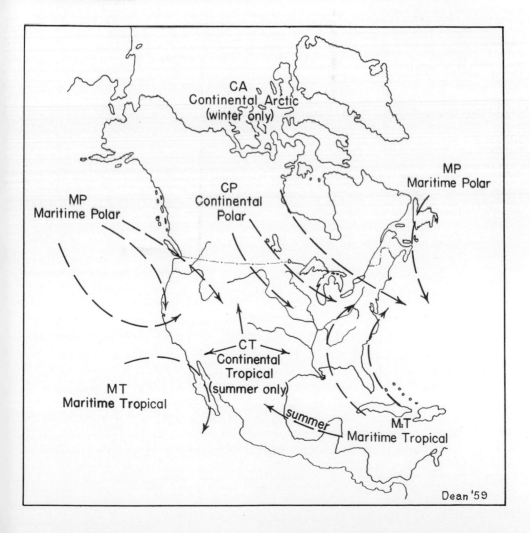

Fronts. The contact between air masses of different properties is called a front. Where the leading edge of a cold air mass is moving under and lifting up warmer air we have a *cold front.* On the other hand the trailing edge of a cold air mass that is followed by warm air is called a *warm front.* In each case precipitation is likely to occur, because warm air is rising over cold air. The duration and the intensity of the precipitation along the two fronts is quite different. The cold front is steep and produces showery, and sometimes violent, precipitation of short duration; whereas the warm front may produce steady precipitation for a longer period of time. See Figure 7-4.

At times the protruding tongues of cold air may trap projections of the opposing warm air mass. Such a pocket of warm air is a cyclone, into which the colder air moves, giving to the central part of the system a counterclockwise direction of motion. If the cold front moves faster than the warm front in such a trap, part or all of the pocket of warm air may be lifted from the surface, thus producing an *occluded front.* This process marks the dying stage of a cyclone. On being raised aloft the warm air mass gives up much of its moisture and its temperature and thus loses its earlier characteristics.

Thunderstorms. Thunderstorms are developed by strong updrafts of warm, moist air. They are of two main types, (1) the local convection thunderstorm and (2) the cyclonic squall-line (frontal) thunderstorm.

Local Convection Thunderstorms. These storms typically occur on hot, humid, calm days in the afternoon or early evening. As the ground is warmed the air rises and, if the air is humid, cumulus clouds appear. If the convection currents are strong the clouds grow to cumulonimbus, or thunderheads, and give rise to a heavy downfall of rain with attendant thunder and lightning. Hail occasionally develops in very intense thunderstorms. These disturbances are usually small in area and of short duration. On a hot summer afternoon in the middle latitudes dozens of them may occur in a single state, and in the equatorial belt of calms local thunderstorms are almost a daily occurrence.

Cyclonic Squall-Line Thunderstorms. This type of thunderstorm is associated with the middle latitude cyclones. The squall-line is the windshift line in a cyclone, which marks the abrupt meeting place of warm humid air from low latitudes with the colder heavier air from higher latitudes. When these winds of contrasting direction, humidity, and density meet, the warm air is forced rapidly aloft and violent thunderstorms sometimes result. Since these storms are not dependent on local surface heating, they may occur at any time of day or night and even occasionally in winter. The squall-line thunderstorm is usually followed by a shift of wind to the northwest and a sudden drop in temperature.

Tornadoes are sometimes associated with squall-line thunderstorms

FIG. 7-6A and 6B. Above is Toler Huff's farmstead in North Dakota before the tornado. Below is the scene a few minutes after the tornado struck. This illustrates the sharp boundary of the path of a tornado. The barn was unroofed, while the nearby house was not damaged.

and are of exceptionally great violence. When two highly contrasting air masses meet at a sharp angle a gyratory whirl is caused which results in a very low pressure in the center. In the center of the whirl the pressure may be so low that the air in houses expands with such force as to blow out the windows and even the walls. Wind rushes toward the center with velocities up to 500 miles per hour. Fortunately, tornadoes are of small size, and, with the exception of the Mississippi Valley region where they strike most frequently, are relatively rare.

Waterspouts are essentially the same as tornadoes, except that they occur over bodies of water. The low pressure and rapidly rising air at the center actually carry surface water up into the cone-shaped spout. Ships are sometimes swamped by the deluge from a waterspout.

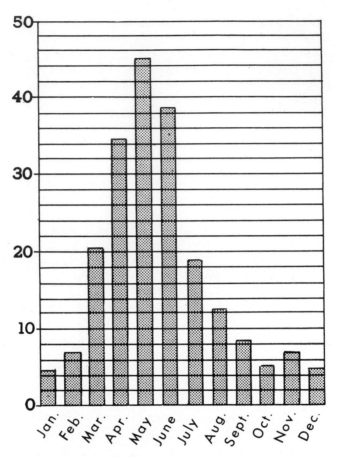

FIG. 7-7. Tornado seasons in the United States. Based on data from 1916 to 1957. The average number of tornadoes ranges from 24 per year in one of the midwestern states to less than one per year in most of the northeastern and far western states. The national average is around 200 a year, over half of which occur in three months—April, May, and June. Tornadoes can occur at any hour of the day or night, but they appear to form most readily in the hours closely following the warmest parts of the day. Forty-three per cent of these storms have occurred between the hours of 3 to 7 p.m.; 82 per cent have occurred between noon and midnight. The individual hours of 4 to 5 p.m. and 5 to 6 p.m. are those during which the greatest number have been reported. These two hours account for 23 per cent of the storms. (U. S. Weather Bureau)

118

Lightning is an electric spark passing from cloud to cloud or from a cloud to the ground. The immediate cause of lightning is a difference of electrical potential. Since the ground is negatively charged, the accumulation of a positive charge in a cloud near the ground will cause a discharge from the cloud to the ground. Most lightning, however, is from one cloud, or portion of a cloud, to another. Authorities do not

FIG. 7-8. A tornado. *(U. S. Weather Bureau)*

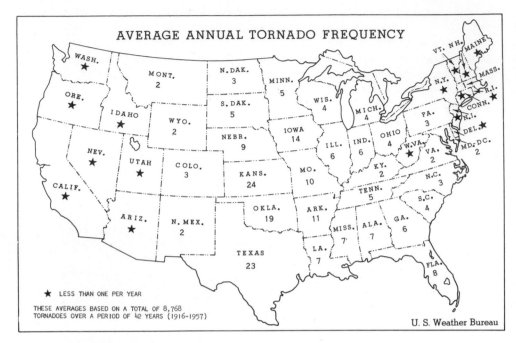

FIG. 7-9. Average annual tornado frequency. *(U. S. Weather Bureau)*

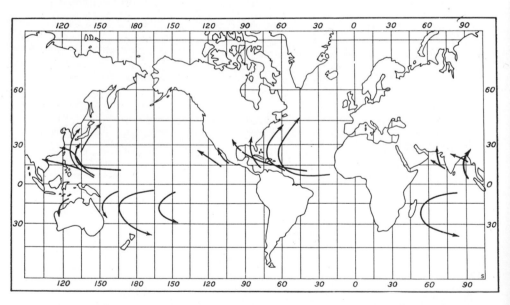

FIG. 7-10. Principal world regions of tropical cyclones. Arrows indicate general areas of occurrence and direction of motion. *(U. S. Weather Bureau)*

agree upon the cause for both positive and negative charges in the clouds. Some state that raindrops are positively charged when growing and negatively charged when evaporating; others think that the larger raindrops in the lower clouds are positively charged while the smaller drops, carried higher aloft, are negative. In any case, *thunder* is the result of the sudden violent expansion of the air caused by the great heat in the path of the lightning.

Tropical Cyclones. Tropical cyclones differ from those in middle latitudes in that they originate only over water; they have no anti-cyclonic companions; they are most common in the late summer rather than in winter, and they often are violent and destructive. These storms usually develop along the poleward margins of the doldrums in the late summer and early fall when that belt of calms is farthest from the Equator. At first they move westward with the trade winds, but then curve poleward. As a rule they soon lose their intensity on reaching land or on moving into the middle latitudes. Occasionally, however, they carry their destructive power from the West Indies region as far north as New England. In the West Indies and the South Pacific the tropical cyclones are known as *hurricanes*; around the Philippines and southern China they are called *typhoons*; in the Indian Ocean they are simply cyclones.

In tropical cyclones of the hurricane or typhoon variety the pressure gradient is very steep. The total diameter of the whirl is usually no more than 100 to 200 miles and the pressure at the center is often below 28 inches. Wind velocities are very high, occasionally reaching a speed of 130 miles per hour. Rainfall is heavy, especially in front of the center.

WEATHER FORECASTING

Reports are regularly received by the central office of the United States Weather Bureau from several hundred weather stations throughout the country. From these data the daily weather map is constructed and forecasts for various sections of the country are made. Until recent years the forecasters depended almost entirely on ground observations; their chief aims were to estimate the paths and velocities of highs and lows and their influence on the weather as they traveled across the country.

Air-Mass Analysis. In contact with the earth's surface, land or water, air becomes warm or cold, moist or dry, depending on the surface over which it lies. Any large portion of the atmosphere which becomes somewhat stagnated, that is moves slowly over a uniform surface, acquires characteristics which mark it as an individual *air mass*. On moving from its source region an air mass is modified by the surface over which it moves, the degree of modification depending on the nature of the new surface with which it is in contact and the length of time spent in passing.

With the rather widespread acceptance of the Polar Front Theory of origin of cyclones and anticyclones and the improvement of methods of observation aloft, weather forecasting is now based on detailed study of the structure of the air by means of frequent observations at the surface and also aloft. The method of air-mass analysis now in common use in Europe and the United States involves a more detailed measurement of the actual physical conditions of the air, especially aloft, than the older pressure-system method. In this analysis the forecaster attempts to ascertain the location and the physical properties of the different air masses and their relations to each other. He then locates the boundary surfaces between the air masses of contrasting origin and properties, for along such boundaries, or fronts, most of the weather changes originate. Another fact, essential in forecasting, is that these air masses and their fronts generally travel in an easterly direction. Even so, forecasts are not always accurate, because of changes in direction, velocity, and physical properties of the moving air masses.

FIG. 7-11. Diagram of wind circulation in a hurricane. *(U. S. Weather Bureau)*

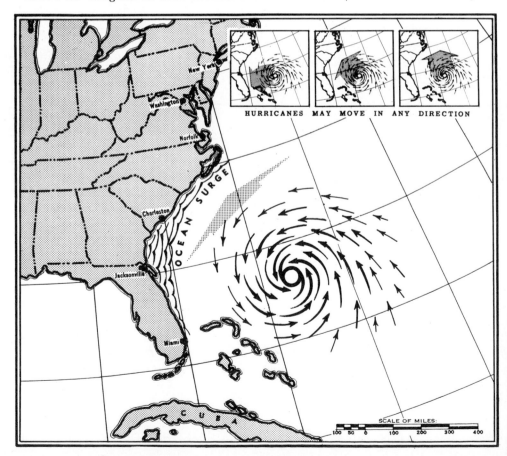

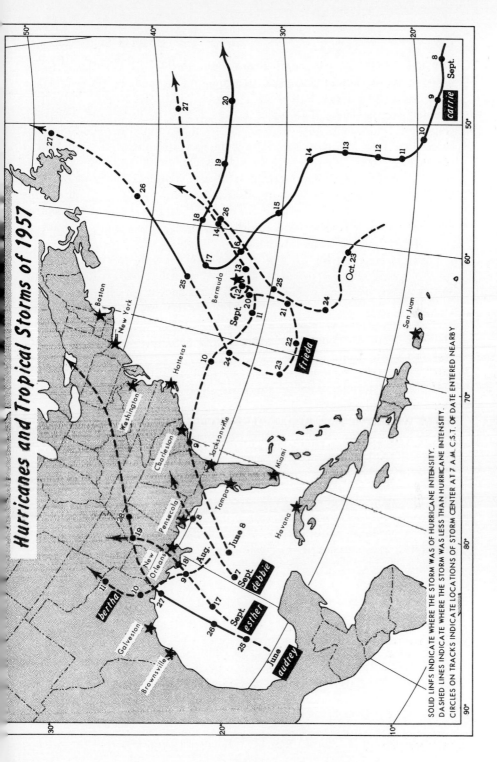

FIG. 7-12. Hurricanes and tropical storms of 1957. (*U. S. Weather Bureau*)

Types of Air Masses, and Fronts. On the U. S. Weather Bureau weather maps, letters are used to show the source, or origin, of the air masses. The large letters A, P, and T indicate Arctic, Polar and Tropical, respectively. The small letters c and m distinguish between continental and maritime, that is, those that originate over land and those that originate over sea. The principal air masses that make the weather of North America are: (1) cA, Arctic continental, (2) cP, Polar continental, (3) mP, Polar maritime, (4) mT, Tropical maritime, and (5) cT, Tropical continental. Figure 7-5 shows the sources and directions of movement of these air masses. The air masses leave their source regions and move across the middle latitudes where they interact to form the cyclones and anticlones.

Contacts between the air masses are shown on the weather maps by the front symbols. A warm front is shown by a line with a row of semicircles on the advancing side. A cold front is shown by a line with a row of sharp projections (saw teeth) pointing in the direction of movement. An occluded front is indicated by a line with alternating semicircles and saw teeth. In general, the cold fronts tend to move southeastward and the warm fronts northeastward. At the same time both drift eastward. The position of a front on any particular day can be predicted with more or less accuracy on the basis of its position and rate of movement on preceding days.

The weather of any locality is determined by the characteristics of the air masses present and by the phenomena that accompany the passage of the boundaries, or fronts. Success in forecasting weather depends in large measure on detailed information on the structure of the various air masses and the accurate location of fronts. The forecaster must also anticipate changes that will take place in the air masses and along the fronts. As the movements and other phenomena of the atmosphere are in accordance with known thermodynamical and hydrodynamical principles, the successful forecaster will make liberal use of these principles in his calculations.

Suggestions for Further Reading

BLAIR, T. A., *Weather Elements*, revised by R. C. FITE (Englewood Cliffs, N. J., Prentice Hall, 1957).

BLAIR, T. A., *Climatology* (Englewood Cliffs, N. J., Prentice-Hall, 1942).

BYERS, Horace R., *General Meteorology* (New York, McGraw-Hill, 1959).

HOLNABROE, J., GUSTIN, W., and FORSYTHE, G., *Dynamic Meteorology* (New York, Oxford University Press, 1943).

STARR, V. P., *Basic Principles of Weather Forecasting* (New York, Harper, 1942).

STEWARD, George R., *Storm* (New York, Random House, 1941).

TREWARTHA, Glenn T., *Introduction to Climate*, 3rd Ed. (New York, McGraw-Hill, 1954).

U. S. NAVY, *Aerology for Pilots* (New York, McGraw-Hill, 1943).

WILLETT, Hurd E., *Descriptive Meteorology* (New York, Academic Press, 1944).

—— 8 ——

Climatic Types

VARIATIONS in the amount, intensity, and seasonal
distribution of the elements controlling weather and climate give rise to
a great variety of climates on the earth, for which a considerable number of classifications have been devised. The ancient Greeks broadly
divided the earth into the winterless tropical region, the summerless
polar regions and the intermediate regions having both winter and
summer. This classification is too simple to be of much use, giving as
it does only a very generalized picture of temperature and taking no
account of precipitation. Among the more detailed classifications of
climates, that devised by W. Köppen of the University of Graz, based
on temperature and precipitation differences, has become more or less a
world standard. Insead of long descriptive names, Köppen uses a combination of letters, each one of which has precise meaning. As Köppen's
complete classification is probably too detailed for the average user of
this book we shall include only the main types, with the designating
letters and some of the secondary divisions as follows:

A. Tropical rainy climate

B. Dry climate
    Desert
    Semiarid

C. Humid mesothermal climate
    Marine west coast
    Mediterranean
    Monsoon

D. Humid microthermal climate

E. Polar climate
    Glacial
    Tundra

A. CLIMATE: TROPICAL RAINY

Characteristics. In regions possessing the tropical rainy climate the sun is never far from the zenith and the temperature is always high. According to Köppen's limits the average temperature of the coldest month must not be below 18°C. (64.4°F.); neither does the temperature rise often above 90°F. Variations fom day to night are greater than from season to season, except toward the poleward boundary, where a short season of coolness breaks the monotony of the high temperature. Even so, this type of climate has no true winter.

Thirty inches of rain is about the minimum for the tropical rainy climate and most localities have very much more. Because of the northward and southward migration of the vertical sunrays the rainfall in many areas is more or less seasonal, and most of it is either convectional or orographic. In the belt of calms near the heat equator the pecipitation is mainly convectional, coming in heavy afternoon showers often accompanied by lightning and thunder. Poleward from the belt of calms the eastern or windward sides of the continents receive orographic rain where the trade winds coming onshore must rise over the land.

Location. The region of the tropical rainy climate occupies an irregular belt extending from the Equator 10° to 20° both north and south. Because of the easterly direction of the trade winds the rainy belt is wider on the eastern than on the western sides of the continents, and in western South America it is notably interrupted by the high Andes Mountains. The three major land areas with this type of climate are in (1) northern South America, (2) central Africa and (3) the East Indies and adjacent portions of Asia.

Temperature and Precipitation Data for Representative Stations

(T = temperature in degrees Fahrenheit; P = precipitation in inches)

Singapore, Malaya. Lat. 1°14′N.; Long. 103°55′E.

	Jan.	Feb.	Mar.	Apr.	May	June	July	Aug.	Sept.	Oct.	Nov.	Dec.	Year
T.	78.3	79.0	80.2	80.8	81.5	81.1	81.0	80.6	80.4	80.1	79.3	78.6	80.1
P.	8.5	6.1	6.5	6.9	7.2	6.7	6.8	8.5	7.1	8.2	10.0	10.4	92.9

Calcutta, India. Lat. 22°32′N.; Long. 88°24′E.; Alt. 21 ft.

	Jan.	Feb.	Mar.	Apr.	May	June	July	Aug.	Sept.	Oct.	Nov.	Dec.	Year
T.	65.8	70.6	79.6	85.3	86.0	85.0	83.3	82.6	83.1	79.7	72.7	65.7	78.2
P.	0.4	1.1	1.4	2.1	5.3	11.5	12.4	12.5	9.5	4.6	0.5	0.2	61.5

It should be noted that Singapore, near the Equator, has a fairly uniform temperature, and precipitation is well distributed throughout the year, whereas Calcutta, farther from the Equator, has a difference of more than 20° between the coolest and the warmest months and distinct wet and dry seasons. These wet and dry seasons of Calcutta are due in large measure to the monsoon winds that are so strongly developed in southeastern Asia.

B. CLIMATE: DRY

Definition and Subdivisions of Dry Climate. The aridity of a climate depends not only on the amount of rainfall but also on the rate of evaporation, which in turn is controlled largely by temperature. A climate in which the rate of evaporation is greater than the precipitation—one in which there is no surplus of water to maintain a constant ground-water supply and to form permanent streams—is a dry climate. There are, of course, different degrees of aridity in the dry climate, so that two main subtypes are recognized: (1) the arid, or desert climate and (2) the semiarid, or steppe climate. The steppes usually more or less surround the deserts and form transitional zones between them and humid climates.

Location and Causes of Dry Climate. Dry climate is typical of the following locations: (1) the centers and western (leeward) sides of continents in the trade-wind belts, (2) the horse latitudes or subtropical high-pressure belts and (3) the interiors of continents in the middle latitudes or westerly wind belts. These dry regions receive scanty precipitation because of their location with respect to pressure and wind belts, to sources of moisture and to highland barriers. In the subtropical highs the air is slowly descending and increasing in temperature, so that there is little occasion for it to give up moisture. The trade winds, moving Equatorward from the subtropical highs, become warmer as they pass to lower latitudes and consequently absorb and retain their moisture, except where they are forced by land barriers to rise and cool. In the middle latitudes the westerly winds bring abundant rain to the western sides of the continents, and the cyclonic storms carry a fair amount to the eastern sides. The interiors of the continents, however, especially Asia and North America, far from the sources of moisture and more or less shut in by highland barriers, receive very little precipitation.

The principal dry deserts of the world are located as follows:

1. Colorado-Sonora, western interior of North America
2. Atacama, western South America
3. Sahara, northern Africa
4. Kalahari, southwestern Africa
5. Arabian, southwestern Asia
6. Gobi, interior of Asia
7. Victoria, central and western Australia

Characteristics of Dry Climate. Both daily and seasonal ranges in temperature are greater in a dry climate than in a humid climate of the same latitude. The scarcity of moisture in the air and the scarcity of vegetation on the ground allow rapid heating and cooling of the land, and it is not uncommon for a night of frost to be followed by a daytime temperature of 80°. Since the dry regions are mainly in the interiors and on the leeward sides of continents where the modifying influence of the oceans is negligible, extreme annual as well as diurnal ranges in temperature are common.

The general circulation of the winds in any dry region depends on the main wind belt in which it is located. The local winds, however, are distinctly more variable than they are in a humid climate. Because of the rapid heating and consequent convectional circulation and also because of the scanty vegetation, the days are usually windy and the air is filled with dust. Frequently the wind becomes strong enough to move the larger rock particles, producing sand storms. The nights are relatively calm.

Temperature and Precipitation Data for Representative Stations

(T = temperature in degrees Fahrenheit; P = precipitation in inches)

Lima, Peru. Lat. 12°3′S.; Long. 76°8′W.; Alt. 500 ft.

	Jan.	Feb.	Mar.	Apr.	May	June	July	Aug.	Sept.	Oct.	Nov.	Dec.	Year
T.	71.1	73.4	72.9	70.0	66.0	62.1	60.6	60.6	61.3	61.9	65.8	69.8	66.3
P.	0.1	0.0	0.0	0.0	0.0	0.2	0.3	0.5	0.5	0.1	0.0	0.1	1.8

Urga, Mongolia. Lat. 47°56′ N.; Long. 106°55′E.; Alt. 3800 ft.

	Jan.	Feb.	Mar.	Apr.	May	June	July	Aug.	Sept.	Oct.	Nov.	Dec.	Year
T.	—16	—4	13	34	48	58	63	59	48	30	8	—17	28
P.	0.0	0.1	0.0	0.0	0.3	1.7	2.6	2.1	0.5	0.1	0.1	0.1	7.6

Rainfall is scanty at all seasons and very variable in its occurence. Years may pass without rain in some regions, as along the coast of northern Chile. When it does come, the rain usually falls in torrential showers of convectional origin with rapid runoff. Relative humidity is low, evaporation rapid, and there are few clouds except dust clouds.

Lima, situated in a low latitude and not far from the sea, has a fairly small range in temperature between the warmest and coldest months; its low precipitation is principally due to its position on the leeward side of the Andes Mountains. Urga, on the other hand, deep in the interior of Asia and located in the middle latitudes, has a difference of 80° between the warmest and coldest months. Here, highland barriers and great distance from the source of moisture account for the small precipitation. As is true of most continental locations, maximum precipitation comes from convectional showers during the warm season.

C. CLIMATE: HUMID MESOTHERMAL

Definition. Both temperature and rainfall are important in this type of climate. According to Köppen, the average temperature of the coldest month must be between 64.4°F. and 26.6°F.; in order to be humid, the rainfall must exceed evaporation. There is a definite seasonal rhythm of temperature with a moderate range between winter and summer.

Location and Subdivisions. This climate is found on the western sides of continents in latitudes about 30° to 60° and on the eastern sides in latitudes about 25° to 40°. Three subdivisions are recognized as follows: (1) the marine west coast, (2) the dry summer, or Mediterranean and (3) the dry winter, or monsoon.

The Marine West-Coast Climate. Those portions of the western sides of the continents that are in the belt of the westerly winds have a marine climate. Here the summers are cool, the winters are mild and rain is abundant at all seasons. The Gulf Stream and the Japanese Current carry these conditions far north along the western coasts of Europe and North America, respectively. The presence of high north-south mountains in western North America limits the marine climate to a narrow strip adjacent to the Pacific, whereas the plains of western Europe allow the oceanic influence to penetrate far inland. In the Southern Hemisphere land areas with this type of climate are small, because of the lack of land in suitable latitudes.

The Dry Summer, or Mediterranean, Climate. Shifting of the zenithal position of the sun and the resulting seasonal migration of the wind belts brings those portions of the western sides of continents between latitudes 30° to 40° north and south under the control of the westerlies in winter and into the horse latitudes and trade-wind belts in summer. In these latitudes the western coasts of continents have mild, rainy winters and hot, dry summers. The type region is that of the lands surrounding the Mediterranean Sea. Smaller regions with a similar climate are found in southern California, central Chile, southwestern Africa and southwestern Australia. The summer months have average temperatures between 70° and 80°, the winter months between 40° and 50°, with occasional frost. Annual rainfall is generally 15 to 25 inches, most of it coming during the winter season. The mild rainy winters with their green vegetation contrasted with the hot, desert-like summers make the Mediterranean type unique among the climates of the world.

The Dry Winter, or Monsoon, Climate. Where land masses are large, as in Asia and to some extent in North America, and seasonal differences in temperature consequently great, monsoons are well developed. The stronger the monsoon tendency, the greater the concentration of precipitation in the warm season. Much of the southeastern part of Asia, the largest continent, has the very pronounced monsoon climate of rainy

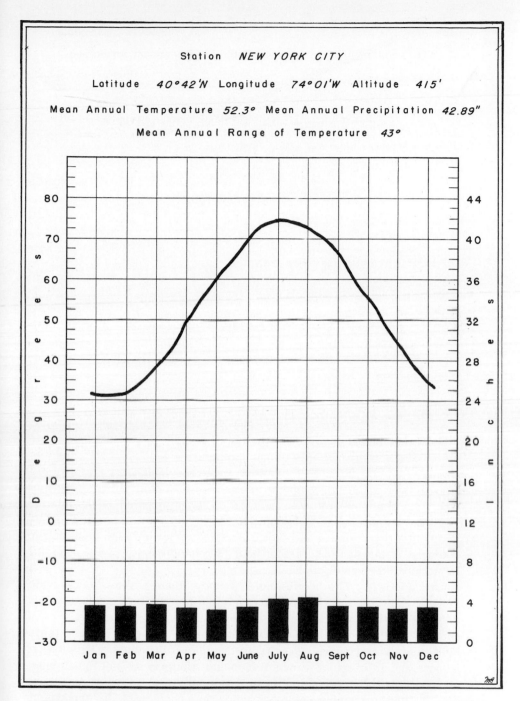

FIG. 8-1. Climatic chart for New York City. Based on data compiled by the U. S. Weather Bureau over a period of more than 80 years. Mean temperature for each month is shown in degrees by the curve; mean monthly rainfall is shown in inches by columns at the bottom of the sheet.

131

Temperature and Precipitation Data for Representative Stations

(T = temperature in degrees Fahrenheit; P = precipitation in inches)

MARINE WEST COAST TYPE

Seattle, Washington. Lat. 47°45′N.; Long. 122°25′W.

	Jan.	Feb.	Mar.	Apr.	May	June	July	Aug.	Sept.	Oct.	Nov.	Dec.	Year
T.	40	42	45	50	55	60	64	64	59	52	46	42	51.4
P.	4.9	3.8	3.1	2.4	1.8	1.3	0.6	0.7	1.7	2.8	4.8	5.5	33.4

MEDITERRANEAN TYPE

Los Angeles, Cal. Lat. 34°3′N.; Long. 118°15′W.; Alt. 293 ft.

	Jan.	Feb.	Mar.	Apr.	May	June	July	Aug.	Sept.	Oct.	Nov.	Dec.	Year
T.	54.5	55.5	57.3	59.7	62.1	65.2	70.2	71.1	69.4	65.1	60.9	55.3	62.2
P.	3.3	3.2	2.9	0.9	0.4	0.1	0.0	0.0	0.2	0.7	1.2	2.7	15.6

MONSOON TYPE

Delhi, India. Lat. 28°38′N.; Long. 77°12′E.; Alt. 718 ft.

	Jan.	Feb.	Mar.	Apr.	May	June	July	Aug.	Sept.	Oct.	Nov.	Dec.	Year
T.	60	61	70	82	89	93	87.5	86	84	79	68	60	76.6
P.	1.8	0.9	0.5	0.4	0.8	3.3	8.3	8.0	4.6	0.3	0.3	0.8	30.0

summers and dry winters that comes with marked seasonal changes in wind direction.

D. CLIMATE: HUMID MICROTHERMAL

Definition and Location. In the D or humid microthermal climate the coldest month has an average temperature below 26.6°F. and the warmest month above 50°F. Colder winters, longer frost seasons, and larger annual ranges in temperature distinguish it from the mesothermal type. The humid microthermal climate is mainly located in the interior and leeward portions of continents in the higher middle latitudes. Thus it is confined to Eurasia and North America, because broad lands in the Southern Hemisphere are not present far enough south of the Equator to produce this type of climate.

Characteristics. The humid microthermal climate covers a fairly wide range of latitude and therefore has notable temperature contrasts in its different portions. On the whole, however, it exhibits a characteristically continental climate with relatively hot summers and cold winters, fairly light rainfall, and rapid and extreme temperature changes. Precipitation is more or less irregular in occurrence and droughts are not uncommon, especially in the interiors. Summer is normally the season of maximum rainfall, most of which comes as convectional showers. In portions of the interiors of the continents the rainfall is no greater in the humid microthermal than in the dry climate, but the lower temperature and slower rate of evaporation distinguish the former from the latter.

Temperature and Precipitation Data for Representative Stations

(T = temperature in degrees Fahrenheit; P = precipitation in inches)

Moscow, Russia. Lat. 55°32'N.; Long. 37°0'E.

	Jan.	Feb.	Mar.	Apr.	May	June	July	Aug.	Sept.	Oct.	Nov.	Dec.	Year
T.	12	15	23	38	53	62	66	63	52	40	28	17	39
P.	1.1	1.0	1.2	1.5	1.9	2.0	2.8	2.9	2.2	1.4	1.6	1.5	21.1

Winnipeg, Canada. Lat. 49°47'N.; Long. 97°15'W.

	Jan.	Feb.	Mar.	Apr.	May	June	July	Aug.	Sept.	Oct.	Nov.	Dec.	Year
T.	—4	0	15	38	52	62	66	64	54	41	21	6	35
P.	0.9	0.7	1.2	1.4	2.0	3.1	3.1	2.2	2.2	1.4	1.1	0.9	20.2

E. CLIMATE: POLAR

Definition and Location. In the polar climate the average temperature of the warmest month is below 50°F. Two subdivisions are recognized: (1) the *glacial*, or ice-cap climate with the warmest month below 32°F., and (2) the *tundra* with the warmest month between 32°F. and 50°F. Polar climate is found in high latitudes and at high altitudes in a variety of latitudes. Northern North America, Greenland, northern Eurasia, Antarctica, and the very high mountains of the world come within the limits of this climate.

Characteristics. Monotonous cold is characteristic of the high latitude climate. At and near the poles the seasons are the alternating periods of light and darkness, rather than of cold and warmth or rain and drought. At the poles the sun is constantly below the horizon for about six months and above the horizon, although never very high, for an equal period. At the Arctic and Antarctic circles the longest day (at the time of the summer solstice) is 24 hours and the longest night (at the time of the winter solstice) is also 24 hours.

Because of the high latitude and the consequent low angle or absence of the sun, insolation is weak and the temperature low. Occasional warm days may occur in the season of highest sun, but they are rather unusual. High pressure prevails because of the low temperature, especially in Greenland and Antarctica. Winds blowing outward from the centers of these high-pressure areas are deflected by the earth's rotation and constitute the northeast and the southeast polar winds in the Northern and Southern hemispheres, respectively. As cold air can never gather much moisture, precipitation is low and most of it comes as snow; but even if melted to water it would amount to less than ten inches a year for most of this region. Slow melting and evaporation have allowed the snowfall to accumulate year after year to form the great ice caps of Greenland and Antarctica. Outside the ice caps, in the tundra, the snow may disappear and the deeply frozen ground thaw to a depth of a few inches for a short time each year.

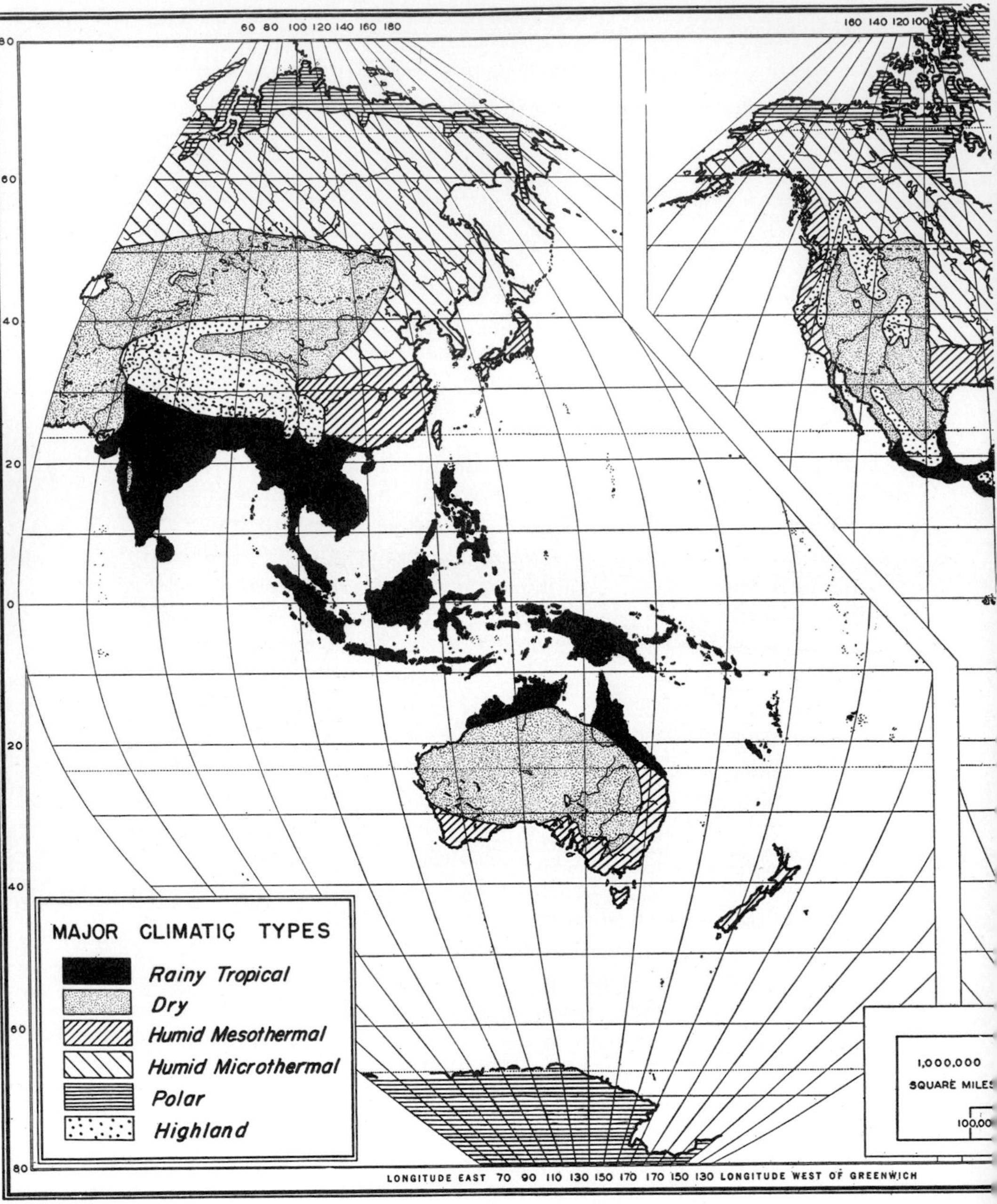

60 80 100 120 140 160 180
160 140 120 100
80
60
40
20
0
20
40
60
80
MAJOR CLIMATIC TYPES
Rainy Tropical
Dry
Humid Mesothermal
Humid Microthermal
Polar
Highland
1,000,000
SQUARE MILES
100,00
LONGITUDE EAST 70 90 110 130 150 170 170 150 130 LONGITUDE WEST OF GREENWICH

FIG. 8-2. Major climatic types. *(Base map reprinted by permission from* Outline Maps and Graphs *by*

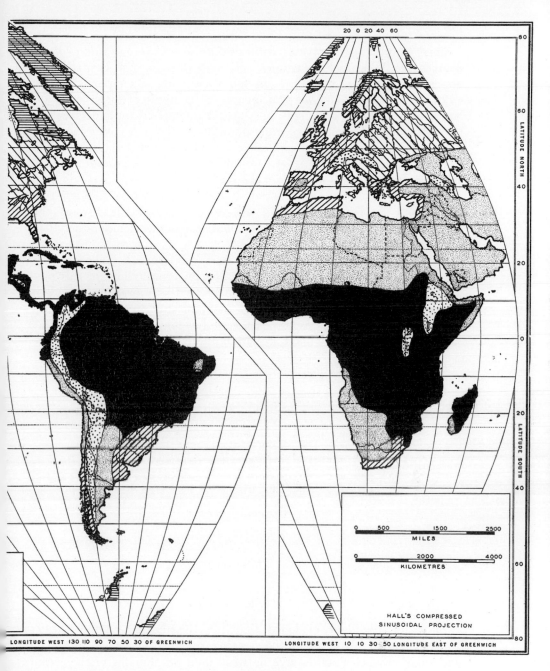

Robert B. Hall, published by John Wiley and Sons, Inc. Climatic data added by Marie Bohrn.)

Since temperature decreases with altitude at an average rate of three degrees per 1,000 feet, mountains and high plateaus rise into the cool upper layers of air. In fact, from the standpoint of temperature, one mile of altitude is equivalent to nearly 1,000 miles of latitude. Highlands, as contrasted with lowlands, are characterized by a decrease in pressure, temperature, and absolute humidity, and, on the other hand, by more intense insolation and radiation and usually greater precipitation. Exposure, or orientation, as well as altitude, is an important climatic factor in highlands. Mountains in the path of vapor-bearing winds have abundant precipitation on the windward slopes, while the opposite slopes and the country beyond are dry. Slopes facing toward the Equator have greater insolation and therefore higher temperature than those facing the poles.

Many mountains rise so high that there is perpetual snow on their summits and glaciers in their valleys. The lowermost limit of this perpetual snow is called the *snow line*. Below the snow line is a belt where the ground is frozen most of the year and trees cannot grow; the lower boundary of this belt is the *timber line*. The altitudes of the timber line and the snow line vary with latitude and exposure.

Temperature and Precipitation Data for Representative Stations

(T = temperature in degrees Fahrenheit; P = precipitation in inches)

TUNDRA TYPE

Upernivik, Greenland. Lat. 72°47′N.; Long. 56°7′W.

	Jan.	Feb.	Mar.	Apr.	May	June	July	Aug.	Sept.	Oct.	Nov.	Dec.	Year
T.	−7.8	−9.2	−6.3	5.9	24.8	35.1	41.0	40.8	33.4	24.8	13.8	1.4	16.5
P.	0.4	0.5	0.7	0.6	0.6	0.5	0.9	1.1	1.1	1.1	1.1	0.5	9.1

GLACIAL TYPE

South Victoria Land, Antarctica. Lat. 77°S., Long. 165°E.

T.	24	16	3	−9	−11	−12	−16	−17	−14	−3	14	26	1
P.	All in the form of snow. Amount not available.												

CLIMATES OF THE PAST

There is abundant evidence that the distribution of the world's climates has not always been the same as it is now. Old trees, salt lakes, and ruins of ancient cities give us some data on climates of the recent past. Variation in the thickness of growth rings of the great Sequoia trees of California show that the climate of that region has fluctuated considerably during the past 3,000 years. Great Salt Lake, in Utah, was formerly a fresh-water lake and covered an area ten times its present size. The old shoreline and outlet channel of this lake are 600 feet above the present water surface. Decreased rainfall and increased evaporation are evidently responsible for the salinity and shrinkage of this lake. Variations in the size of glaciers in the Rocky Mountains and elsewhere show changes in climate. Those in Glacier National Park have shrunk noticeably and some have disappeared entirely within recent years, because of a slight increase in average temperatures.

Huntington gives evidences of increasing aridity in western Asia. He cites among other examples the changes that have taken place in Palmyra. Two thousand years ago Palmyra, in Syria, was a great and wealthy city of 150,000 people. Ancient writers tell of its sweet water, beautiful gardens and temples. Today Palmyra is mostly a desolate ruin in the desert. Its 1,500 people still obtain water from the old aqueducts, but it is no longer sweet and is barely enough to irrigate the small gardens on which they depend for a livelihood.

Climates of the more distant geologic past have left various records of their existence. Arid climates have existed at various periods of the earth's history in regions which have humid climates at the present time, and warm humid climates have prevailed in regions which are now arid. In portions of New York, Ohio, and Michigan are ancient deposits of salt and gypsum that could have been laid down only in an arid climate, whereas the petrified trees of Arizona tell of the moist climate and luxuriant vegetation that once existed in that desert region. Fossil trees are found in eastern Greenland, above the present timber line; coal, formed from luxuriant plant growth, occurs in Spitzbergen and in Antarctica; and fossil coral reefs are found about the shores of Hudson Bay, although reef-building corals at present are practically limited to tropical and subtropical waters.

Some regions that were formerly glaciated now experience moderate to mild climates. At one period in the earth's history there were extensive glaciers in South Africa, Australia, and India, regions that now have tropical and subtropical temperatures. Not so far back in geological time much of northern North America and northwestern Europe was covered by enormous ice sheets. At the same time mountain glaciers were larger and more numerous in the mountains of North America and Europe than they are now. Glacial till, glacial lakes, and other evidences of this latest ice age are prominent features of the landscapes.

Changes in climate have been explained by various hypotheses. Some ascribe such changes to diastrophism and gradation, which bring about changes in the topography of the land and in the relations of land and water. Others propose that changes in the shape of the earth's orbit, variations in the sun's energy discharge, and other astronomical factors have been responsible for the changes in climate. It has been observed that the energy output of the sun varies as much as 10 per cent in short cycles; perhaps larger variations have occurred over long

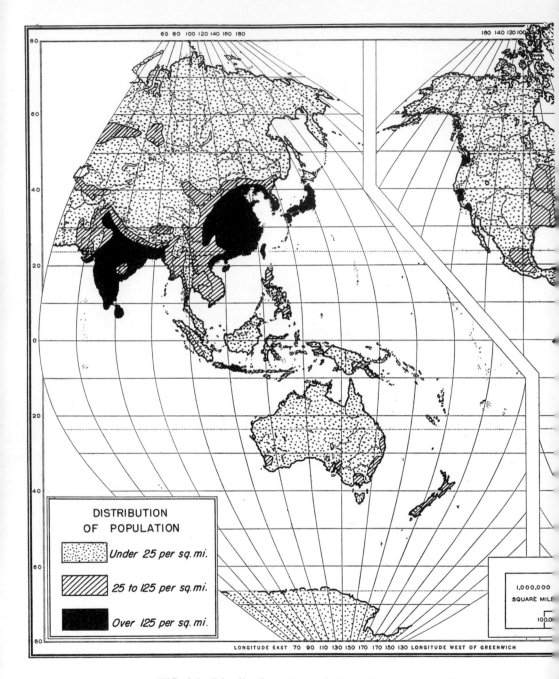

FIG. 8-3. Distribution of population. Compare with Fig. 8-2 and note th
relationship between climate and population. *(Base map reprinted b*

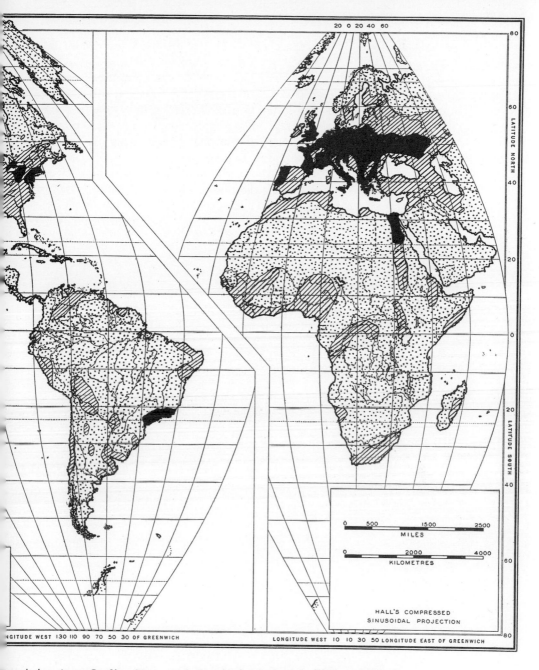

20 0 20 40 60

LATITUDE NORTH

80

60

40

20

0

20

LATITUDE SOUTH

40

60

80

0   500   1500   2500
MILES

0   2000   4000
KILOMETRES

HALL'S COMPRESSED
SINUSOIDAL PROJECTION

LONGITUDE WEST 130 110 90 70 50 30 OF GREENWICH

LONGITUDE WEST 10 10 30 50 LONGITUDE EAST OF GREENWICH

ermission from Outline Maps and Graphs *by Robert B. Hall, published
John Wiley and Sons, Inc. Population data added by Marie Bohrn.)*

139

periods. Changes in the composition of the air itself, especially in its carbon dioxide, water vapor, and dust content, are believed by some to have been important in causing changes in the climates of the past. We know that these constituents of the air are important in absorbing and retaining the heat of the sun, and variations in their amounts resulting from volcanic activity, the formation of coal and other processes might have affected the climate of the past considerably. Still another proposal to explain past climates is that of the drifting of continents. According to this hypothesis the solid continental masses rest on a substratum which yields to long-continued stresses; therefore, the continents may slowly change their latitudes, crowd together, drift apart, or otherwise change their positions, affecting the climate of any particular locality.

Suggestions for Further Reading

BLAIR, T. A., *Climatology* (Englewood Cliffs, N. J., Prentice-Hall, 1942).

HUNTINGTON, Ellsworth, *Mainsprings of Civilization* (New York, Wiley, 1945).

KENDREW, W. G., *The Climates of the Continents*, 3rd Ed. (New York, Oxford University Press, 1942).

KIMBLE, G. H. T., *Our American Weather* (New York, McGraw-Hill, 1955).

SHAPLEY, Harlow, Editor, *Climatic Change* (Cambridge, Harvard University Press, 1953).

TANNEHILL, Ivan R., *Weather Around the World* (Princeton, Princeton University Press, 1943).

— 9 —

Weathering
and Mass Movement

$\mathbf{M}$OST OF THE ROCKS of the lithosphere are stable as long as their original environments remain unchanged. A granite, for example, will exist indefinitely if allowed to remain in the depths of the earth where it was formed. If it is exposed to the atmosphere, however, it will break down. Although most rocks are formed under conditions which exclude the atmosphere, uplift and erosion are constantly exposing rocks that were once buried, and volcanic eruptions pour out material from the interior. These rocks adjust themselves to their new environment by *physical* and *chemical* interaction with it in the processes of weathering.

Man-made structures also succumb to the attacks of the atmosphere. A house constructed of the strongest stone, brick, or other materials will fall into ruins in a few centuries or less, unless it is frequently repaired. Bridges, roads, fences, monuments and all other structures are subject to destruction by weathering. Man is continually in conflict with the weather. He selects the most resistant materials for his buildings, he paints the exposed surfaces and fills the cracks to delay weathering, but eventually all of his structures are destroyed and must be rebuilt of fresh materials.

Closely following the processes of weathering are those that are involved in the *mass movement* of the broken-down material without benefit of transporting agents, that is, by gravitation. In the breaking down of earth materials both physical and chemical processes are active. In mass movement the down-hill pull of gravity is the dominant force.

PHYSICAL WEATHERING

Physical weathering includes the processes whereby rocks are broken apart into smaller units without change in the chemical composition.

141

FIG. 9-1. Exfoliation at high altitude in the Sierra Nevada, Calif. *(Photo by Gilbert, U. S. Geological Survey)*

FIG. 9-2. Weathered fragments fallng from the upper portion of the cliff accumulate at the foot as talus. *(Photo by C. H. Tozier. Dept. of Geology, Harvard University)*

This phase is also known as mechanical weathering, and as disintegration. Physical weathering is accomplished mainly by changes in temperature, by the wedgework of ice, by wetting and drying, and by plants and animals.

Temperature Changes. Most solids expand when heated and contract when cooled. The buckling of concrete walks and roads in summer and the opening of joints in winter are familiar examples. Rocks are subjected to alternate heating and cooling by daily and seasonal changes in temperature, and the more rapid and extreme the temperature changes the greater the stresses on the exposed rocks. In dry regions and high mountains, marked by the most rapid and extreme temperature changes, a daytime temperature above 100° might be followed by a night below freezing. Under such conditions disintegration is extremely effective. Since rock is a relatively poor conductor of heat, the surface may become highly heated while the temperature a few inches beneath the surface is scarcely affected. This continual rapid expansion and contraction causes the surface zone to break loose from the material beneath and peel off in chips, sheets, and slabs. This peeling off of thin and more or less concentric layers is known as *exfoliation*. Chemical weathering, especially hydration, is also an important factor in exfoliation.

Most rocks consist of more than one mineral, each mineral reacting in different degrees to changes in temperature. Such rocks are subjected to complex stresses which tend to separate the minerals from each other into granular fragments. Where loosened material is rapidly removed, fresh surfaces are constantly being exposed and the process of rock disintegration continues, but where weathered material remains in place it protects the underlying rock and thus retards mechanical disintegration. Dislodged rock fragments fall to the base of steep slopes and cliffs and accumulate as *talus*. This talus, if allowed to remain, protects the lower portion of the cliff while the upper portion continues to recede. Eventually the accumulated talus may reach the top and give some protection against weathering to the entire cliff.

Frost Action. All rocks contain pores, cracks, or other openings into which moisture from the atmosphere or from the ground penetrates. As the water changes to ice it expands and requires more space. At a temperature of 30°F. a pressure of about 138 tons per square foot is exerted by the ice forming in a closed cavity. For this reason bottles of water, automobile engines, and cannon, are broken by the powerful expanding force of freezing water. Even entire buildings may be heaved up if their foundations are not below the frost line.

To this enormous pressure the rocks near the surface in regions of frost are frequently subjected. Water in minute openings as well as in larger cracks must, on freezing, somehow find space for increase in volume. With alternate freezing and thawing, such as accompanies a succession of cold nights and warm days, the wedgework of ice is repeated again and again during a single season, and minute bits as well as large masses are broken loose from the bedrock. Mechanical disintegration of this kind is, of course, limited to those parts of the earth where the changes in temperature frequently cross the freezing point of water and is further confined to a thin surface zone. In the cooler parts of the earth, in high mountains and upper latitudes, frost action is often the most effective process of weathering.

The effect of frost action in soil is often very noticeable. Freezing of water in soil particles helps to break them apart and make the soil finer in texture, lighter and more easily worked. Frost heaving also brings boulders to the surface. In New England and other parts of the northern United States where there are boulders in the soil and subsoil, the farmer may clear his fields of surface boulders and yet find more on the same surface the next year. The continuous appearance of these frost-heaved boulders has given rise to the erroneous belief that boulders grow from smaller pebbles.

Wetting and Drying. Alternate wetting and drying is an effective method of physical weathering. Many minerals react to wetting by expanding and then contract when drying. In a rock composed of inhomogeneous materials the different minerals will react differently to wetting and thus set up stresses. After chemical alteration of feldspar to kaolin (clay), the kaolin swells when wet and thus aids disintegration.

Plants and Animals. The widening of cracks in rocks by the growth of plant roots, the overturning of trees by the wind and the burrowing of worms, ants, and rodents all aid in the disintegration of rocks. Man, also, by quarrying, mining, tunneling, and excavating, and by clearing the forest and cultivating the land contributes greatly to rapid erosion, which thereby allows fresh rock to be exposed to the processes of weathering.

CHEMICAL WEATHERING

By combining with or removing certain elements in minerals, air and water alter the appearance and composition of rocks. One or both of these agents of chemical decomposition is almost universally present at and near the surface, and usually penetrates to a considerable depth. A rock may, therefore, be almost completely altered before it is actually exposed at the surface by any or all of the processes of chemical weathering, namely, oxidation, hydration, carbonation, and solution.

Oxidation. In the process of oxidation, oxygen is added to the constituent minerals of rocks, especially to the iron compounds, to form oxides. Oxidation is greatly aided by the presence of water, the water in most cases as well as the oxygen combining with the rock materials

FIG. 9-3. Exfoliation domes in Yosemite National Park. *(Photo by J. Walter Thompson Co.)*

FIG. 9-4. Exfoliation dome, Looking Glass Rock, Pisgah National Forest, N. C. *(U. S. Forest Service)*

FIG. 9-5. Blocks loosened by ice-wedging creeping downhill, Mt. St. Helena, Wash. *(Photo by Matthes, U. S. Geological Survey)*

FIG. 9-6. Tree growing in a joint crack, Bear Mountain, N. Y. Eventually its trunk will split the rock apart.

to form hydrous oxides. The nature of this change by oxidation is well illustrated when an ordinary nail is exposed to damp air; first it becomes dull, then rusty, and ultimately is reduced to a powder of iron rust. This change involves both oxidation and hydration, and the resulting rust is the hydrated oxide of iron. Oxygen and moisture acting upon those minerals which contain iron produce an iron rust like that resulting from the rusting of a nail. The red, brown, and yellow colors so common in rocks and soils are stains due to the rusting or decay of iron-bearing minerals.

Hydration. The chemical union of water with the minerals in a rock is called hydration. This phase of weathering is especially effective on some of the aluminum-bearing minerals. Feldspar, a very common aluminum silicate, is broken down by hydration into kaolin, the principal constituent of common clay. Some highly aluminous minerals, like nephelite, are converted to bauxite, the ore of aluminum, by prolonged weathering. Hydration of minerals usually results in marked increase in volume, and thereby is a great aid to mechanical weathering, especially in the case of exfoliation.

Carbonation. Minerals containing the oxides of certain basic metals, such as sodium, potassium, calcium, and magnesium, are often decomposed by the union of carbon dioxide with these metals to form carbonates or bicarbonates. These carbonates, being more or less soluble, may be carried away in solution or remain in the soil as soluble plant foods.

Solution. Water is often called the universal solvent, since almost all rock materials are more or less affected by its solvent action. Meteoric water absorbs carbon dioxide in its passage through the atmosphere or absorbs it in its flow along the surface of the ground. This slightly acid water dissolves many substances more readily than does pure water. The carbonates of sodium, potassium, calcium, and magnesium are especially soluble in carbonated water, so that solution of these materials, going on together with carbonation, plays an important part in the breaking down of rocks. In rocks that consist of two or more minerals which are intimately bound together in a solid mass, the removal of one of these minerals by solution will cause the others to crumble to an incoherent mass.

Some rocks consist almost entirely of one readily soluble mineral. The most common of these is limestone, composed largely of calcium carbonate. Others are gypsum (hydrated calcium sulphate) and rock salt (sodium chloride). When the bulk of these rocks is removed by solution, only a small residue of insolubles is left.

WEATHERING OF GRANITE

A discussion of the weathering of granite in a temperate humid climate will serve to illustrate the complex nature and interaction of the processes. Mechanical agents break apart the solid rocks into fragments ranging in size from enormous boulders to fine dust. On these fragments and also on the unbroken rock the chemical agents are constantly at work, attacking every exposed surface and penetrating into the cracks, vesicles, pores and other openings.

A typical granite consists essentially of the three minerals, orthoclase feldspar, quartz, and biotite mica. The alteration of orthoclase, a silicate of potassium and aluminum, involves chiefly hydration into a hydrous aluminum silicate clay mineral, colloidal silica, and potassium hydroxide. Carbonation of some of the potassium also takes place. Biotite, a silicate containing iron and magnesium in addition to aluminum and potassium, is altered by oxidation, hydration, and carbonation, the iron uniting with oxygen and also with water to form iron oxide and hydrous iron oxide, and the magnesium becoming carbonated, to form a soluble compound readily carried away in solution. Because it is quite stable chemically, quartz undergoes only disintegration during weathering of the granite, the larger grains becoming smaller particles.

The weathering of small quantities of various accessory minerals usually occurring in granite produces some additional alteration products, such as sodium carbonate, calcium carbonate, iron carbonates, and calcium phosphate. Soil formed by the weathering of granite therefore consists of the insoluble aluminous clay (kaolin), iron oxide and hydroxide, and quartz grains and some of the soluble carbonates and phosphates, much of the latter material having already been carried away in solution.

RELATION OF WEATHERING TO CLIMATE

The character of the climate has a great influence on the nature and rate of weathering. In a hot, moist climate, such as that of many equatorial regions, where rainfall is heavy and the temperature high, chemical processes are very active. The rock generally decays to great depth, and heavy rains leach the surface soil of most of its soluble materials.

In desert regions where changes in temperature are often rapid and extreme and rainfall is sparse, the mechanical effects of expansion and contraction assume major importance, whereas solution by downward percolating water is comparatively negligible. Much of the water that soaks into the ground during a rainfall is soon brought to the surface by capillary action and rapidly evaporated. Because of this excessive evaporation, the soluble salts of sodium, calcium, and magnesium are concentrated at and near the surface, especially on flat ground and in depressions, where the slight rainfall is not sufficient to wash them away.

In subpolar regions and in high mountains, the wedgework of ice is the most important phase of weathering. The rock is usually saturated with water which periodically freezes and thaws, shatters the rocks and produces a mantle of angular fragments. Chemical weathering, although present, is of minor importance.

In the middle latitudes, where there are marked seasonal differences in climate, the nature of weathering varies from season to season. In summer, solution and chemical decomposition are the dominant processes; in winter, frost action is most effective, particularly in those regions where the temperature frequently fluctuates above and below the freezing point of water, as it does from day to night during much of the winter in northern and central United States.

INTERRELATIONS AND RESULTS OF THE PROCESSES OF WEATHERING

Although the various processes of weathering may be analyzed separately, in nature they are usually closely interrelated. Mechanical weathering is a great aid to chemical weathering, the enlarge-

FIG. 9-7. Mechanical weathering or rock disintegration, Emery County, Utah. In dry climates decomposition or chemical weathering is relatively unimportant. (*Photo by Hunt, U. S. Geological Survey*)

FIG. 9-8. The Slumgullion mud flow into Lake San Cristobal, Hinsdale County, Colo.
(*U. S. Geological Survey*)

ment of cracks and pores and the breaking down of rocks into smaller
pieces greatly increasing the effectiveness of chemical action, because
of the increase in exposed surfaces. The various chemical processes are
often at work on a rock simultaneously, and even a single mineral may
be subjected to two or more processes of chemical decay at the
same time.

Weathering is but the initial step in a series of processes whereby
the exposed surface of the lithosphere is worn down and carried away.
Weathering breaks down the bedrock into smaller bits and decomposes
the hard minerals into loose material. Wind, water, and moving ice carry
this broken-down material away and deposit it in other places, much of
it eventually in the sea. From the standpoint of man's welfare, weathering is one of the most important processes of nature, for soil is formed by
it, and, except for the air we breathe, the water we drink and the sunshine
that lights the earth, this soil is man's most important natural resource.

FIG. 9-9. Typical landslide topography, Ouray County, Colo. *(U. S. Geological Survey)*

MASS MOVEMENT

Most of the preceding discussion in this chapter has been concerned with the breaking down of earth materials by physical and chemical weathering. Now we come to a consideration of the mass movement of that broken-down material and of the loose material derived in other ways. In this process the earth material moves down hill under the influence of gravity alone, that is, without being transported by some other moving agent.

The accumulation of talus below a steep slope results from the falling of fragments loosened from the cliff above. On falling, the fragments may be broken into smaller ones, which tend to roll or slide still farther down the talus slope.

The slow *creep* of soil down a hillside is a gravity movement that is aided by alternate freezing and thawing. On freezing, the material is heaved up perpendicular to the sloping surface. On thawing, the frag-

151

ments settle straight down, that is, perpendicular to the horizontal. Thus each freezing and thawing moves the material down hill.

Landslides are sudden, or rapid, movements of large masses of loose material on steep slopes. Such slopes have been oversteepened, that is, beyond the angle of repose of loose material, by natural or artificial processes. On these slopes the debris will slide more readily when wetted by heavy or long-continued rains. Glacial erosion in valleys tends to oversteepen the valley walls. After the glacial ice has melted and the surface is exposed to atmospheric weathering, landslides are common on the steep valley walls. In their downcutting and lateral swinging, streams often make valley walls steeper than they will stand and landslides result. Landslides on valley walls sometimes dam the streams and produce lakes. Waves cutting into a shore produce cliffs on which landslides may occur. Scarps produced by faulting are also common sites of landslides.

Man causes landslides by such engineering operations as digging canals and making road cuts. In these cases the cut walls are left steeper than they will long stand. The famous Culebra Cut in the Panama Canal has been the site of many landslides. In the Hudson Valley, where clay deposits are abundant, road builders and maintenance men have much difficulty due to mass movement of the soft clay. The movement of such plastic material as a clay is designated as a *slump* rather than as a slide.

Suggestions for Further Reading

JENNY, Hans, *Factors of Soil Formation* (New York, McGraw-Hill, 1941).

KELLER, W. D., *Principles of Chemical Weathering* (Columbia, Mo., Lucas Brothers Co., 1955).

SHARPE, C. F. S., *Landslides and Related Phenomena* (New York, Columbia University Press, 1938).

— 10 —

The Work of Streams

STREAM SYSTEMS

A STREAM is water flowing over the land in a more or less distinct channel or depression. In most cases a stream is a part of a system. Such a stream system, consisting of a trunk, or master stream, and many tributaries, may be compared with a branching tree—except that the stream branches are limited to the ground surface while a tree branches out in various planes, and with the further exception that the water in a stream system flows toward and into the trunk whereas the sap in a tree trunk rises and moves outward into the branches.

Stream systems are of various sizes. The Mississippi system is a gigantic network covering most of the United States between the Appalachian and the Rocky Mountains, and carrying water from thousands of square miles to the Gulf of Mexico through one main trunk. East of the Appalachian Mountains, most of the drainage is divided among several much smaller stream systems, such as the Delaware, the Susquehanna, and the Potomac. At the other extreme are the numerous small streams that run down the slopes of coastal plains, each entering the sea independently and each only a few miles or a fraction of a mile in length.

Sizes of Streams. Although there are no exact criteria of distinction, streams are commonly divided in diminishing order of size into rivers, creeks, brooks, and rills. Because there is no precise distinction, two streams of the same size might be placed in different categories in different localities.

In a typical stream system one finds numerous little rills, or rivulets, which join to form the brooks; a number of brooks, sometimes designated as branches, will join to form the creeks; and the union of the creeks makes the large rivers. Of course, some rills and brooks flow directly into a river without the intermediary creek.

Source of Streams. Precipitation from the atmosphere is the source of the water that flows as streams. It is estimated that nearly 27,000 cubic miles of water in one form or another falls on the land surface of the earth each year. Some of this moisture is evaporated from the ground or is transpired through plants and therefore does not enter into stream flow. Another part of the water soaks directly into the ground and may not appear at the surface again before reaching the sea. Nevertheless, a considerable portion of the precipitation falling on the land is carried off by streams and constitutes the *runoff*. This runoff is of two kinds: (1) immediate, or surface, runoff and (2) delayed, or ground-water, runoff. The relative proportions of the immediate and the delayed runoff vary with the rate of rainfall, the porosity of the soil and rock, the steepness of the slope, and the vegetation cover. The immediate runoff commonly swells the volume of streams during wet weather, sometimes causing floods. On the other hand, the delayed runoff, which passes through the ground and comes out in springs, stream beds and other places of seepage, tends to keep the streams flowing during dry weather.

Gradient and Velocity of Streams. The slope of the surface followed by a stream channel is known as the *gradient* and is commonly expressed in feet per mile. For example, a stream that descends 10 feet vertically in a horizontal distance of one mile has a gradient of 10 feet per mile. Stream gradients vary greatly from place to place and from one portion of a stream to another. The lower Mississippi has a gradient of only a few inches per mile, whereas some of the small streams in the Rocky Mountains descend two or three thousand feet per mile.

Obviously, the steeper the gradient the greater the velocity of the flow; but other factors, such as the volume of water and the shape of the channel, also affect the velocity of a stream. The effect of volume on the velocity can be readily appreciated by noting the increase in the velocity of any stream during high water. The velocity of a stream is of great importance in determining its ability to erode the land.

GRADATIONAL WORK OF STREAMS

Importance and Nature of Streams in Gradation. Running water is by far the most important agent of gradation that modifies the greater part of the land surface of the earth. In humid climates, except in regions of active glaciation, stream work is heavily dominant over all other agencies of erosion. Even in arid climates running water carves out most of the major landscape features during and after the sporadic rains. On most of the land surfaces running water is more or less constantly at work, removing the products of weathering, breaking down rock with its own tools, and carrying the accumulated material to some lower position.

Stream gradation may be outlined as follows:

> Erosion
> > Corrasion, or mechanical wear
> > Corrosion, or chemical wear, mainly solution
> > Transportation of sediment
>
> Deposition

Stream Erosion. *Corrasion.* Running water, like the wind, can do little mechanical work without its tools, the boulders, pebbles, sand, and silt which it carries along. With the finer fragments a stream grinds away the rock of its channel as sandpaper abrades and scrubs, while the impact of the boulders is comparable to blows by a hammer. Not only is the bedrock over which a stream flows worn away, but the tools with which the water works are also worn to smaller and rounder bits.

The corrasive power of a stream, that is, its capacity for mechanical work alone, varies approximately as the square of the velocity of the water. This relationship may be better understood if one considers that if the velocity be doubled, even without any additional tools, twice as many particles strike against any obstacle in a given time and each strikes with twice the force. The nature and amount of the tools carried by a stream of course affect the rate of corrasion: the more hard sharp particles a stream carries the faster its channel is worn. Another factor is the resistance of the rock, commonly called the country rock, over which a stream flows. Rocks vary greatly in resistance to the abrading and dissolving power of running water, and some portions of the stream bed are worn away more rapidly than others.

Corrosion. The corrosive work of streams is chiefly a matter of solution. Many of the constituents of rocks are to some extent soluble, some much more than others, and streams in regions of readily soluble rocks accomplish much of their work by solution. It frequently happens that by taking one kind of material into solution, water will thereby increase its solvent power over other materials. For example, water can more effectively dissolve limestone after absorbing carbon dioxide from the air and from vegetation. Unlike corrasion, the corrosive power of streams is not affected by velocity and some sluggish streams perform a large portion of their work by corrosion.

Transportation. *How the Load Is Obtained.* The material a stream gathers from a variety of sources and by various processes and carries along in its seaward progress is its load. Some of their load the streams obtain by their own action of corrasion and solution. In addition, the

FIG. 10-1. Smooth, rounded, water-worn cobbles in a stream channel, Williamette National Forest, Ore. *(U. S. Forest Service)*

FIG. 10-2. Intricate system of gullies in Death Valley, Calif. *(National Park Service)*

wind contributes an appreciable amount of sand and dust, especially
in regions of sparse vegetation; the erosive action of glaciers produces
great quantities of fine material, and streams that flow from melting
glaciers are often turbid with the products of ice erosion. In some
regions volcanic eruptions occasionally contribute large quantities of
volcanic ash. And finally, the ground water brings material in solution
from underground.

By far the greater portion of the load of streams, however, consists of
the products of weathering. The surface runoff feeding countless rills
is an almost universal means of bringing sediment to the streams.
Weathered soil creeps down slope and into the streams and in steep-
sided valleys talus and landslides contribute to their load.

How the Load Is Carried. Part of the load of streams is carried in
mechanical *suspension.* As practically all of the rock and mineral fragments are considerably heavier than water, they are kept in suspension
only by the movement of the water. The faster the water moves the
greater is the total quantity of sediment and the larger are the particles
that it can transport. The rate of increase in both categories is very
great. For fragments of any given density, the size that can be carried
varies as the fifth power of the velocity of the water. Thus, a stream
flowing two miles an hour is able to carry fragments 32 times as large
as can be carried by a stream flowing one mile an hour. Because of this
high rate of increase in carrying power with velocity, rushing torrents,
such as those that develop at flood times, are able to move great
amounts of material, including large boulders and other heavy objects.
Particles too heavy to be carried in suspension may be moved by
traction, that is, by pushing, rolling, and jumping along the bottom.
The carrying power of a stream will vary with changes in volume from
season to season, and some of the load moved by traction during low
water is carried in suspension during high water.

In addition to the mechanical load, the waters of every stream carry
a considerable amount of mineral matter in *solution.* The amount varies
in different streams with the solubility of the country rock. In any
stream the proportionate amount is greater during dry seasons when
most of the water carried is not surface runoff but ground water.

ORIGIN AND GROWTH OF VALLEYS

Valleys Made by Streams. Most streams flow in valleys which they
have carved by their own erosion. This obvious principle of the origin
of valleys was not commonly recognized until about the beginning of
the nineteenth century. Before then it was widely believed that water
courses, especially canyons, gorges, and ravines, had been formed by
cataclysms which split the earth asunder, and that the highlands and

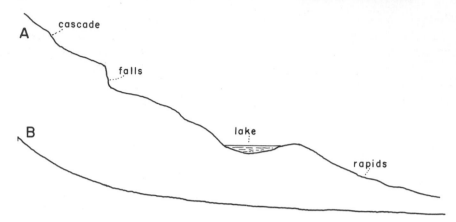

FIG. 10-3. Longitudinal profile of a valley in youth (A) and in maturity (B). Rapids, falls, and lakes result from initial irregularities in the land surface and disappear when the stream has worn down its channel to a smooth curve.

lowlands had always been as now. James Hutton of Edinburgh, the father of modern geology, was among the first to recognize that valleys and other land features are created by the long slow action of every-day forces. Hutton set forth his views on the origin of valleys, as well as of many other earth features, in a two-volume work entitled the *Theory of the Earth*, in 1795. Unfortunately, Hutton's style of writing was so cumbersome that his ideas did not gain immediate wide acceptance. In 1802 John Playfair, a friend of Hutton's and a lucid writer, published his *Illustrations of the Huttonian Theory*, in which he made clear Hutton's ideas and gave numerous examples of the principles involved.

Regarding the origin of valleys Playfair says:

Every river appears to consist of a main trunk, fed from a variety of branches, each running in a valley proportioned to its size, and all of them together forming a system of valleys, communicating with one another, and having such a nice adjustment of their declivities that none of them join the principal valley either on too high or too low a level; a circumstance which would be infinitely improbable if each of these valleys were not the work of the stream which flows in it.

The principle stated above has become known as *Playfair's Law*. Like most other laws, it has some exceptions, but the exceptions can be readily explained.

The excavation of valleys by running water can be readily observed on a small scale in roadside cuts and in steep plowed fields. The rills

FIG. 10-4. Recently formed gully in the semiarid grazing land of Rio Arriba County, N. M. *(Photo by Dane, U. S. Geological Survey)*

FIG. 10-5. An enormous and intricate gully system—the canyon of the San Rafael River, Utah. *(Photo by Dr. Barnum Brown)*

from a heavy rain gouge out numerous small gullies, which are deepened, widened, and lengthened by each successive rainfall. As time goes on some gullies grow faster than others because they are located on weaker material or where they can gather more water or where the slope is steeper. Smaller gullies adjacent to the larger ones become tributaries; the number of independent gullies decreases and integrated systems develop; the larger systems encroach on the smaller and make them tributary; the number of systems becomes fewer and each system larger. By magnifying the scale we can visualize the development of systems of valleys over a large region, even a continent, in a manner similar to the development of systems of gullies. The Colorado River system, with its gigantic main canyon and numerous tributary canyons, is a thousand-fold enlargement of a system of gullies.

Valleys grow in three directions, in depth, length, and width. In regions where the gradients are steep and the velocities of streams are great, downcutting of the channels proceeds at a relatively rapid rate. Valleys in such regions are narrow and steep-sided. There is a limit to downcutting, however, for a stream cannot cut below its outlet. In fact, in order to flow at all it must have some slope toward its mouth. The gradient of a stream gradually decreases as it deepens its valley until finally it is so low that the stream is too weak for further down-cutting. Such a stream is said to be *graded,* or has reached *grade.* In this case there is equilibrium between the energy (velocity and volume) of the stream and the load it has to transport.

A graded stream is more or less a theoretical condition, which may never be reached and, if reached, may not be long maintained. When reached, it may best be viewed as an average condition, for seasonal changes in volume and in load will cause it to deposit at some times and to erode at other times. Even when the average graded condition has been reached, it may not last, because diastrophic movement may change the gradient and thus upset the equilibrium.

Valleys grow in length by erosion at the head. As the channel downstream is deepened, the water entering the head of the valley has a steeper gradient and is therefore able to cut into the slopes forming the valley head. Weathering, rain wash, slumping, the upstream migration of waterfalls, and the sapping action of springs greatly aid in the *headward erosion* of valleys.

Weathering, rain wash, and slumping cause valleys to grow wider at the same time that they are deepened and lengthened. Lateral corrasion by the stream as it swings from side to said also widens the valley. With decrease in the rate of downcutting and the approach of grade, the rate of valley widening becomes relatively faster. Eventually downcutting stops, but the processes of widening continue until broad lowlands are excavated.

Any valley made by a stream must necessarily have a small beginning and increase in size with time. The rate at which it grows and the shape it develops will depend on such factors as the volume of water, the elevation of the land, the structure and resistance of the rocks and the length of time the stream works. A canyon, for example, cannot be excavated in a region which is only slightly above sea level. A stream located where the rock is very weak may reach grade and level the bottom of its valley to a width of several miles in less time than it takes a stream of the same size merely to cut through resistant rock to grade.

Structural Valleys. Although most valleys are chiefly the result of stream excavation, some owe their existence primarily to warping and faulting, or breaking, of the surface of the earth. The Great Valley of California, through which the Sacramento and San Joaquin rivers flow, was formed when the parallel Sierra Nevada and Coast Range Mountains were uplifted and a long depression was left between them. The valley of the Jordan River along the eastern border of Palestine and a portion of the Rhine Valley in Germany were formed by the sinking of long and narrow blocks of the earth between sets of parallel fractures. Even though some valleys begin life as structural features, they become more or less modified by the streams that flow in them.

RATE OF STREAM EROSION

Calculations of the average rate of erosion in the drainage basin of a stream system can best be made by measuring the average annual volume of water discharged by the trunk stream and weighing its content of mechanical and chemical sediment. Careful calculations of this nature made by the Hydrographic Branch of the United States Geological Survey and by other investigators reveal that the Mississippi River annually carries to the Gulf of Mexico about 340,500,000 tons of material in suspension, 40,000,000 tons moved along the bottom, and 136,400,000 tons in solution. This makes a total of 516,900,000 tons of rock material annually removed from the Mississippi drainage basin. On this basis it is calculated that the Mississippi River is lowering its drainage basin at the average rate of about one foot in 9,000 years. Although some of the other stream systems in the United States are lowering their basins faster and some more slowly than the Mississippi, because of differences in climate, altitude, and the nature of the rocks, the average rate of reduction of the whole United States is not far from the above figure of one foot in 9,000 years.

Differential Erosion. In any drainage system some parts of the land surface are eroded faster than others. In fact, portions of the surface are built up by deposition while other portions are being eroded. Among the factors that cause such differential erosion are differences in climate, in altitude and steepness of slope, and in rock resistance. Streams are more effective agents of erosion in humid than in dry climates. High altitude and steep slopes provide declivities down which the rock waste can be readily moved. The relative resistance of rocks is extremely important in determining the rate and pattern of stream erosion, as well as of all other processes of erosion. Practically everywhere the streams have excavated valleys where the rock is relatively weak and have left the more resistant rock to form the hills and ridges.

STREAM DEPOSITION

Causes of Deposition. It will be remembered that streams carry a part of their load in chemical solution and a part in a mechanical manner. The solution load of streams is usually considerably below the saturation point, so that practically all of this material is carried into the sea. Most of the mechanical load also eventually reaches the sea, but sometimes part of it is deposited on land, at least temporarily, and at the margin of the sea.

Two factors favor the deposition of sediment by streams: (1) decrease in velocity and (2) decrease in volume. Since the transporting power of a stream increases and decreases at a high rate with changes in velocity, it is evident that a loaded stream must drop some of its load when the velocity is checked. It is also evident that a loaded stream will become overloaded if some of its volume is lost by evaporation and seepage.

Kinds of Deposits. *Alluvial Fans.* Alluvial fans are commonly found at the base of steep slopes. Small ones may be seen at the foot of roadside cuts, at the lower end of gullies in plowed fields, and at the foot of bluffs where intermittent rills from heavy rains carry material down the steep slope and deposit it at the base. A stream tumbling down the face of a mountain finds its gradient and velocity abruptly checked at the foot and there deposits a portion of its load. Such a deposit spreads out from the base of the steep slope in the shape of a fan. Where several streams flow from a mountain into a lowland near each other, their fans may coalesce and form *compound alluvial fans* or a *piedmont alluvial plain.*

In some localities the loss of water by evaporation and seepage into the ground is a factor in the formation of alluvial fans. Where streams flow from humid highlands into dry lowlands the loss of volume may be as important as the loss of velocity in causing deposition of sediment.

Large alluvial fans are found at the eastern base of the Rocky Mountains in Colorado, at many places in the Great Basin of Nevada, at the western base of the Sierra Nevada in California and in the intermontane basins of southern California. Many of the large orange

FIG. 10-6. Alluvial fans at foot of Lost River Range, Butte County, Idaho.
(Vertical photo, U. S. Geological Survey)

orchards of California are located on the fertile soil of alluvial fans.

Channel Deposits. Variations in volume and velocity from season to season cause deposition in the stream channels themselves during periods of low water. Such deposits are, of course, only temporary and are swept away during succeeding high-water stages. The inner slopes of bends or curves are common places of deposition; here the velocity is less than on the outside of the curve, and bars of silt, sand, or gravel are developed.

Some streams, especially those that suffer loss of volume in dry regions, are constantly overloaded and deposit sediment in their channels most of the time. The South Platte River in Nebraska is a good example. The headwaters of this river arise in a region of fairly abundant rain in the Rockies. On crossing the semiarid plains the volume and velocity become so low that the river cannot move all of its sediment at one time. Numerous sand bars choke the stream and divide it into many interlacing streamlets, which continually shift as the sand bars are changed. Such a stream is a *braided stream.*

Floodplain Deposits. Valleys in which streams have developed broad, flat bottomlands, or *floodplains,* are subject to flooding in times of high water. As long as a stream is confined to its channel the high velocity of the rising flood waters enables it to carry a great load of sediment. But when the flood water breaks over the top of the channel banks and spreads far and wide over the flat valley floor the current is slowed and deposition takes place. Each flood adds another layer to the existing deposits, so that some valleys have a covering of alluvium several score or even a few hundred feet thick.

Since the velocity is suddenly checked at the point where the water overflows the channel banks, the amount of deposition on the floodplain is greatest at that point. In this way the floodplain is built up into a pair of broad low ridges or *natural levees* that are highest just beyond the borders of the channel and slope gently toward the valley sides.

FIG. 10-7. Diagram of a floodplain and associated features. Oxbow lakes are seen where meanders are cut off from the main stream and also from its Yazoo tributary. Back swamps often occur behind the natural levee. Alluvium covers the rock floor of the valley.

These natural levees tend to keep a river in its channel during moderately high water, but the very high floods either break through or rise over them and flood the flat ground beyond.

Where levees are well developed the lowlands behind them are apt to be poorly drained and swamps are common. Such swamps back of the levees are known as *back swamps*. Some of the tributary streams flow along the back lowlands for a considerable distance before they find a break in the natural levee and join the main stream. One of the most striking tributaries of this kind is the Yazoo River in the state of Mississippi, which follows the floodplain of the Mississippi River for about 150 miles before entering the main stream near Vicksburg. The name *Yazoo tributary* is applied to streams which behave like the Yazoo River.

Rivers with high natural levees and broad floodplains often change their courses in time of flood. A breach in the levee may be cut so deep and the back lowland may be so low that the water does not return to the old channel when the flood subsides. Instead, the river cuts a new channel in the lower ground and builds up a new pair of levees.

Floodplain deposits make rich soils and are usually intensively cultivated. In spite of the danger of floods, many cities are built on floodplains because they offer flat ground near cheap water transportation. Although periodic floods are normal events, the result of heavy precipitation and rapid runoff, man has contributed to their intensity and frequency by clearing forests and plowing steep land, thereby causing even more rapid runoff. He has also attempted to reduce floods by building artificial levees along the main streams and by straightening their channels, but his efforts in that direction have not been eminently successful. Probably the most promising method of flood control is to slow up the runoff and establish some control over the numerous tributaries that feed a main stream. This can be accomplished, in part at least, by reforestation, terracing of hillsides, and building a multitude of dams along the tributaries.

Deltas. We have seen that the deposition of sediment along a stream's course is in most cases due to loss of velocity. So, too, is the deposit at the stream's mouth, or *debouchure.* Where a stream flows into a quiet body of water, such as a lake or the sea, its velocity is all but lost and deposition of most of its remaining load follows. Long ago the deposit at the mouth of the Nile River was given the name *delta* from its resemblance to the shape of the Greek letter, delta. Deposits at the mouths of other streams are given the same name, although some depart considerably from the delta shape.

The accumulating sediments partially choke the mouth of the stream and cause it to divide into branches, or *distributaries.* Deposition continues in the distributaries until they too are choked and split into other branches. In this way a network of dividing, coalescing, and shifting channels develops on most deltas. One or more channels are kept open for navigation by dredging or by building jetties which confine the current and thereby increase the velocity.

Some streams have no visible deltas. In most such cases waves, currents, and tides remove material as fast as the streams deliver it. Again, streams may empty into such deep water that the delta has not yet been built up to sea level although a great amount of material may already have been deposited on the bottom. Other streams, like the Niagara River, carry so little sediment that there is almost no deposition at their mouths.

Deltas, like floodplains, are subject to the hazards of floods and shifting channels, but since they usually have fertile soils and are accessible to water transportation many of them support large populations. Some of the great deltas, such as those of the Nile and of the Tigris and Euphrates, are sites important in the history of man's early development. One of the oldest and densest populations of the world lives on the delta of the Hwang Ho, or Yellow River, of China, and the deltas of the Rhine and adjacent streams support an intensive modern agricultural and commercial civilization.

CONSEQUENT AND SUBSEQUENT STREAMS

The direction taken by stream valleys depends on a number of factors, the most important of which are the slope of the land and the distribution of weak rocks. Any newly uplifted land area will slope directly or indirectly toward the sea. Streams that follow this original slope of the land are *consequent*. Their direction is a consequence of the topography, without regard to the character of the rock. Most of the streams on the Atlantic Coastal Plain flow down the original slope of the surface to the sea and therefore are consequent streams.

As streams deepen their valleys and develop tributaries they discover differences in resistance to erosion. Weak rock layers, zones of closely spaced joints, faults, and other weaknesses provide lines along which erosion proceeds more rapidly than elsewhere. As a result many valleys develop along these zones of structural weakness. Such valleys are adjusted to the structure of the rock and are known as *subsequent* valleys. The Shenandoah Valley in Virginia and the Mohawk Valley in New York are examples of subsequent valleys.

STREAM PIRACY

Streams compete with each other in the processes of valley development and the expansion of their drainage areas. The conditions that may favor one stream against another in this contest are (1) steeper gradient, (2) weaker rock and, (3) greater volume. A stream situated where conditions for growth are favorable will deepen and lengthen its valley until it steals some of the runoff feeding the headwaters of its less favorably located neighbors and by continued aggression may divert large portions of the competing streams to its own channel. This diversion of drainage from one stream channel to another is *stream piracy*.

Stream piracy is most common in headwater regions along asymmetrical divides where streams on one side have steeper gradients than those on the other side of the divide. One of the classic examples of recent capture is found in the Catskills of New York. Kaaterskill Creek flows down the steep eastern front of the plateau with a gradient of

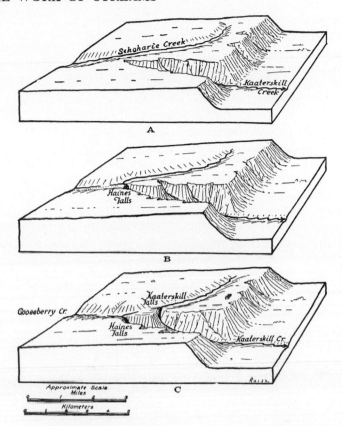

FIG. 10-8. Stream piracy. The three diagrams represent three successive stages in the capture of the headwaters of Schoharie Creek by the swifter-flowing Kaaterskill Creek, Catskill Mountains, N. Y. Gooseberry Creek (C) is the beheaded remnant of the ancient Schoharie. *(From Guidebook 9A, 16th International Geological Congress)*

several hundred feet per mile, while Gooseberry Creek, a tributary of the Schoharie, flows westward with a much more gentle gradient. Because of its much steeper gradient, Kaaterskill Creek has extended its valley westward by headward erosion and has cut off a few miles of the headwaters of Gooseberry Creek. A few miles south of this locality, is a case of imminent piracy where the Plaafekill and the head of Schoharie Creek are in opposition. In the not too distant future the rushing Plattekill will behead the gently flowing Schoharie.

In the Appalachian Highlands, along the divide between the Atlantic and the Gulf of Mexico drainage basins, numerous cases of recent and imminent piracy can be seen. The streams flowing to the Atlantic have shorter courses and steeper gradients than those flowing to the Gulf. As a consequence the Atlantic streams are stealing the headwaters of the Gulf streams and gradually shifting the divide westward. Other examples of this type of capture are found in the Andes Mountains along the boundary between Argentina and Chile. It is said that the Chilean rivers, with their short, steep courses to the Pacific Ocean, have beheaded nearly all of the Argentinian rivers.

Although steeper gradient alone is sufficient cause for the capture of one stream by another, the process is accelerated if the pirate stream is further favored by weaker rock and greater volume. In any case the pirate must be able to deepen its valley below that of its victim. It is commonly believed that many of the dry gaps in the hard rock ridges of the Appalachians were cut by through-flowing streams which were subsequently captured by neighboring streams having the advantage of location in the adjacent weak-rock areas.

Suggestions for Further Reading

GILBERT, G. K., *Geology of the Henry Mountains* (U. S. Geographical and Geological Survey of the Rocky Mountains Region, 1877).

LEOPOLD, L. B., and WOLMAN, M. G., *River Channel Patterns: Braided, Meandering, and Straight* (Washington, D. C., U. S. Geological Survey Professional Paper 282-B, 1957).

SCHULER, E. W., *Rocks and Rivers of America* (Lancaster, Pa., Jacques Cattell Press, 1945).

THORNBURY, William D., *Principles of Geomorphology* (New York, Wiley, 1954).

TRASK, Parker D., *Applied Sedimentation* (New York, Wiley, 1950).

— 11 —

The Cycle
of Stream Erosion

STAGES IN VALLEY DEVELOPMENT

W E HAVE SEEN that most valleys are made by streams, and that even those valleys initiated in other ways are modified by the streams that later flow in them. The growth of a valley follows a more or less orderly sequence: first a stream develops a small, narrow valley in which downcutting or deepening is the dominant process; as the lower limit of downcutting is approached, the effect of sideward cutting becomes more and more important, the bottom of the valley widens and becomes a floodplain. With continued widening of adjacent valleys the divides between streams become narrower and lower until eventually a whole region is worn down to an almost featureless surface sloping gently toward the sea.

The stages through which a valley passes in its normal development are conveniently divided into youth, maturity, and old age. Although the time required for a stream to reach old age cannot be stated definitely, it must ordinarily be expressed in hundreds of thousands, even millions of years. Because of the various factors such as the original altitude of the land, the resistance of the rocks, and the climate, that control the rate of valley development, streams actually the same age in years may be in different stages of development, and a stream that is chronologically younger than another may yet be more advanced in development. Also, a single stream can be in different stages of development along different parts of its course, because of differences in rock resistance.

Young Streams and Valleys. A young stream, or valley, is one in which downcutting predominates over lateral planation, one in which

169

FIG. 11-1. Resistant rock makes the vertical scarp over which the small stream plunges, Thacher State Park, N. Y. At the base of the falls weaker rock is worn back more rapidly into a cave. *(Photo by the author)*

FIG. 11-2. Potholes in granite ledges in James River, Henrico County, Va. *(U. S. Geological Survey)*

the processes of valley *deepening* are more active than those of valley-floor *widening*. The stream has sufficient gradient and velocity to carry its load and at the same time to deepen its channel. Perhaps the most distinctive features of a young valley are (1) an irregular gradient and (2) a V-shaped cross-profile.

Irregular Gradient. Although the average gradient of a youthful stream is steep, it is usually irregular. At some places in the channel flow is swift, at other places more gentle. Sometimes the irregular gradient is the reflection of the original irregularities of the surface on which the stream took its course. In other cases the stream finds differences in resistance of the rocks in its bed and develops an irregular gradient by cutting down the weak rock more rapidly than the resistant rock. Probably the most striking expressions of its irregular gradient are the waterfalls and lakes in a stream's course.

Waterfalls and *rapids* indicate that the youthful stream has not yet graded its course to a smooth, uniform slope. In the life history of a stream, waterfalls are but temporary features, for as the valley is deepened the falls become lower and lower and disappear entirely when maturity is attained.

Waterfalls are commonly found where resistant rock crops out in the stream bed and are especially abundant in regions of rugged topography. At Niagara Falls a nearly horizontal bed of hard rock forms the brink of the escarpment over which the water plunges. The Great Falls of the Potomac, as well as the falls and rapids in other streams along the so-called "Fall Zone," are located where the streams flow from the more resistant rocks of the Piedmont onto the weak rock of the Coastal Plain. Many other examples are found in the Appalachian Mountains, in the Adirondacks, and in fact in most rugged regions where a variety of rocks occur.

Mountains that have been glaciated generally have numerous waterfalls. Mountain glaciers commonly excavate the main valleys more deeply than the tributary valleys. After the ice melts and the glaciated valleys again become water courses, the numerous tributary streams plunge into the main valleys over steep precipices. Yosemite Falls in the Sierra Nevada of California is an example of this kind of falls. During a period of recent glaciation the valley of the Merced River was gouged out much more deeply than that of its tributary, Yosemite Creek. Now, since the ice has disappeared, the Yosemite must plunge 2,500 feet over a precipice into the main valley.

Then, too, some waterfalls are made by dams behind which water ponds into a lake or pool before it rushes over the embankment. Lava flows and landslides cut across established stream courses; silt, sand, and boulders left in the wake of receding ice temporarily choke glaciated valleys; beavers build dams of logs and sticks across creeks; and man builds concrete barriers across rivers.

FIG. 11-3. Yosemite Creek, in two leaps, drops almost 2,500 feet from the high tributary into the more deeply glaciated Merced River Valley. (*U. S. Dept. of Interior*)

Many waterfalls move slowly upstream. Niagara Falls affords an ideal example of the conditions that cause the upstream retreat of an escarpment. Here the hard rock layer which forms the cliff over which the Niagara River plunges is underlain by a very weak layer. The swirling water at the base of the cliff loosens the weak rock and removes it, thus undermining the overlying hard rock and producing the Cave of the Winds. As the cave grows deeper the overhanging rock is left unsup-

FIG. 11-4. Lower Falls (308 feet) and the canyon of the Yellowstone River, a youthful valley. Note the V-shaped cross profile. *(U. S. Dept. of Interior)*

ported and large blocks fall into the plunge pool. In this manner the falls have slowly receded upstream a distance of 7 miles from Lewiston.

Lakes and *swamps* as well as falls and rapids in a stream course indicate an irregular gradient. Lakes are formed in a variety of ways which will be discussed later. But whatever their origin, streams eventually destroy lakes by filling them with sediment and by cutting down their outlets so that they are drained. While falls and rapids mark the abrupt

173

FIG. 11-5. Although the Grand Canyon of the Colorado River, shown
above, is about a mile deep, it is still in the youthful stage of development.
The step-like appearance of the valley walls results from the alternation
of weak and resistant rock beds. *(Photo by Fairchild Aerial Surveys, Long
Island City, N. Y.)*

slopes of a youthful stream course, lakes and swamps fill the depressions
and flat places. All of these features disappear when the gradient
becomes uniform.

V-Shaped Cross Profile. A young valley commonly has a V-shaped
cross-profile which may be wide at the top with gently sloping sides, or
narrow and steep-sided, the steepness depending on the nature of the
material in which the valley is cut and also on the climate of the region.
In any case the valley is narrow at the bottom, being no wider there
than the stream itself. In other words, there is no floodplain.

V-shaped valleys are of various sizes. A gully in a plowed field, a
ravine in the side of a mountain, the gorge of the Hudson through the
Highlands and the mighty Grand Canyon of the Colorado are all young
valleys. Although the Grand Canyon has been in the process of formation for more than a million years the river is still vigorously deepening

174

its channel. The effects of rock resistance on steepness of slope are seen in the step-like appearance of the walls of the canyon. The bold cliffs made by resistant beds alternate with the gentle slopes formed by the weak layers.

Mature Streams and Valleys. The most prominent features that distinguish a mature stream from a young stream are (1) a regular gradient and (2) a floodplain. In maturity the falls, rapids, lakes and other irregularities of a youthful gradient have disappeared. A completely mature stream has graded its course so well that deepening of the channel is no longer important. Instead of growing deeper, the valley bottom grows wider by lateral planation. The V-shaped cross profile of youth gives way to the broad floodplain and flat bottomed U-shape of maturity.

As the floor of a valley grows wider the stream develops a series of more or less regular serpentine curves called *meanders*. In fact, the sideward swinging of the stream which results in meanders plays a major role in further widening the valley. The size of the meanders is roughly proportional to the size of the stream; thus, the diameter of a fully developed meander is from 10 to 20 times as great as the width of the stream which produced it. In times of high water a stream may shorten its course by cutting directly across the spur instead of following the curve of a meander. The arc of a meander abandoned in this way is called an *oxbow lake*.

Old Streams and Valleys. The distinction between old and mature valleys is in all cases purely arbitrary, and different authorities use different criteria. Perhaps the most common basis of classification is the relation between the width of the floodplain and the width of the meander belt, that is, the transverse distance between two lines that are tangent to the outside curves of the meanders. If the floodplain is 8 or 10 times as wide as the meander belt the valley is classified as old. A portion of the lower Mississippi meets this requirement for an old valley.

As the floodplain grows in width the various features associated with it become more pronounced. Meanders become closely spaced and cutoffs, or oxbows, more numerous; back swamps are widespread; Yazoo tributaries are common; and natural levees grow broader and higher, until the stream bed is sometimes at a higher elevation than the rest of the valley floor.

Many streams are in different stages of development in different portions of their courses. Where the bedrock is weak, a valley may be well graded and have a floodplain, while upstream or downstream the same valley may be a youthful gorge in resistant rock. As a general rule, main streams are in a more advanced stage of growth than their tributaries and most streams become younger upstream.

FIG. 11-6. Crooked Creek, in California, meanders lazily through a flat-bottomed, mature valley. *(Photo by Lee, U. S. Geological Survey)*

STAGES IN REGIONAL EROSION

So far in our discussion of the cycle of erosion we have considered only the valleys. Now let us take a larger view which embraces the entire land surface of a region, and includes many valleys and the divides between them. Observation and deduction have shown that large portions of continents pass through cycles of erosion. Of course the process is slow and we cannot in one lifetime observe the sequence of events as they progress in any one region, but the study of many regions in various stages of erosion enables one to form a concept of the succession of changes in any given region.

The cycle of stream erosion may be visualized by considering a land area recently uplifted above the sea. Streams immediately attack this new land surface, carving out valleys and carrying material away. If they are given enough time and are not interrupted, the streams will eventually remove all of the land down to their base level of erosion.

FIG. 11-7. Oblique aerial view of the Red River Valley at Shreveport, La. Here, where the floodplain is many times the width of the meander belt, the valley is old. *(Photo by Fairchild Aerial Surveys, Long Island City, N. Y.)*

When this task is accomplished they can do no more, and the stream cycle is completed.

Base level may be defined as that level below which streams cannot degrade. Inasmuch as water flows downhill, the base level of erosion cannot be lower than the outlet of the streams. For streams that empty into the sea, sea level is the ultimate base level. This level rises inland so that the local base level of streams 1,000 miles from the sea may be some hundreds of feet above sea level. Temporary base level may be provided by a lake, into which the stream empties, or by a hard rock barrier, through which the stream cuts slowly. In some localities, such as Death Valley and the basin of the Dead Sea, base level is below sea level. Streams flowing into these low basins do not reach the sea.

In the regional cycle of erosion, as in the development of individual valleys, we recognize the stages of (1) youth, (2) maturity, and (3) old age. The erosional stage of a region, however, does not always correspond to the developmental stage of the streams which drain it. For example, a region may be eroded to maturity by young streams, and a youthful region may include some streams that are in the mature stage.

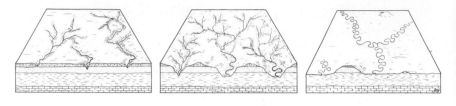

Youth   Maturity   Old Age

FIG. 11-8. **Diagrammatic representation of the successive stages in regional dissection.** In youth, broad interstream areas predominate; in maturity, the landscape consists mostly of slopes; and, in old age, most of the surface has been worn down to a peneplane, broken only by a few scattered monadnocks.

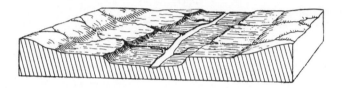

FIG. 11-9. Diagram of the middle Hudson Valley, showing the terraces left after rejuvenation by re-peated uplift. *(New York State Museum)*

Youth. Now let us follow the dissection of an uplifted region, such as a high plain or a plateau, from the time the streams begin their work until they have reduced the whole area to a lowland. At first all of the surface is uneroded upland. As time goes on this upland is cut up by stream valleys. In the early, or youthful, stage of regional development the valleys are relatively few and narrow and the divides between them are broad. We may, therefore, designate as youthful any region in which the principal element of the landscape consists of the original undissected upland surface.

Maturity. The stage of youth gradually develops into that of maturity. Stream valleys become more numerous and grow wider; the divides become narrower, the upland areas grow smaller. The upland is no longer the dominent element in the surface of the region. Now the slopes of the valley walls are the predominant element in the landscape. Perhaps some small areas of the original upland remain; some of the streams, too, may have made floodplains and introduced a lowland element into the landscape; but the slopes between the upland and the lowland are still the largest element. This is the stage of maturity.

Old Age. When maturity has passed, all parts of the original upland have disappeared. With continued erosion the valley bottoms grow wider, the divides lower, and the slopes, more gentle. When the area of the lowlands, or valley bottoms, exceeds the area of slopes or valley walls, the old-age stage is reached.

Peneplane. A peneplane is the final result of stream work. It is the ultimate product, the end of a complete cycle of regional erosion. The valleys are broad, the streams sluggish and the divides low. Much of the surface is worn down as low as running water is able to wear it. Here and there small hills of resistant rock and low divides along the headwaters remain as *monadnocks* above the monotonous lowland surface.

The formation of a perfect peneplane over a large region would require a great span of time, for the process of erosion becomes slower and slower as the slopes grow gentler. Perhaps no region of considerable size has remained undisturbed sufficiently long for complete peneplanation. However, more or less imperfect peneplanes now uplifted and dissected can be observed in the Canadian Shield of Ontario and Quebec and in the Piedmont Province of the United States.

INTERRUPTIONS IN THE CYCLE OF EROSION

Had there been no interference with normal stream erosion most of the lands of the earth would long ago have been reduced to peneplanes. As a region passes through the successive stages of erosion it may be interrupted at any stage in the cycle by various other processes. Among these processes that disturb the normal cycle of stream erosion are (1) uplift, (2) subsidence, (3) glaciation, and (4) volcanic action.

Effects of Uplift. Uplift of a region causes rejuvenation of both the streams and the land mass as a whole. If a region drained by mature streams is elevated, the gradients of the streams are increased and young valleys are cut in the bottoms of the mature valleys. The valleys thus become double, or step-like in form, and remnants of the bottom of the former mature valley, below which the young valley is cut, remain as terraces or benches.

If an old, or peneplaned region is uplifted, a new cycle of erosion is inaugurated. The rejuvenated streams begin to cut down and the whole region again takes on the characteristics of youth. Remnants of the old eroded surface may long remain as flattish interstream areas, giving evidences of former peneplanation. In cutting down, the streams may retain their old meandering courses and become intrenched in narrow, winding, steep-sided valleys.

Effects of Subsidence. Whereas uplift brings a region renewed youth, depression hastens the development of old age by lowering the land

FIG. 11-10. Maturely dissected slopeland topography in the Appalachian Plateau, Kanawha County, W. Va. *(U. S. Dept. of Agriculture)*

FIG. 11-11. Old age topography, with monadnocks. Piedmont of Virginia. *(Courtesy, John L. Rich and the American Geographical Society)*

and thereby decreasing the amount of material that the streams must remove in order to complete the cycle. Depression may make the streams so sluggish that they deposit sediment and build flat-bottomed valleys. If the land is depressed below sea level, the invasion of the sea puts an end to the cycle of stream erosion. When subsidence takes place along the sea coast, the mouths of the valleys are drowned and become bays and estuaries; the higher ground between the streams forms peninsulas and islands. The St. Lawrence, Hudson, Delaware, Susquehanna, Potomac and other streams along the Atlantic Coast of North America are all drowned for some distance inland.

Effects of Glaciation. Some portions of the earth's surface are now covered with glacial ice; other portions have been glaciated in the past but are now free from ice. During regional glaciation, streams are, of course, blotted out. When the ice melts away, a surface quite different from the preglacial surface is exposed. The ice has smoothed and gouged and scraped the land, and large amounts of glacial debris, irregularly deposited, obscure the former stream erosion surface. Streams that go to work on this new surface, therefore, assume the characteristics of youth. Much of northeastern North America had reached the mature stage of regional dissection before the recent great Ice Age, but when that ice disappeared it left behind numerous lakes, waterfalls, and other features of youth.

Effects of Volcanic Action. Volcanic action too may rejuvenate individual streams or even the entire topography of a large region. Small lava flows sometimes dam up stream valleys and impose the features of youth on them. In some cases large areas are more or less completely covered with thick layers, or flows, of lava. The Columbia Plateau which covers an area of more than 200,000 square miles in northwestern United States is a great lava field of comparatively recent origin. The older erosion surface beneath the lava was more or less completely covered by the volcanic material. The earlier cycle was interrupted and a new cycle was initiated on the surface of the lava field.

OTHER CYCLES OF EROSION

The discussion of this chapter has dealt mainly with the cycle of stream erosion. One reason for this is the fact that streams are the most widespread and important agent of erosion; another reason is that the cyclic aspects of stream erosion are better understood. The other agents of erosion, however, namely, wind, ground water, glaciers, and waves and currents, do follow a more or less definite sequence in their actions, which following chapters will to some extent reveal.

Suggestions for Further Reading

LOBECK, A. K., *Geomorphology* (New York, McGraw-Hill, 1939).

SHULER, E. W., *Rocks and Rivers of America* (Lancaster, Pa., Jacques Cattell Press, 1945).

THORNBURY, William D., *Principles of Geomorphology* (New York, Wiley, 1954).

VON ENGELN, O. D., *Geomorphology* (New York, Macmillan, 1942).

— 12 —

Ground Water

ORIGIN, DISTRIBUTION, AND MOVEMENT

W ATER NOT ONLY FLOWS *over* the ground in channels as streams; it also trickles slowly from pore to joint to crack *through* the rocks and soil of the upper lithosphere. Because the results of its work are often hidden, because it appears at the surface only occasionally in springs and wells, the significance of this underground water as a gradational agent is perhaps underestimated.

Sources of Ground Water. The greater part of the water in the ground is of *meteoric* origin; it was precipitated from the atmosphere. Some of the total annual precipitation falling on the earth, estimated at nearly 27,000 cubic miles of water, immediately runs off through the streams to the sea, some is evaporated from the land surface, and some soaks into the ground.

A small portion of the underground water is derived from molten rock masses beneath the surface. Such water is *magmatic*. In volcanic regions some of the water flowing out of hot springs and erupted as steam by volcanoes is coming to the surface and seeing the light of day for the first time. These waters are eventually taken into the atmosphere and later precipitated as meteoric water.

Still another small part of the water in the ground is *connate* water. This water was incorporated in some rocks when they were sediments accumulating on the bottom of the sea and has remained there ever since. The salt water found associated with petroleum in many oil fields is believed to be connate water.

Porosity of Soil and Rock. The mantle of soil that covers the bedrock is more or less porous, and will absorb some of the surface water. The porosity of this mantle rock, and consequently its capacity for retaining water, varies from place to place with the number and size of the pores

183

between the grains. The bedrock beneath the soil also has some capacity for holding water, but because of cementation, compaction, or crystallization, the bedrock ordinarily does not have as much pore space between the grains as the soil; joints, and fissures, however, provide additional openings for the admission of water. The porosity of different types of rocks varies greatly, ranging from 1 or 2 per cent in massive crystalline rocks up to more than 30 per cent in poorly cemented and closely jointed sandstones.

In general, rocks become less porous with depth; however, differences in the inherent porosity of rocks provide many exceptions to this rule. As the depth increases, the pressure must eventually become great enough to close all openings in all rocks. Although very strong rocks may retain pore spaces to a depth of as much as 10 miles, in most rocks the openings are eliminated at a much shallower depth.

Zone of Saturation. Under the impetus of gravity the ground water will percolate downward as far as the openings in the rocks will allow. The rock openings thus become filled from the bottom upward. The process is similar to that of pouring water into a bucket of sand. If only a little water is supplied, the sand is saturated only at the bottom. As more water is poured in, the level of *saturation* rises. Correspondingly, there is in the lithosphere, between the downward limit of percolation and the upper limit of saturation, known as the *water table,* a zone of rock completely saturated with water.

The Water Table. The position of the water table, that is, the upper limit of saturation, varies greatly in different regions; it also varies to some extent from time to time in any one region. In humid climates the water table is usually found within less than 50 feet of the land surface; in dry plateaus where the surface is cut by deep canyons it may be more than 3,000 feet beneath the surface. The water table is farther beneath the surface in hills than in valleys; yet it is not level for it conforms to some extent with the configuration of the land surface. In valley floors it may be at, or even above, the surface of the ground. Furthermore, alternation of periods of wet and dry weather causes the water table to move up and down so that there is a transition zone that is above the upper limit of saturation in dry periods and below it in wet periods.

Man can, and does, affect the position of the water table. On Long Island, N. Y., where considerable quantities of domestic water are obtained from wells, strict limits of withdrawal are enforced in order to keep the local water table above sea level. If too much fresh water is withdrawan, the salt water seeps in and spoils the wells.

Zone of Aeration. Above the water table, where it does not intersect the ground surface, there is a *zone of aeration.* In wet periods, water from the surface percolates through this zone down to the water table; in dry periods, some water moves upward by capillarity from the water table. Although the amount of water in this zone obviously must vary greatly from time to time, the rocks never become completely saturated. There is always some air present, filling the openings that are not occupied by water. The air and water together greatly accelerate the chemical decomposition of the rocks just beneath the surface.

Movement of the Ground Water. Most of the ground water eventually reaches the surface again. Some of it is carried upward by capillarity; some is absorbed by plants and transpired; a considerable quantity is drawn out through wells. Underground water emerges as springs and seepages on hillsides, in valleys and in the beds of streams, lakes, seas and oceans. Only a very small percentage of the ground water enters into chemical combination with minerals and is thus more or less permanently taken out of circulation.

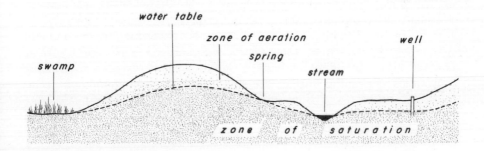

FIG. 12-1. Idealized diagram showing the relationships between surface features and the underground water.

As a rule the ground water percolates slowly through the pores and crevices of rocks, moving only a fraction of a mile a year. In some places, however, where distinct tunnels have been dissolved out of soluble limestone or where large open fissures occur, it may flow as much as several miles a day. In such situations the springs and wells are prone to pollution from the surface, for they do not have the benefit of slow filtration.

The water tends to migrate along the paths of least resistance to points where it can come to the surface again. Since gravity is the principal impelling force in its movement, the ground water always comes to the surface at points lower than those where it entered the ground. Sometimes the combined actions of capillarity and plant transpiration locally counteract the major force of gravity.

Springs and Wells. A *spring* is water issuing naturally from the ground in sufficient volume to create a distinct current; a slow escape of ground water at the surface is known as *seepage*. Springs are common on the sides of valleys below the water table. They are especially likely to occur at the top of impervious rock layers and where joints, fissures and porous beds allow the free exit of water to the surface.

Springs are designated by various adjectives which indicate their characteristics. Some springs have deep sources and are continuous in their flow; these are *permanent* springs; others, with shallow sources, flow in wet weather, but dry up during droughts when the water table falls below their outlets; these are *intermittent.* The water that supplies *thermal,* or hot springs, has been heated by contact with hot rock underground and has temperatures that range up to the boiling point of water. The term *mineral* springs is somewhat misleading, since all springs contain some mineral matter in solution. In the popular sense of the term, however, mineral springs are those which contain an unusually large amount of mineral matter or some unusual mineral. The various types of mineral springs are named according to the mineral matter which gives them their distinctive character. Calcareous springs contain abundant lime carbonate; saline springs carry a noticeable amount of salt; sulfur springs are rich in odorous compounds of sulfur.

While springs issue from natural orifices, *wells* are man-made. Any hole that penetrates the zone of saturation will fill up to the level of the water table. From there the water is raised to the surface by a suction pump or by containers on a pulley system. The rapidity with which a well fills and therefore the amount of water which can be obtained from it depends on the amount and rate of movement of the water in the rock penetrated by the well. If an abundant continuous source of water is desired, the well must be sunk into a porous rock formation which is saturated with water. Such a formation is known as an *aquifer.* A study of the topography and the rock structure of a region will indicate the most likely place to locate a well.

In some localities the relationships of rainfall, elevation, and rock structure are such that water will flow from a well under its own pressure. Such a flowing well is an *artesian* well. In some sections of the world, however, the term "artesian" is loosely applied to any notably deep well.

The following conditions are essential for a flowing well: (1) a pervious layer of rock which acts as a reservoir or aquifer, (2) outcrop of the pervious bed at an altitude higher than the site of the well, (3) adequate rainfall in the region of outcrop to supply the reservoir with water, (4) an impervious layer of rock overlying the porous bed to

FIG. 12-2. Artesian well, San Luis Valley, Colo. *(Photo by Siebenthal, U. S. Geological Survey)*

FIG. 12-3. Delighted throng watches "Old Faithful" Geyser spout stream of scalding water and steam 150 feet into the air at an average interval of 64 minutes, Yellowstone National Park, Wyoming, Idaho, Montana.

prevent the water from escaping. Under these conditions the water in the aquifer is confined under hydrostatic pressure and will rise to the surface through the well hole. Around the Black Hills of South Dakota and in the high plains east of the Rocky Mountains the conditions are favorable for artesian water, and much of the water supply was formerly obtained from flowing wells. As the number of wells has increased, the water in the aquifer has been drawn out faster than it has been replenished, the hydrostatic head has been reduced and many of the wells have stopped flowing.

Geysers. Geysers are hot springs which have periods of violent, intermittent activity, instead of flowing quietly and continuously. Some geysers spout every few minutes, others once in several months. A few, such as Old Faithful in Yellowstone Park, have regular periods of eruption, but most are very irregular. Geysers occur only in regions of present or recent volcanic activity, and in but some of them. They are found in Yellowstone Park of the United States, in Iceland, New Zealand, Japan, Malaya, and the Kamchatka Peninsula. In Yellowstone Park alone, there are more than 100 geysers and about 4,000 hot springs active at the present time.

Most of the water erupted by geysers is meteoric water which has percolated downward from the surface, but a little is probably magmatic, condensed from cooling igneous rocks below the surface. The surface water sinks downward until it comes into contact with rock sufficiently heated to boil it. If the outlet of the heated water to the surface is unobstructed, a quiet, continuous flow, a hot spring, is the result. But if the water becomes heated beyond the boiling point in a narrow or crooked tube where circulation is not free, the accumulation of steam in a pocket far down the tube will create enough pressure to cause an eruption which suddenly throws out the whole column of water in a fountain, or geyser. Before another eruption can occur, water must accumulate in the tube until the lower portion is superheated and the pressure is built up again.

As the constant loss of hot water cools the rock beneath the surface, the time between eruptions becomes longer and longer, until eventually they cease entirely. Unless the sources of heat are renewed, all existing geysers will become extinct within a relatively short geological time. As the present geyser regions disappear, new ones may develop. Then, too, changes in the supply and circulation of the ground water also affect the eruptions of geysers.

SOLUTION BY THE GROUND WATER

Because of its widespread distribution and its ability to dissolve many different kinds of substances, even though slowly, water is called the universal solvent. In moving through the rock openings, the underground water comes in contact with materials of various degrees of solubility. The effectiveness of solution therefore varies greatly in different kinds of rocks.

Solution in Limestone, Gypsum, and Rock Salt. Since limestone is the most common of the readily soluble rocks, the work of ground water is most important in limestone regions. Gypsum and rock salt are more soluble than limestone, but they are not nearly as common, and solution features in these rocks are more restricted in their occurrence.

Caverns and Tunnels. Even in limestone and other soluble rock some layers or zones are more susceptible than others. Also, solution is most effective along joints and bedding planes where the water can circulate most freely. It frequently happens that large quantities of material are removed from certain parts of the rock while other portions remain undissolved. In this way caverns and tunnels of various sizes and shapes are formed.

Many of the limestone caverns have been commercialized. Artificial lighting has been installed, narrow passages enlarged and other improvements have been made that make the caves more accessible and presumably attractive to the public. Numerous caverns are found in the Shenandoah Valley of Virginia and in the Ohio River basin of Kentucky and Indiana. Of these, the best known are the Luray Cave of Virginia, Mammoth Cave in Kentucky, and Wyandot Cave of Indiana. Perhaps the largest cave ever opened to the public is Carlsbad Caverns in southeastern New Mexico. Its total extent has not yet been fully explored. One chamber alone in this huge cave, the Big Room, is over a half-mile in length and has a maximum width of 400 feet and a maximum height of 348 feet.

The Natural Tunnel in southwestern Virginia, near Big Stone Gap, is a rather unusual solution feature. Cutting through a ridge for a distance of 1,500 feet, it connects the two valleys on opposite sides of the ridge. This tunnel is now followed by a considerable stream of water and is utilized by the Southern Railroad.

Sinkholes and Natural Bridges. If the bedrock is soluble and cavernous, funnel-shaped depressions on the surface of the ground are commonly found. Some of these *sinkholes* or swallow holes are formed directly by the solvent action of descending surface water which enlarges cracks or joints; others appear where the roofs of caverns collapse. In the middle of the city of Staunton, Virginia, in 1910, such a sinkhole was formed by the collapse of a cavern roof.

Much of the surface water in limestone regions drains into the sinkholes and thence follows underground channels. Some streams of considerable size flow into sinkholes and disappear underground, becoming *lost streams*. When the bottoms of sinkholes become choked with sediment so that the water cannot drain out readily, lakes or ponds appear. Lakes and swamps are also common where the bottoms of sink-holes are below the water table. The latter is the case in the Lake District of Florida.

Where sinkholes and caverns are numerous there are few surface streams, except short ones that empty into sinkholes. These sinkholes and the short gullies that lead to them create a rough, pock-marked surface which is difficult to traverse and to cultivate. Sinkhole topography of this kind is well developed in the Karst region east of the Adriatic Sea and has come to be called *Karst topography*. In this country similar topography is found in portions of central Tennessee and northern Kentucky.

FIG. 12-4. Sinkhole (Swallow hole) in the Minne-kahta limestone near Boyd, Wyo. *(American Museum of Natural History)*

Natural bridges, such as the Natural Bridge of Rockbridge County, Virginia, are often the direct result of underground solution. The stream whch now flows under the Natural Bridge formerly flowed underground in a long tunnel. The Bridge is all that is left of the former roof of that tunnel; the portions both upstream and downstream have collapsed and been carried away.

DEPOSITION BY GROUND WATER

Ground water precipitates any material with which it has become oversaturated. Among the often varied and complex causes for over-saturation are loss of water by evaporation, reduction in temperature, the addition to the solution or subtraction from it of certain materials

FIG. 12-6. Natural Bridge, Virginia, the remnant of the roof of a natural tunnel. (*Photo by Hillers, U. S. Geological Survey*)

FIG. 12-5. Natural Tunnel, Va. The railroad utilizes the natural passage made through the ridge by the underground stream at the left.

FIG. 12-7. Concretions. At the left are concretions of iron-bearing clay (dark) and calcium carbonate (white). The large circular concretion is about 1½ inch in diameter. At the right is a concretion with a leaf inside. *(Photos by the author)*

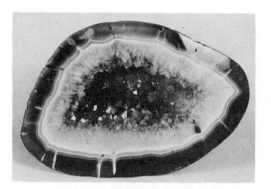

FIG. 12-8. Geode lined with quartz crystals cut open and polished. *(American Museum of Natural History).* FIG. 12-9. Polished section of petrified tree trunk. Replacement of the wood fiber by mineral matter, molecule by molecule, has preserved the minutest details of the original structure. *(American Museum of Natural History).*

which may cause precipitation of other substances. A considerable portion of the dissolved load of the ground water is therefore deposited underground, at least temporarily, or on the ground where the water issues to the surface.

Cave Deposits. Because of changes in the composition or circulation of the ground water, caverns which were hollowed out by solution frequently become places of deposition. Calcium carbonate is the most common mineral matter deposited in caves, although gypsum, rock

FIG. 12-10. "Old Faithful Log," Petrified Forest, Ariz. A log that was buried by sediment and volcanic ash long ago (Triassic time) and was recently exhumed by erosion. While buried the wood was replaced by silica.

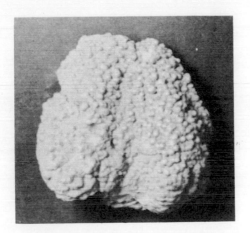

FIG. 12-11. Geyserite from Yellowstone Park. *(Photo by the author)*

salt and other materials are sometimes found. As lime water slowly seeps into the cave, it evaporates and deposits lime carbonate or *travertine* in various forms. *Stalactites* hang downward from the roof; *stalagmites* grow upward from the floor; post-like forms or *pillars* extend from floor to roof. Water trickles down the walls and through cracks, leaving various fluted and curtain-like deposits, and the floor is often covered with flat sheet-like layers of travertine. When pure, all travertine is white, but the inclusion of other mineral matter imparts various colors.

193

FIG. 12-12. Long slender stalactites, a few stubby stalagmites, and a small pool in Skeleton Cave, Jenolan, Australia. *(Geological Survey of Canada)*

FIG. 12-13. Stalactites and stalagmites joined in columns and curtains, Carlsbad Caverns, N. M. *(U. S. Dept. of Interior)*

195

Cementation. Below the water table, in the zone of saturation, the ground water tends to fill the pores and cement the cracks in rocks with material which it has carried down from the zone of leaching. Thus a compact sandstone is formed by the deposition of material between the grains of loose sand, and veins are formed by the deposition of minerals in cracks and joints. The composition of the cementing material varies from place to place with the constituents of the rocks from which the ground water has dissolved its load. Calcium carbonate, silicon dioxide, and iron oxide are the most common cements.

Concretions. Precipitation by the ground water frequently starts about some nucleus and continues with the addition of more or less concentric layers around the outside. The shape of the nodule or concretion thus formed depends in large measure on the shape of the nucleus, which may be a fossil, a pebble or other object. Concretions are most common in porous or weak sedimentary rocks. As a rule they differ in composition from the enclosing rock. Silica, or flint, concretions are plentiful in some limestones; lime or iron carbonate concretions are often found in clays and shales; and many coal beds contain concretions of iron sulphide in the form of marcasite.

Geodes. Geodes are cavities partly filled with crystals or some other form of mineral matter growing inward from the surface of the cavity. The cavities themselves may have been formed by solution or by the expanding force of steam in lava. Most geodes are lined with some form of calcite or silica, the latter often in the form of quartz crystals, amethyst, onyx, or opal.

Replacement. Under some circumstances solution of one substance and the deposition of another in its place may occur simultaneously, so that the form and structure of the original material are perfectly preserved. If a mineral is replaced in this manner the result is a *pseudomorph* having the form and structure of one mineral and the chemical composition of another; if the material attacked is of organic origin, it becomes *petrified*, or literally turned to stone, by the substitution of mineral matter, molecule by molecule, for the original material. The logs in the Petrified Forest of Arizona are tree trunks that have been buried in sand so long that all plant tissue has been replaced by silica from the ground water.

Spring Deposits. Sometimes springs are so heavily charged with mineral matter that they precipitate their load soon after reaching the surface. Calcium carbonate, the most common material deposited by springs, often forms large mounds and terraces near the outlets. While travertine is the general name applied to this material as well as to cave deposits, the very porous variety is called *calcareous tufa,* and the compact crystalline variety which takes a good polish is known as *Mexican onyx.* Among the largest of all travertine deposits are the great limestone beds at Tivoli in Italy, from which was quarried much of the stone used in St. Peter's Church at Rome and in the interior of the Pennsylvania Railroad Station in New York. At Mammoth Hot Springs in Yellowstone Park great deposits of travertine are still growing. If the deposit made by springs is siliceous, it is called *geyserite* or siliceous sinter. All of the geysers and many of the other hot springs in Yellowstone Park are depositing geyserite.

MECHANICAL WORK OF GROUND WATER

Landslides. Although ground water generally moves much too slowly to erode mechanically, its presence in the ground is an important contributory factor in the movement of landslides. Loose mantle rock, such as talus and glacial debris, tends to glide down steep slopes when it is heavily laden with water. The water not only increases the weight of the loose material but also provides lubrication to make gravity more effective. Landslides usually occur after prolonged periods of rain when the ground is well saturated with water, on mountain slopes and the sides of oversteepened valleys.

Landslides are sometimes destructive to man and his works. One of the most disastrous slides occurred on the Rossberg in Switzerland in 1806. Great masses of loose rock and soil suddenly slid from the mountainside into the valley, burying the village of Goldau and killing several hundred people. In Italy, in 1855, a great mass of rock waste slid into the valley of the Tiber River, damming the valley and flooding the village of San Stefano to a depth of 50 feet. The Turtle Mountain slide at Frank, Alberta, in 1903, also caused considerable damage. Here the whole face of the mountain, a mass estimated at 40 million cubic yards, broke loose and slipped into the valley below. And in the Culebra Cut of the Panama Canal the steep slopes created by artificial excavation experience frequent landslides and will continue to do so until the slopes become gentle.

Suggestions for Further Reading

KUENEN, P. H., *Realms of Water* (New York, Wiley, 1956).

LOBECK, A. K., *Geomorphology* (New York, McGraw-Hill, 1939).

MEINZER, O. E., *Ground Water in the United States: A Summary* (Washington, D. C., U. S. Geological Survey, Water Supply Paper 836-D, 1939).

SHARPE, C. F. Stewart, *Landslides and Related Phenomena* (New York, Columbia University Press, 1938).

THORNBURY, William D., *Principles of Geomorphology* (New York, Wiley, 1954).

— 13 —

Glaciers and Glaciation

IN PARTS OF THE WORLD where temperatures are below freezing much of the time, a considerable portion of the precipitation falls as snow. If more falls than melts, some snow is left on the ground to accumulate from year to year. At high altitudes in any latitude and at all altitudes in high latitudes there are regions of perpetual snow. These regions are said to be above the snow line. At the Equator in the Andes the snow line is 16,000 to 18,000 feet above the sea. As the latitude becomes higher the snow line becomes lower in altitude until it finally reaches down to sea level in some of the polar lands.

As the flaky snow accumulates to great depths above the snow line, the weight of the upper layers gradually compacts the lower layers. During the summer, meltwater at the surface trickles downward and freezes in the pores beneath. In this manner hard ice masses of great thickness are formed. These ice masses commonly have a stratified or layered structure, the layers representing successive seasons of snowfall. On attaining considerable thickness this snow-ice begins to move from its place of accumulation. As soon as it begins to move, it becomes a *glacier*.

Glaciers may be conveniently divided into three types, as follows: (1) the alpine type, (2) the piedmont type and (3) the continental or ice-cap type. Alpine glaciers are often designated as mountain, or valley, or local glaciers.

ALPINE GLACIERS

While alpine glaciers are so named because of their abundance in the Alps, they are also commonly found in other great mountains, such as the Rockies, the Andes, and the Himalayas. In fact, all of the continents except Australia have glaciers of this type. These glaciers are distinguishable from other types not only because of the mountain location but also

FIG. 13-1. Louis Agassiz (1807-1873), the Father of Glacial Geology, was one of the first men to recognize and prove the former existence of an ice age in Europe and North America. *(American Museum of Natural History)*

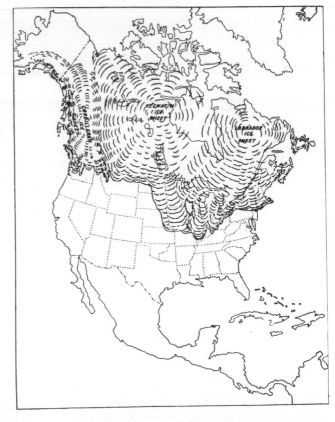

FIG. 13-2. Map showing centers of accumulation and maximum extent of the ice cap in North America during the last Ice Age. *(American Museum of Natural History)*

FIG. 13-3. High snowfields and glacier heads in the Canadian Rockies.
(Geological Survey of Canada)

because they occupy only the valleys in the mountains. Since the snow is blown over or slides down from the peaks and steep slopes, accumulation is greatest in the high portions of valleys. Here the glaciers originate and move down the valleys as tongues or rivers of ice, from a fraction of a mile to as much as thirty miles in length, and separated from others in nearby valleys by ridges and peaks.

Crevasses. *Crevasses* are fissures or cracks in glacial ice, commonly formed where glaciers move over irregularities in the valley bottoms. Ice, being rigid, can accommodate itself to abrupt changes in slope only by breaking and gaping apart. Differences in the rate of movement between the central and marginal portions of a glacier may cause oblique crevasses to open along the sides. At the head of a glacier where the ice breaks away from the snowfield above, a prominent crevasse, the *bergschrund,* often develops. All crevasses are a source of danger to mountain climbers, especially when they are concealed by a fresh fall of loose snow.

Movement of Valley Glaciers. Glaciers do not flow like a stream of water, neither do they slide like a block of ice. There are several factors which contribute to the movement of glaciers and influence their rate of motion. Among them are the thickness of the ice, the amount of melting and refreezing, and the slope of the surface over which the ice moves. The fact that glaciers move faster in summer than in winter and faster in the afternoon than in the forenoon indicates that melting and refreezing is an important cause of movement. Nevertheless, the relative values of the factors involved in ice motion are not very well understood.

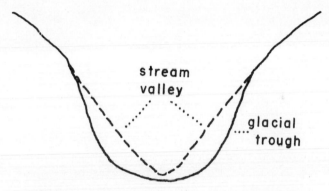

FIG. 13-4. **Cross-profile of a young valley before and after glaciation.** The V-shaped stream valley is deepened and widened into a round-bottomed U by ice erosion.

As compared with stream velocity, glacial motion is very slow, one to three feet a day being an average rate. Some, however, move only a few inches and a few others as much as 100 feet a day. The movement is usually differential, the center moving faster than the sides and the top faster than the bottom.

Growth and Decay. Mountain glaciers move down their valleys until they reach a point where melting is equal to the forward movement. In most cases the lower end, or front, is below the snow line, and sometimes even below the timber line. When melting exceeds the forward movement, the front of the glacier retreats (melts back) up the valley; when melting is less, the glacier advances. Thus, variations in temperature and in the amount of snowfall cause the lower limits of glaciers to oscillate back and forth. Small glaciers respond to changes in temperature and snowfall more rapidly than do the larger ones. The small glaciers in Glacier National Park are longer in winter than in

FIG. 13-5. Typical glacial trough. Glaciated valley of Leckie Creek in the Coast Range of British Columbia. *(Geological Survey of Canada)*

summer, whereas the fronts of the large glaciers in the Alps do not noticeably shift their positions with the seasons.

Long-term observations on various glaciers in the Alps and elsewhere show that many of them have cycles of advancing and retreating extending over a period of years. There seems to be such a climatic cycle of about thirty-five years during which many glaciers pass through a cycle of advancing and retreating. Doubtless there are longer cycles, but they are not well known. It is certain, however, that the glaciers in the Alps, the Rockies, and other mountains were formerly much larger and more numerous than they are now.

Methods of Erosion. Glaciers erode by (1) plucking, (2) scouring, and (3) transportation. Along the contact between a glacier and the ground, finger-like extensions of ice penetrate cracks in the rocks; movement plucks out the ice-gripped blocks and drags them along. These ice-plucked blocks, as well as debris gathered from other sources, are the tools that make the moving ice a powerful force in deepening and widening pre-existing valleys. Loose material is scrubbed off and the solid rock is scratched, gouged, and scoured smooth by the grinding and polishing action of the fragments frozen in the base of the ice. In addition to the material the glacier gathers by its own efforts, other debris is brought to it by slumping and landslides from the upper valley walls, by little streams that flow down from above in summer, and by the wind.

Transportation of debris by a glacier is markedly different from transportation by running water. Moving ice will incorporate in its own mass

FIG. 13-6. Avalanche "busting" by use of a 75 mm. shell exploded in a suspected wind slab area, showing giant avalanche in motion 10 seconds after the shell exploded, Wasatch National Forest. *(U. S. Forest Service)*

and take along fragments of practically any size, even those as large as a house. Everything is carried together, completely unsorted and regardless of the size, weight, or shape. Furthermore, the size of the particles transported is not dependent on the velocity of the moving ice. It is important to remember this fact when we consider ice deposits.

Results of Erosion. Glaciers are, and have been, responsible for most of the scenic beauty of high mountain regions. The striking topographic features characteristic of glaciated highlands can best be observed after the ice has disappeared and the results of erosion are exposed to full view. Since the mountain valleys that are now being glaciated, or have been in the past, were initiated by stream erosion, the glacial features are superimposed on and follow the grain of a pre-existing stream-sculptured landscape.

Glacial Troughs. Ice erosion of a young mountain valley converts the V-shaped cross-profile to that of a round-bottomed U. The sides are attacked as well as the bottom, projecting spurs are worn off, and the walls are made smooth, straight, and steep. The former stream valley is now a glacial trough.

Where rock resistance varies, the floor of the trough may be irregular. At places where weak rocks crop out, the valley is gouged more deeply, and depressions are left to form lake basins after the ice disappears. A long, narrow lake occupying a large part or all of a glacial trough is a *finger lake,* (see Fig. 15-2). A series of small lakes, filling only the hollows in the floor of the trough and strung along the course of one stream, are known as *paternoster lakes,* from their resemblance to beads

FIG. 13-7. Yosemite Valley, a steep-sided glacial trough. At the right a small stream plunges from a hanging tributary into the main valley. The flat floor of this trough is due to occupancy by a lake. *(Photo by Hillers, U. S. Geological Survey)*

FIG. 13-8. Glacial trough with hanging tributary, Glacier National Park, Mont. *(National Park Service)*

FIG. 13-9. A fiord on the Labrador Coast. *(Geological Survey of Canada)*

FIG. 13-10. Mt. Robson glacier in the foreground with two small tributaries coming down from the flanks of the matterhorn peak in the background, Canadian Rockies. *(Harvard University Dept. of Geology)*

FIG. 13-11. Cirques in the Torngat Mountains of Northern Labrador.
(Courtesy, Alexander Forbes and the American Geographical Society.)

on a chain. Sometimes they are separated by falls and rapids. These features may also result from ice cap glaciation if the axes of the valleys are aligned with the direction of ice motion.

Where glaciers of either the alpine or ice-cap type discharge into the sea, valleys may be excavated below sea level. When the ice melts away these troughs, filled with sea water, become *fiords*, such as those along the coasts of Norway, Alaska, and Labrador.

Hanging Valleys. In mountains that have long been subjected to alpine glaciation the main valleys are usually more deeply eroded than their tributaries, so that, when the ice disappears, the elevation of the tributaries is higher, sometimes by several hundred feet, than that of the main valley. Such high tributaries are called hanging valleys. Many of the beautiful waterfalls of glaciated mountains, such as Yosemite Falls, are found where streams leap from hanging tributary valleys into the deeper main valleys.

Arêtes. Mountain glaciers not only deepen their valleys, but also widen them and make their sides steeper. The widening of two parallel

206

valleys often makes the dividing ridge between them narrower and steeper until the crest becomes very sharp, like the blade of a cleaver. Such knife-edge ridges between troughs are called *arêtes*.

Cirques. Perhaps the most striking features of Alpine topography are the amphitheater-like depressions, or *cirques*, at the heads of the glacial troughs. Here at the heads of the valleys the ice begins its motion, and here it remains longest when the period of glaciation draws to a close. Consequently, the head of a glacial trough is commonly deeper, wider, and more steep-sided than the lower valley. In many cases the cirque is excavated so deeply that a lake, or *tarn,* forms in it when the glacier disappears.

Matterhorn Peaks. As the cirques grow deeper and wider the mountain peaks above them grow steeper, narrower and relatively higher. Where several cirques cut into the flanks of a mountain peak from different directions they more or less isolate it from its neighbors and reduce it to a spectacular horn, or needle peak. Hundreds of these peaks, often called matterhorns after the famous mountain in the Swiss Alps, are found in the Alps and in other glaciated mountains.

Deposition by Alpine Glaciers. Inasmuch as the ice is incapable of sorting the load that it gathers and carries, materials of all kinds are necessarily dumped together when it melts. In fact, the unsorted nature of ice deposits is their most outstanding characteristic. This material, consisting of a heterogeneous mixture of boulders, gravel, sand, and clay, is designated as *till.* Meltwaters from a glacier pick up some of the finer material dropped by the ice and redeposit it. Such material is, of course, carried and deposited according to the principles of stream action and is therefore sorted. Since it is derived from glacial deposits and redeposited by water it is called *glaciofluvial* material. More or less of the glaciofluvial material is in close association with the till. Some is carried beyond the limits of the ice and deposited in the valley of the meltwater stream as a *valley train.* The terms till and glaciofluvial deposits are lumped together in the term glacial *drift.*

Whereas the term drift applies to the nature of the material deposited by a glacier and its meltwaters, the term *moraine,* with a modifying adjective, refers to the topographic form and the position of the deposits with respect to the glacier. Melting is most rapid along the front, or toe, of a glacier. As the melting ice drops its load more ice moves in with more load. The deposit at the front may accumulate to considerable thickness and form a hummocky ridge called the *terminal* moraine. After melting from the entire valley the valley floor is littered with drift, called the *ground* moraine. In many cases the two sides of the valley, where the ice acquired abundant material from the valley

FIG. 13-12. A matterhorn peak in Glacier National Park, Mont., Going-to-the-Sun Mountain. St. Mary's Lake is at the foot. *(National Park Service)*

walls, are marked by ridges of drift, called *lateral* moraines. Glacial deposits are further discussed in the following section on continental glaciers.

Differences Between Glaciated and Nonglaciated Mountains. Mountains that have never been subjected to alpine glaciation usually have a relatively smooth surface outline. The peaks and other summits are rounded and covered with residual soil. The valleys are V-shaped and crooked, with narrow ravines at their heads. Tributaries usually enter the main valleys at accordant junctions, that is, at a common level, and waterfalls and lakes are scarce:

Where glacial erosion has been active over an extended period of time and the ice has disappeared, the rounded surfaces produced by weathering and by stream work are modified and more or less replaced by the features of ice erosion. The V-shaped stream valleys are deepened, widened, and steepened to glacial troughs, spurs are cut back and the valleys made straighter, and tributary streams enter the main valleys in waterfalls. The former narrow valley heads are broadened into cirques, and lakes abound, both in the cirques and in other portions of the valleys. Bare rock surfaces, scarred by scratches and grooves, crop out on the steep valley sides. Sharp, pyramidal matterhorn peaks and narrow ridges rise to etch a jagged skyline. In all, the landscape produced by alpine glaciation is more rugged, more varied and picturesque, and more spectacular than the landscape of nonglaciated mountains.

PIEDMONT GLACIERS

Valley glaciers in high latitudes sometimes extend down to the foot of the mountain and spread out on the foothills as piedmont glaciers. The best known of these is the Malaspina Glacier on the west side of Yakutat Bay in Alaska. Formed by the union of several valley glaciers which move down from the St. Elias Mountain Range and coalesce on the nearby flat lowland, this glacier covers an area of about 1,500 square miles. Its movement is so slow and the amount of debris supplied to it by its feeders is so great that many feet of moraine have accumulated on the upper surface where melting is rapid. Forests even grow on the moraine at some places near the margin, in spite of several hundred feet of ice beneath.

Today piedmont glaciers are limited to high latitudes, and are well developed only in Alaska. During the Ice Age, however, they were more numerous, and evidences of their former presence are abundant at the foot of the Alps, the Rockies, the Andes, and other localities.

FIG. 13-13. Glaciers on Mount Lewis Case, Alaska. Note that the drainage is ponded behind the moraine in the foreground. *(U. S. Forest Service)*

FIG. 13-14. The Blue Ridge of Virginia has the rolling, tree-blanketed profile of the typical unglaciated mountain. Compare with Fig. 13-15. *(U. S. Dept. of the Interior)*

FIG. 13-15. The steep, bare and angular slopes of the Rockies in Glacier National Park show the effects of alpine glaciation. Just to the right of the center is a needle peak or matterhorn. *(U. S. Dept. of the Interior)*

FIG. 13-16. Poorly drained, glaciated landscape of Superior National Forest, Minn. *(U. S. Forest Service)*

FIG. 13-17. Masses break off from the ice margin and float out to sea as icebergs, Glacier Bay National Monument, Alaska. *(Photo by Lowell Summer)*

CONTINENTAL GLACIERS

Character and Distribution. Continental glaciers, or ice caps, differ from valley glaciers in that they cover the entire surface of a large region, filling the valleys and extending over the hills and ridges. If a valley glacier is likened to a stream of ice, a continental glacier must be compared with a large lake or sea of ice, with here and there a bare mountain peak, or *nunatak,* above the surface as an island in the ocean.

Nearly 6 million square miles of the earth's land surface are now covered by continental ice sheets. Practically all of Antarctica's 5 million square miles are ice-covered; the Greenland glacier is about 720,000 square miles in area, and smaller ice caps are found in Iceland, Spitzbergen, and other Arctic islands. During the Ice Age an additional 10 million square miles or more of land in northern North America and Europe were loaded with thick ice sheets. Thus we can not only observe the processes of continental glaciation operating today over large portions of the earth, but we can also study other equally large areas which show the effects of former glaciation.

The ice cap on Greenland reaches the sea with a thickness of 2,500 feet in some places. Inland the ice surface rises gradually, whereas the ground surface beneath the ice is lower in the interior than at the margins. In 1930-1931 the Wegener Expedition, which measured the thickness of the ice at several places with a seismograph, found it to be in the vicinity of 4,400 feet, 40 miles from the margin; 5,500 feet, 75 miles inland and about 6,500 feet near the center.

More recent observations have recorded thicknesses of 11,000 feet, even though the ice surface is not that high above sea level. Evidently portions of the landmass of the Greenland subcontinent are below sea level.

The ice in the continental glaciers moves from the high central portions outward in all directions. Measurements of the rates of motion in different localities vary from one inch to 50 feet a day, movement being most rapid toward the margin where melting is fastest. On reaching the sea the ice breaks off into *icebergs*, which float away to melt slowly in warmer waters.

Erosion by Continental Glaciers. Since a continental glacier caps the entire surface of a region, it erodes the hills as well as the valleys. Loose mantle rock is scraped off and the bedrock is ground and scoured by the pebbles and boulders frozen in the moving ice. When they are angular, these pebbles and boulders scratch parallel *striations* and *grooves* in the bedrock over which they are dragged. In Canada and the northern United States there are many large areas of bare rock surface which still preserve the evidences of Ice-Age scratching, grooving, and grinding.

Where the ice sheet moves over rocky hills, it usually smooths off the stoss side by grinding and steepens the lee side by plucking. The result is an asymmetrical hill called a *rôche moutonée*, or "sheep rock." Many of the small hills in Bronx Park, New York exhibit this form of ice erosion. Then, too, ice moving in the direction of a preglacial stream valley may deepen and widen that valley as would an alpine glacier. The valleys of the Finger Lakes and the Hudson Gorge in the Highlands of New York State have been deepened by tongues of ice in this manner.

Deposition by Continental Glaciers. In general make-up and appearance the till deposited by continental glaciers is very like that left by alpine glaciers. Since the continental ice sheets cover larger areas and may move greater distances, their moraines are apt to include a greater variety of materials. Boulders and pebbles left by the ice that are foreign to the bedrock beneath are called *erratics*. Many such erratics, some of them more than 50 feet in diameter, have been found in the northern part of the United States, scores and hundreds of miles south of their places of origin.

Terminal Moraine. When melting at the margin is about equal to the forward motion of the ice, and the front remains nearly stationary for a long time, a considerable deposit of material will accumulate at the edge of the melting ice. This terminal, or end moraine marks the ice

FIG. 13-18. Rock surface scoured and striated by glacial movement. *(New York State Museum)*

FIG. 13-19. Deep grooves in solid rock made by glacier just below Lace Lake, Glacier Creek, Flathead National Forest, Mont. *(U. S. Forest Service)*

limit at the time of deposition. It takes the form of a hummocky belt of small rounded hills, ridges, and basins distributed in a disorderly and irregular manner. Many of the basins are closed depressions which contain lakes or swamps. This gently rolling, patternless landscape, sprinkled with ponds and bogs, is sometimes given the name of *knob and kettle topography*. Where the terminal moraine is deposited on flat ground it is a conspicuous feature in the landscape. On Long Island, New York, for example, it runs the length of the island from east to west and forms its so-called "backbone."

Ground Moraine. On melting and disappearing from a region, a continental glacier leaves ground moraine of variable thickness scattered more or less unevenly over the entire surface it once covered. On some hilltops and steep slopes it is absent or very thin, whereas in some lowlands it may be as much as 500 feet thick. The ground moraine is thicker in the United States than in Canada, the southward moving ice being forced to deposit more and more of its load as it reached lower latitudes. Lakes and swamps are common in regions covered by glacial drift because of the unequal deposition of the till and consequent damming of streams.

In some localities a part of the ground moraine is in the form of smooth, elliptical hills, called *drumlins*, whose long axes are parallel to the direction of ice motion. They are commonly from 25 to 150 feet high, one-fourth to one mile long, half as wide as long, and steepest, as a rule, on the end facing the direction from which the ice came. Drumlins are abundant in only a few localities in this country: in the region south of Rochester, New York, where several thousand are found; in and around Boston Bay, and in eastern Wisconsin.

Drumlins consist of unsorted material, though the fine textured constituent usually predominates. There is good evidence to show that drumlins are formed where the lower part of a glacier becomes so overloaded with debris that there is more debris than there is ice to carry it. This condition may occur where the ice has moved over an area of weak rock and has gathered a heavy load of fine material. Concentrations of the overload may lodge against small rock bosses or other irregularities of the surface. Movement of the ice over the lodgments streamlines them into an ellipsoidal shape.

Glaciofluvial Deposits. The meltwaters at the ice margin unite to form numerous streams which carry much of the finer glacial debris out beyond the terminal moraine. Each of these streams is so heavily laden with gravel, sand, and silt that it builds an alluvial fan, the coarser sand and gravel being deposited near the terminal moraine, the finer sand and clay carried farther along. As the fans coalesce they form a gently sloping *outwash plain*. The southern half of Long Island, south of the

FIG. 13-20. Glacial erratic of granite resting on schist, Central Park, New York City. *(Photo by Ronald Strauss)*

FIG. 13-21. Glacial till consisting of boulders of various sizes and shapes embedded in clay, Bangor, Pa. *(Photo by Hardin, U. S. Geological Survey)*

FIG. 13-22. The irregular hills and depressions of knob and kettle topography, Iron County, Utah. *(Photo by Gregory, U. S. Geological Survey)*

FIG. 13-23. Drumlin in bay, Chester Harbor, Nova Scotia. The steeper end faces the direction from which the ice sheet advanced. *(Geological Survey of Canada)*

217

terminal moraine, is such an outwash plain. Large blocks of ice from the glacier front are sometimes floated out and buried in the moraine or in the outwash material. When these ice blocks melt, the surface of the ground is marked by pits, or *kettle holes*.

Associated with the unsorted till in areas covered by terminal and ground moraines are great quantities of sorted, or stratified material deposited by water during times of rapid melting and waning of the ice sheet. Some of these deposits take the form of narrow, winding ridges, from a few feet to 100 feet high and a few yards wide at the summit, running in a direction roughly parallel to that of the ice movement. Some of these ridges, or *eskers*, are several miles long and so regular in form that they resemble railroad embankments. It is believed that eskers are formed by deposition from subglacial streams and probably also from streams that flowed in crevasses. They are most common in New England, Scandinavia, Finland, Ireland, and other regions where the front of the ice formerly stood in bodies of water.

Conical, oval, and irregular deposits of assorted sand and gravel, known as *kames*, are doubtless formed under various local conditions during times when the ice melted rapidly. Some kames are formed in water ponded at the ice margin; others are deposited in depressions on the ice surface, and still others in crevasses. The gravel and sand of many kames and other glaciofluvial deposits are excavated for building and road material.

Ice-Damned Lakes. Where the land surface in front of the continental glacier slopes toward the ice edge, the ice front serves as a dam for the meltwater and other drainage in front of the glacier. In this way temporary marginal lakes are formed, only to disappear when the ice dam melts.

The largest marginal glacial lake that was formed in North America during the Ice Age is known as Lake Agassiz. At the time of its greatest extent it covered more than 100,000 square miles in Minnesota, North Dakota, and Manitoba. When the ice melted and the surface water could find its way northward to Hudson Bay, the lake disappeared almost entirely, leaving Lake Winnepeg and Lake of the Woods as small remnants of a once great body of water. The exposed floor of Lake Agassiz, covered with fine, rich sediment, is now a fertile wheat-growing region.

Fine sediment carried into marginal glacial lakes is generally deposited in pairs of thin layers, or *laminae*. In each set, one lamina is thinner and finer grained than the other. Each pair of layers is called a *varve* and is believed to represent one year's deposition. Most of the sediment was probably carried into the lakes with the summer meltwaters. The coarser particles soon settled to the bottom, but the finer material remained suspended until winter. When the lakes froze over and the water became calm beneath the ice cover even the finest particles settled. By

FIG. 13-24. Strata in a glacial esker, taken in a gravel pit south of Ely, Minn., Superior National Forest. *(Photo by Leland J. Prater, U. S. Forest Service)*

cutting into the bed of one of these extinct lakes and counting the varves of clay, the number of years the lake was in existence can be calculated. (See Fig. 3-5.)

Drainage Changes. Since a continental glacier covers the entire surface of a region, it blots out the preglacial streams. Ice erosion and the deposition of till change the configuration of the preglacial surface. On the new surface exposed when the ice melts, the streams do not always follow their former courses. Many of the old valleys are filled with glacial till, and the earlier stream divides have been shifted. Even those streams that do return to their preglacial valleys may find that differential ice erosion and uneven deposition of till have left the valleys with irregular gradients, so that they must be graded anew. Thus, in general, the effect of continental glaciation is to rejuvenate drainage. The numerous lakes and waterfalls of the northern United States and Canada give striking evidence of the youthfulness of the drainage in this region that was glaciated during the recent Ice Age.[1]

[1] See Chapters 25 and 26 for further information on earth history.

219

CAUSE OF GLACIATION

In the preceding pages it has been indicated that glacial climates come and go. A number of regions of the earth, some of which are in fairly low latitudes, show evidences that they have been glaciated in past times. The most recent Ice Age (Pleistocene) was multiple in its occurrence. That is, within the past million years there have been four ice invasions of the middle latitudes, separated by warm interglacial stages. One naturally inquires as to the cause, or causes, of the coming and passing of glacial climates. Many hypotheses have been proposed, but no one has gained universal acceptance. One hypothesis lays great stress on the variation in solar radiation; another has to do with changes in the composition of the atmosphere; a third gives great importance to the elevation and subsidence of the land; still another explains the changes in climate by the drifting of the continental masses to different positions on the globe.

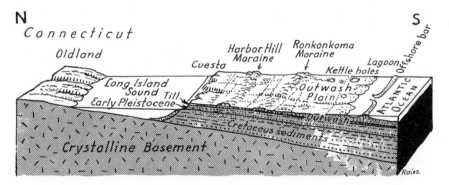

FIG. 13-25. Section through Long Island, New York, showing terminal moraine and outwash plain. Vertical scale greatly exaggerated.

Perhaps a combination of circumstances is more likely to be the cause of the coming and going of ice ages. A recent hypothesis proposed by Ewing and Donn is a combination which includes the shifting of the poles to different positions on the earth, or a sliding of the earth's crust so that land areas change their latitude, together with changes in the circulation of sea water caused by these changes in latitude and by diastrophism, as well as other circumstances and inferences which are beyond the scope of this book. As data of many kinds accumulate over a longer period of time, this, one of the greatest unsolved problems of earth science, will doubtless become better understood.

Suggestions for Further Reading

FLINT, Richard F., *Glacial Geology and the Pleistocene Epoch* (New York, Wiley, 1957).

THORNBURY, William D., *Principles of Geomorphology* (New York, Wiley, 1954).

THWAITES, F. T., *Outline of Glacial Geology* (Madison, Wis., Published by the Author, 1953).

VON ENGELN, O. D., *Geomorphology* (New York, Macmillan, 1942).

ZEUNER, F. E., *The Pleistocene Period; Its Climate, Chronology, and Faunal Succession* (London, Ray Society, 1945).

— 14 —

Wind Work

THE WIND is one of the several gradational agents that modify the surface of the lands. Although wind work is of some importance in all climates, its greatest fields of activity are in regions where the earth's surface is poorly protected by vegetation or other cover. Arid regions, some sea coasts, and river floodplains in semiarid climate provide favorable sites for effective wind action. Given these favorable environments, the effectiveness of the wind, like that of running water, depends on its velocity; the stronger the wind the greater its carrying power and the more rapidly it will abrade. The work of the wind consists of abrasion, transportation, and deposition.

EROSION

Abrasion. To be an effective abrading agent, the wind must have tools which it can drive against rock to grind off particles. Its tools are the loose sand and dust particles it picks up from surfaces not entirely protected by vegetation. Swept along by the wind, sand scours and grooves rock surfaces and slowly wears them away in a blasting process similar to that by which man cleans stone buildings or cuts figures in stone by means of pressure-driven sand.

Where rocks of different degrees of resistance crop out at the surface, or where orientation exposes some surfaces more than others, the wind carves out the weak or more exposed rock faster and produces the varied forms of differential erosion. In flat regions, broad shallow depressions known as *blowouts* may be scooped out. In the Gobi Desert, for example, these basins range from 300 yards to 30 miles in length and from 50 to 400 feet in depth. In hilly regions, differential wind erosion on hillsides produces *wind caves*, which in some cases grow deeper and deeper until a tunnel, or *blow hole*, extends entirely through the hill. Many other picturesque and unusual forms, such as mushroom rocks, table rocks, pedestals, and hoodoos, are developed by differential erosion.

The sand particles used by the wind as tools are themselves worn, chipped, pitted, and reduced in size in the process of abrasion. Originally angular grains are worn off at the corners and reduced to well-rounded grains with frosted surfaces. Such typical wind-blown sand is sometimes designated as "millet-seed sand." Pebbles and cobbles that are too heavy to be moved by the wind are polished and sometimes faceted or grooved by the wind-blown sand, and are named *ventifacts*. *Dreikanters* are a special type of faceted pebble with a triangular cross section. Bedrock, too, may be polished, and sometimes grooved in the direction of the prevailing wind. The polished surfaces of both loose fragments and bedrock may have a dark, enamel-like, appearance, due to the evaporation of solutions containing iron or manganese. Such surfaces are designated as *desert varnish*. In many places the fine particles are so completely blown away as to leave only pebbles and cobbles, forming the *desert pavement*, or *hammada*.

Structures made by man suffer no less than natural objects from wind abrasion. In lighthouses and other buildings along sandy beaches the windows become frosted and eventually destroyed by the constant grinding and chipping of wind-blown sand. In deserts the telegraph poles may be cut off just above the ground in a short time by the gnawing, shifting sand, unless they are protected by metal coverings.

Transportation. Rock waste formed by weathering is the principal source of the wind's load of dust and sand, although abrasion by the wind also provides some material. From plowed fields, floodplains, beaches, dried-up lake beds, glacial moraines, deserts, gullied hillsides, or any other open surface unprotected by vegetation the wind picks up its load.

The size and weight of transported particles depend on the wind's velocity. Ordinarily, sand grains are too heavy to be picked up and carried in suspension for any great distance, and are usually moved by rolling, skipping, or gliding. In a strong wind, however, sand grains may be actually picked up and carried in suspension, but they do not rise into the upper currents of air and are not carried very far at any one time. Repeated shifting by winds prevailing from one direction may eventually carry sand for considerable distances. In southwestern France sand has been blown inland from the seashore as much as 5 miles, and in the Sahara Desert large sand deposits are now found 100 miles from their apparent source.

Dust is commonly carried suspended in the air and may be transported great distances. A strong wind blowing for a few days in one direction in the semiarid southwestern part of the United States gathers and carries so much dust that the air becomes hazy and the sunsets highly colored. Dust carried from the American "dust bowl" is occasionally visible in the air on the Atlantic seaboard. The "blood" rains of

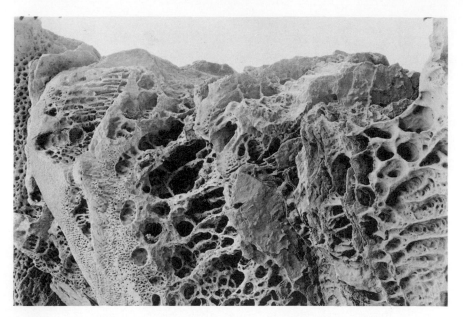

FIG. 14-1. Rock outcrop intricately fretted by wind abrasion, near Livingston, Mont. *(Photo by Walcott, U. S. Geological Survey)*

FIG. 14-2. A shallow blowout, the lowest part of which contains an intermittent lake, near Apishawa, Colo. A small mesa is seen in the background. *(Photo by Gilbert, U. S. Geological Survey)*

FIG. 14-3. Wind caves in a hillside, Dry Valley, Utah. *(Photo by Jackson, U. S. Geological Survey)*

FIG. 14-4. A blowhole or window, sculptured by the wind in Arches National Monument, Utah. *(U. S. Dept. of Interior)*

northern Italy are reddened by dust from the desert area of northern Africa. Strong winds pick up the red dust and carry it across the Mediterranean; as the winds rise to cross the Alps their moisture is condensed and the rain carries the dust down on northern Italy as red mud.

Vast quantities of volcanic ash are sometimes blown into the atmosphere by violent eruptions. Dust from the explosion of Mt. Katmai in Alaska in 1912 formed a deposit a foot thick 100 miles to the leeward of the source, and considerable quantities were carried as far as Seattle, Washington, 1,600 miles away. Dust from the eruption of Krakatoa in the East Indies in 1883 was carried in the atmosphere in such great quantities as to cause brilliant sunsets for several months entirely around the globe. So widespread is the process of dust transportation that it may reasonably be said that every square mile of the land surface of the earth has received dust particles from every other square mile.

DEPOSITION

When the velocity of the wind decreases, it must perforce drop all or part of its load of sediment. The heaviest particles are dropped first and so on down to the lightest and smallest. The very small particles of suspended dust are often washed down by rain and snow. Since particles carried in suspension differ notably in size and weight from those rolled along the ground, and since the two sizes of material are usually sorted and deposited separately, aeolian deposits may be divided on this basis into dust deposits and sand dunes.

Dust Deposits. Dust deposits are generally without special form, or are more or less mixed with other material and so escape notice, but some are of great magnitude and distinctive character. Most of the great wind deposits of fine material are known as *loess*.

Notable deposits of this loess are found in the Mississippi Valley from Louisiana northward to Illinois and Iowa, in eastern Washington, in the pampas of Argentina, in central Europe, and in the interior of China. In the Mississippi Valley the loess deposits average 10 to 20 feet in thickness, and but rarely attain a thickness of 50 to 100 feet. Its rather fine texture and its content of unleached soluble plant foods, make this loess an easily worked and fertile soil, widely cultivated in the midwestern corn and wheat belts. This Mississippi Valley loess was presumably derived in part from the glacial deposits of the recent Ice Age, in part from floodplains of the Mississippi and Missouri rivers, and probably in part from the more arid country to the west. In China the loess deposits reach a thickness of as much as 1,000 feet in parts of Shensi and adjoining provinces. The loess of China apparently had its source in the Gobi Desert of central Asia, whence it was carried east-

FIG. 14-5. Approaching dust storm, Heath, Mont., June, 1937. *(Photo by C. C. Williamson)*

FIG. 14-6. A narrow, steep-sided gully exposes a considerable thickness of vertically jointed wind-blown loess, Helena, Ark. *(Photo by Crider, U. S. Geological Survey)*

ward by the prevailing westerly winds. The Yellow River, or Hwang Ho, of China and the sea into which it empties owe their color to the great amount of fine yellow dust the river derives from the loess area through which it flows. Where it is unprotected by vegetation, loess is easily eroded. Many of the roadways in the loess region of China have become worn down into deep, narrow trenches by the wear of centuries of travel. Some of the farmers live in caves excavated in the walls of these trenches.

Volcanic ash is another wind deposit of considerable importance. Although fine in texture like loess, it consists of finely broken angular fragments of volcanic glass. This material is found in greatest abundance in and near some present-day volcanic regions; however, consolidated deposits known as *bentonites*, are found interbedded with older rocks at many places where volcanoes no longer exist.

Sand Dunes. Dunes are accumulations of sand formed in much the same manner as snowdrifts. They are started by some obstruction which causes an eddy in the sand-laden wind, and, once they are started, the dunes themselves provide the obstacles which cause their further growth. Dunes are of various sizes, ranging from a few feet to as much as 1,000 feet in height and from a few square feet to several square miles in area. They take various shapes according to the amount of sand available and the velocity and constancy of direction of the wind. They may be roundish hills, elongate ridges, crescents (*barchanes*), or irregular hummocks, normally having a long gentle slope on the windward side and a shorter steeper slope on the lee. The surface of the windward side commonly exhibits little ridges and furrows, called *ripple marks*.

The composition of most dune sand is dominantly quartz though small amounts of other rock-forming minerals may be present. Locally, however, there are dune sands that do not contain quartz as the dominant constituent: the beach dunes of Bermuda consist mostly of calcite; and the dunes of the White Sands National Monument in Otero County, New Mexico are made of nearly pure gypsum. The sand composing the dunes is usually well sorted as to size and well rounded in shape.

Dunes may be formed wherever there is a source of sand available to the wind. The most common sources are a sandy beach, a sandy river plain, and a disintegrating sandstone or other granular rock in a dry climate. Small dunes are found at various places along the Atlantic Coast of the United States from Cape Cod southward. Those along the south shore of Lake Michigan and on the southwest coast of France are also derived from beach sand. Dunes are found along rivers in many places in the western United States, notably along the lower Columbia River in Washington and Oregon and along the Arkansas River in western Kansas. In the arid part of the United States as well as in the

FIG. 14-7. Barchan sand dune and rippled sand, White Sands National Monument, N. M. *(U. S. Dept. of Interior)*

FIG. 14-8. A New Mexican sand dune drawn by Robert Balk (1899-1955), an artist as well as a great geologist.

Sahara and other deserts, disintegrating sandstones and other granular rocks are the principle source for the dunes.

All sand dunes migrate to some degree, unless they become so covered with vegetation that the wind no longer has access to the sand. Movement is accomplished by the transfer of sand from the windward to the leeward side, and as the material is shifted, the dune moves to the lee. If the wind direction changes, the direction of dune movement changes with it. On account of the large amount of sand to be moved, the rate of movement is usually slow, rarely exceeding 25 feet a year. In exceptional cases dunes move hundreds of feet a year or several score feet in a single day of strong wind.

Windward   Leeward

FIG. 14-9. **Profile of a migrating dune.** The windward side is gentle and rippled; the leeward side is steep. Compare with Fig. 14-10.

Migrating dunes may overwhelm roads, houses, farms, and forests. Some of the cities of ancient Chaldea and Babylon were covered by dune sand, and the town of Kunzen on the coast of East Prussia was buried by a sand dune in the early 1800's and was exhumed about 60 years later by the migration of the dune. Some of the railroads in our arid West are considerably bothered by shifting sand dunes. The most effective method of stopping migration of dunes is by planting certain hardy grasses and shrubs adapted to sandy soil on the windward slope. This holds the sand in place and thus prevents the advancement of the dune until trees may be planted in the accumulation of humus from the grass and shrubs. In this manner a considerable area of sandy waste in southwestern France has been converted into a profitable pine forest.

The impression is common that deserts are preponderantly characterized by shifting sand dunes. This impression is considerably exaggerated. Great expanses of relatively bare rock are more common than are dunes. In the Sahara, for example, it is estimated that not more than one-ninth of the area is occupied by dunes. In many places the surface is covered by coarse rock rubble, called a hammada, the sand and finer material having been blown away.

Suggestions for Further Reading

BAGNOLD, R. A., *The Physics of Blown Sand and Desert Dunes* (New York, Morrow, 1942).

LEIGHTON, M. M., and WILLMAN, H. B., "Loess Formations of the Mississippi Valley," *Journal of Geology*, Vol. 58, 1950, pp. 599-623.

FIG. 14-10. Migrating sand dunes in Death Valley, Calif. *(U. S. Dept. of Interior)*

— 15 —

Lakes and Swamps

THE INCIDENTAL FORMATION of lakes as the result of certain phases of erosion and deposition has already been discussed; and additional methods by which lakes are formed will be mentioned in succeeding chapters. Nevertheless, it appears desirable to treat systematically these important and conspicuous landscape features by looking backward and forward and also by including material that is not found elsewhere in this book.

A lake may be defined as a body of standing water occupying a depression on the land. Lakes may be large or small and deep or shallow; small ones are often called ponds, and very large ones inland seas. Swamps, or marshes, differ from lakes in that they are so shallow that the water surface is entirely obscured by a thick growth of vegetation.

In general, it may be said that lakes and swamps occur where there is some obstruction to the free runoff of surface water. Such obstructions to drainage may result from the operation of any of a number of natural processes and also from the activities of man.

ORIGIN OF LAKE BASINS

Lakes Formed by Gradational Processes. Basins in which water collects to form lakes may be produced by any of the common processes of gradation. Some of these processes, however, are more fruitful than others in this respect.

In reviewing the activities of those agents of erosion that have already been discussed, we find that lake basins can be formed even by the wind. In dry climates, blowouts excavated by the wind and hollows between sand dunes form basins that are often the sites of intermittent lakes. A number of such wind-formed lake basins are found in the Great Plains, especially in Nebraska, and also in the Columbia Plateau region of the state of Washington. In some cases lakes are formed when wind-blown material dams up a stream valley.

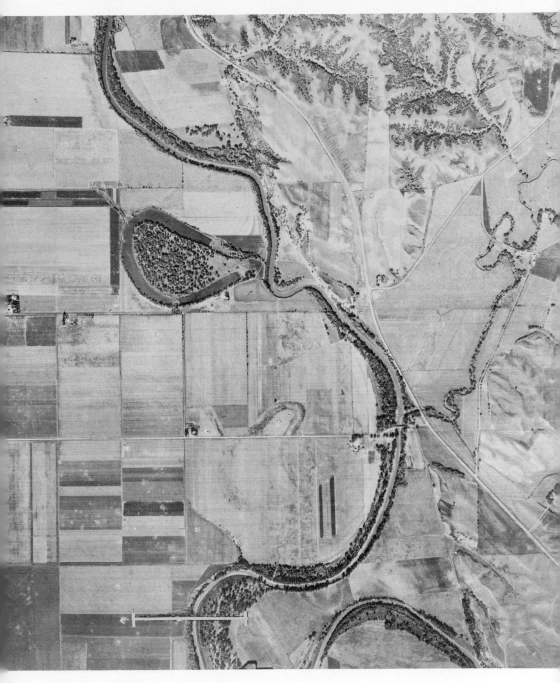

FIG. 15-1. Oxbow lake occupying a cut-off meander of the Big Sioux River, S. D. The white bar represents about half a mile. *(U. S. Dept. of Agriculture, A. A. A.)*

233

FIG. 15-2. A small finger lake in a glacial trough in the Canadian Rockies. *(Geological Survey of Canada)*

As a rule "streams are the mortal enemies of lakes," but a few types of lake basins are the direct result of stream action. Cutoff stream meanders are left on the floodplains of many mature and old rivers as oxbow lakes. Lake Pontchartrain in Louisiana is an example of delta lakes that form in depressions along the margins of deltas where the drainage is obstructed by the deposition of sediment. Similarly, the growth of alluvial fans sometimes obstructs the runoff of surface water. The basin of Lake Tulare, for instance, in the Great Valley of California, is closed by great alluvial fans built out into the valley from the base of the Sierra Nevada.

Lakes formed by glaciation are more numerous than those created by all other processes combined. Comparison of the number of lakes in the recently glaciated portion of North America with those in the unglaciated portion will verify this statement in a striking manner. Most of the thousands of lakes in Maine, in the Adirondack Mountains, in Minnesota, and in other portions of the northern United States are the direct result of glacial erosion or deposition or a combination of both. Some of these lakes occupy basins that were excavated by ice erosion; others were formed where deposition of moraine dammed the valleys; still others are found in kettle holes in the moraine.

In regions of soluble rocks, solution by the ground water often forms lake basins. Many sinkholes do not contain water, however, because they are above the water table and are open or porous at the bottom. Inasmuch as landslides are caused in part by ground-water action we may also include here those lakes formed by landslide dams.

Shoreline lakes, common along both the Atlantic and Pacific coasts of the United States, are usually formed where waves and currents build sand bars across the mouths of bays.

Lakes Formed by Diastrophism. As we previously pointed out, the lithosphere is not stable; some portions of it are being elevated while others are depressed. As a result, basins of various sizes and shapes are formed on the surface. Because they conform with the attitude of the bedrock such basins are called *structural basins*. They are the result of (1) warping, or bending, of the rock strata and (2) faulting, or breaking, of the strata.

Examples of lakes which occupy structural basins may be seen in many parts of the world. Lake Superior occupies a down-warped basin which was later enlarged somewhat by glaciation. The Caspian Sea has been isolated from the Mediterranean by the uplift of mountains. Lake Okechobee in Florida lies in a broad shallow basin on a surface that has recently been elevated from the sea bottom. The Dead Sea in western Asia and Lakes Tanganyika and Nyassa in eastern Africa are long, narrow lakes trapped in down faulted blocks which have sunk far below their surroundings. And many of the lakes in the western United States, such as Great Salt Lake in Utah, Pyramid Lake in Nevada, and Owens Lake in California, are situated in structural depressions. An example of a lake that came into existence in modern times as a result of diastrophism is Reelfoot Lake in western Tennessee. This lake basin was formed when the surface was displaced some 20 feet during the great New Madrid earthquake in 1811.

Lakes Formed by Volcanic Action. Some lakes are found in the craters of extinct volcanoes. Crater Lake, in southwestern Oregon, 5 or 6 miles in diameter and 2,000 feet deep, is one of the largest of this kind, and is of such extraordinary interest and scenic beauty that its

FIG. 15-3. Jackson Lake in Jackson Hole, Wyoming, lies in a down-faulted basin alongside the towering Grand Teton Mountains. *(U. S. Dept. of Interior)*

FIG. 15-4. Crater Lake from the south end, Crater Lake National Park, Ore. *(U. S. Forest Service)*

FIG. 15-5. Typical beaver dam and pond, Yellowstone Park. *(National Park Service)*

FIG. 15-6. Shallow playa lake formed after a rain, San Luis Valley, Colo. *(Photo by Siebenthal, U. S. Geological Survey)*

immediate vicinity has been set aside as a national park. Crater lakes are found in many other volcanic regions, among the most notable being those of the Campagna near Rome, those in the volcanic region of central France and of Central America.

Sometimes lava flows obstruct stream valleys and thereby form lakes. Snag Lake in California, Lac d'Ayat in central France and Tiberias Lake (Sea of Galilee) in the Jordan Valley are examples of this type.

Lakes Made by Plants and Animals. In remote regions, or where he is protected from hunters, the beaver is a lake-maker of considerable importance. This industrious animal builds its dam of sticks across many little streams and lives in the quiet waters of the pond above.

In some cases the growth and accumulation of plants may so greatly obstruct the surface runoff of water as to cause shallow lakes. Lake Drummond in the Great Dismal Swamp was formed, at least in part, in this manner.

Man-Made Lakes. Man's activities have become increasingly important among the agencies that form lakes. By constructing dams across streams, water is impounded for irrigation, water power, municipal supply, flood control, and other purposes. In recent years particularly, lakes of great size have been formed by throwing huge concrete dams across some of the large rivers of western United States. One of these reservoirs, Lake Meade above Boulder Dam on the Colorado River, is 125 miles long.

INTERMITTENT AND SALT LAKES

All so-called fresh water contains a very small amount of dissolved salts. If a lake has no outlet, the water that enters can escape only by evaporation. The salts remain and become more and more concentrated until eventually the water is salty. Lakes with outlets do not become salty because the outflow of water removes the salts as rapidly as they are carried in. In the various salt lakes all degrees of salinity are found, from relative freshness on the one hand to saturation on the other.

In addition to sodium chloride, or common salt, salt lakes usually contain other chlorides as well as sulphates and carbonates. In some cases borax is abundant. The kind of salt which predominates in any lake depends mainly on the composition of the rocks in and around the lake basin.

Some salt lakes, such as Great Salt Lake in Utah, are descended from lakes which were formerly fresh. Because decreased humidity has caused evaporation to exceed the inflow, this lake has shrunk below its former outlet. The fresh water ancestor of Great Salt Lake, known as Lake Bonneville, covered an area about 10 times as large and was about 900 feet deeper than the present shrunken, remnant. The fresh water lake existed during the Pleistocene Ice Age, when precipitation was greater and evaporation less than now.

Other salt lakes originate by the isolation of portions of the sea and are salty from their beginning. The Caspian Sea was cut off from the Mediterranean by the elevation of the intervening land, and Salton Sea was shut off from the Gulf of California by the growth of the Colorado River delta. If evaporation in these lakes exceeds inflow, as it does in Salton Sea, they decrease in size and grow more salty. If, on the other hand, inflow exceeds evaporation, as it does at times in the Caspian, they become less salty. Even though the Caspian and other similar lakes, or inland seas, may fluctuate seasonally or at irregular intervals, the general tendency in recent times has been that of shrinkage in area and lowering of level.

Not all lakes without surface outlets are salt lakes. Some drain away underground and thereby are kept fresh. Crater lakes usually do not fill the crater and flow over the rim. Instead, the water moves through the porous volcanic material and may appear as springs and seeps far down the flanks of the cone. Sinkhole lakes, too, may be kept fresh by underground outlets; and many kettle lakes have rather free circulation underground.

In arid and semiarid regions water fills shallow basins during wet seasons, only to disappear by evaporation during the dry periods. On evaporation the beds of some of these intermittent lakes are left covered with a deposit of muddy sediment which becomes dry and hard and reticulated with cracks. Such deposits are known as *playas*. In some of these the percentage of salts is so high that the lake floor is left as a white alkaline flat, or *salina*. Intermittent lakes are typical of the Great Basin, the arid southwestern United States and dry regions in other continents.

DESTRUCTION OF LAKES

Measured in terms of geologic time, lakes are ephemeral. Some may last only a few centuries or less, while others exist for a million years. It is estimated that there are now only half as many lakes in northern United States as there were 11-12,000 years ago, at the end of the last Ice Age.

One of the important processes which results in the destruction of lakes is the deposition of sediment on the lake floor. Much of the sediment carried into a lake by streams and other surface water settles in the quiet water, making the lake shallower and eventually filling the basin. A second process that destroys lakes is the cutting away of the dam or rim. Although robbed of much of its sediment, the outlet stream still possesses some cutting power. It gradually lowers the outlet

FIG. 15-7. Great Salt Lake is the shrunken remnant of ancient Lake Bonneville. Shorelines of the larger ancestral lake can be traced on the west front of the Wasatch Mountains. (U. S. Forest Service)

channel, making the lake smaller and shallower. The growth and accumulation of organisms, especially of plants, is a third process that contributes to the destruction of lakes. From the shallow water near the shore a choking mass of vegetation gradually creeps toward the center as the lake itself becomes shallower, until the whole basin is ultimately converted into a marsh or peat bog. Change in climate is another factors which sometimes causes the destruction of lakes. A lake formed behind an ice dam drains when the ice melts; and, decreased rainfall and increased evaporation may lower the level of a lake until it disappears.

Deposits in Lakes. Sediments deposited in lakes are of various kinds. Incoming streams, the velocity of which is suddenly checked, deposit coarse sediment at their mouths in deltas. Farther on, the finer sediment is spread more or less uniformly over the lake bottom. When the lake is drained, this fine silt and clay is left to make fertile soil. In some lakes the growth of organisms is so prolific that their accumulated remains make important deposits on the bottom. The microscopic shells of diatoms may form valuable beds of diatomaceous earth, and fatty plants and animals may contribute to the formation of oil shales. In dry regions, where evaporation is rapid, chemical substances, such

FIG. 15-8. Typical vegetation in the Great Dismal Swamp of Virginia-North Carolina. *(Photo by Russell, U. S. Geological Survey)*

as common salt, gypsum, potash, and borax, are deposited on the bottom and around the shores of the shrinking lakes.

SWAMPS

Swamps are areas of ground that are saturated, though not usually covered with water. They result from poor drainage of surface water. Many swamps represent the last stage in filling of lake basins; others may never have been more than damp or boggy places.

Many swamps occur on flat coastal plains which have recently been uplifted from the sea floor. There the land is so low and flat that the water does not drain away readily. The Great Dismal Swamp of Virginia and North Carolina and the Everglades of Florida are examples of large coastal plain swamps. Another favorable site for swamps is on the broad floodplains of rivers, where the building of natural levees leaves parts of the floodplain lower than the river. Along the lower Mississippi River, for example, there are many swamps (back swamps) on the floodplain because drainage to the river is obstructed by the levee. In regions that have been subjected to continental glaciation swamps are common. Such swamps are due mainly to the uneven deposition of glacial drift, which impedes the drainage. Most of the swamps, large and small, of the

241

northern portions of North America and Europe are of glacial origin.

Formation of Peat and Coal. In some swamps the growth of vegetation is luxuriant. When the plants die they are partly protected from oxidation by the water and therefore decay very slowly. Other plants growing on the partly decayed matter add to the accumulation. In the process of change the vegetable matter gives off some of its volatile constituents in the form of carbon dioxide, marsh gas, and water. Since the percentage of carbon becomes higher as the other elements are lost more rapidly, this process of change is known as *carbonization*.

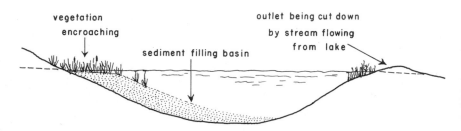

vegetation
encroaching

outlet being cut down
by stream flowing
from lake

sediment filling basin

FIG. 15-9. Diagram showing the processes by which lakes are destroyed.

Considerable thickness of partly carbonized plant material, known as *peat*, may accumulate in this manner. It is reported that the peat in the Great Dismal Swamp averages 10 feet in thickness. In Ireland, Denmark, and other parts of northern Europe where coal and wood are scarce, peat is excavated from bogs, dried, and used as fuel.

Peat is the first stage in the formation of coal. If a peat bog subsides sufficiently, the deeper water drowns out the vegetation and covers it with sediment, such as clay, or silt, or sand. Thus protected from the air, the organic matter undergoes further carbonization and progresses to the successively higher stages of lignite and bituminous coal. The rate of change does not depend on time alone; thickness (weight) of the overburden is important.

Compressional movements, such as those that cause folding of the strata, seem to be essential for the formation of anthracite (hard coal). The bituminous (soft) coal of western Pennsylvania is of the same geological period as the anthracite of northeastern Pennsylvania. The strata in the west are only slightly disturbed by compressional movement; whereas those in the northeast are intensely folded. Still farther east, in Rhode Island, where compressional movements were accompanied by the intrusion of igneous masses, carbonization of the plant material of the Coal Age has reached a more advance stage, some of it occurring as pure carbon in the form of graphite.

Suggestions for Further Reading

HINDS, Norman E. A., *Geomorphology* (Englewood Cliffs, N. J., Prentice-Hall, 1943).

LOBECK, A. K., *Geomorphology* (New York, McGraw-Hill, 1939).

RUSSELL, I. C., *Lakes of North America* (Boston and London, Ginn, 1895).

VON ENGELN, O. D., *Geomorphology* (New York, Macmillan, 1942).

WORCESTER, P. G., *A Textbook of Geomorphology* (Princeton, N. J., Van Nostrand, 1939).

— 16 —

The Ocean and Its Shores

T HE WORLD OCEAN is a great body of water which occupies the depressions in the surface of the lithosphere and surrounds the elevated or land areas of the earth. From the standpoint of area alone this water body is of great importance, for its surface is nearly three times as great as that of the lands, the ocean covering roughly 142 million square miles, the land areas of the earth only 54 million square miles.

The Atlantic, Pacific, Indian, Arctic, and Antarctic oceans are partially separated, major divisions of this world of water; smaller divisions are known as seas, gulfs, and bays. Such partly enclosed water bodies as the Mediterranean Sea, the Gulf of Mexico and the Hudson Bay are all parts of this great world ocean. Since all divisions, large or small, land encircled or open, are connected, anything which affects the level of one will correspondingly affect the others.

The distribution of land and water is not uniform over the earth. The Southern Hemisphere is covered by much more water than the Northern Hemisphere, and the Pacific Ocean is twice as large as any other ocean. Indeed, it is larger than all of the land areas of the earth combined.

As the ocean is also called the sea, its surface may be referred to as *sea level*. Mean sea level is the datum plane, or base, from which measurements of altitude are reckoned. To determine this mean sea level accurately, observations with a tide gauge must be carried on over a period of months or even years, so that not only the daily fluctuations in sea level may be taken into account but also those of a seasonal nature.

THE OCEAN BOTTOM

Sounding. The ocean bottom is naturally not open to direct observation as is the surface of the land. Until recent years soundings had to be made by the slow method of dropping a weight and line to the bottom. By this method the Challenger Expedition was able to make only about

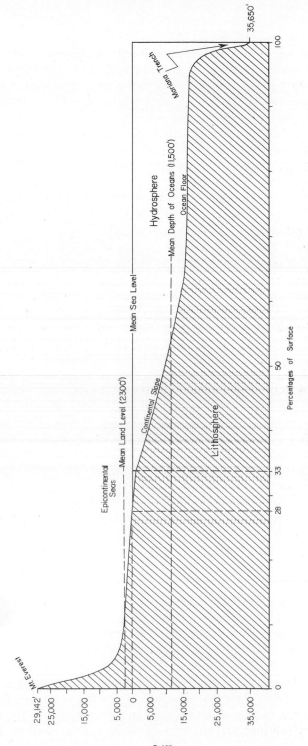

FIG. 16-1. Hypsometric chart of the continents and ocean basins.

245

500 soundings from 1873 to 1876. Since the development of the sonic depth-finder, or fathometer, however, the measurement of the ocean bottom has been proceeding at a rapid rate. This instrument measures the time necessary for a sound wave to travel to the bottom and for its echo to return to the surface. A ship equipped with a fathometer can chart the bottom as it steams along its course.

In spite of the present rapid method of sounding, the ocean bottom is so large an area that much of it is not yet well known. It is calculated that the average depth of the ocean is about two and a half miles. Until recently it was thought that the greatest depth of the ocean was in the Swire Deep, or Philippine Trough, where soundings show a depth of 35,433 feet. Recent measurements by a U. S. Navy bathyscaph show a depth of 37,800 feet in the Marianna Trench.

Subdivisions. The ocean bottom can be naturally divided into three parts: (1) the *continental shelf*, (2) the *continental slope*, and (3) the *abyss*. Because there is more water than can be contained in the ocean basins, around the margins of the continents there is a zone of shallow bottom from a few miles to more than 150 miles in width. This is the continental shelf, the submerged border of the continents. On it lies the epicontinental sea, where the water is rarely more than 100 fathoms (600 feet) deep. At the outer edge of the continental shelf the ocean bottom descends rapidly down the continental slope to the abyss, which in the main is more than 6,000 feet deep.

Submarine Valleys. At a number of places the outer portion of the continental shelf and the continental slope are marked by gigantic grooves and notches which resemble young valleys of stream erosion. Some of these valleys have dimensions comparable in magnitude to the Grand Canyon of the Colorado. They are found off the coasts of all the continents, with the possible exception of Antarctica. A well-known example in eastern North America is the Submarine Canyon of the Hudson River. From near Sandy Hook a channel extends across the continental shelf and the continental slope for a distance of 125 miles. The outer 35 miles of the valley is distinctly a canyon with walls 3,000 feet high. At its outer end the bottom of this canyon is 6,600 feet below sea level.

The origin of submarine valleys is a geological puzzle which has not yet been solved. None of the hypotheses that have been advanced to explain them has received universal acceptance. One hypothesis states that the valleys were cut by streams when the lands were higher, or the sea level lower, by several thousand feet, than now. The principal objection to this hypothesis is that there is not sufficient evidence of other kinds to show that there have been such great changes in the relation of land and sea in recent times. Other hypotheses ascribe the submarine valleys to submarine currents, to submarine springs, and to waves produced by earthquakes. Although the problem is now being intensively investigated, our knowledge of marine processes is not yet sufficient to allow sound judgment on these hypotheses. Recent information gained by M. Ewing and associates strengthens the hypothesis of submarine density (turbidity) currents. Perhaps in the near future a satisfactory explanation of this phenomenon will become apparent.

Ocean Deeps, Troughs, Swells, and Ridges. Beyond the continental slope the ocean bottom is not well known. It is known, however, that the ocean floor is far from uniform. Fifty-seven *deeps* descend more than 18,000 feet below sea level. Some of these deeps are broad, basin-shaped depressions, such as the Canary and Cape Verde basins in the North Atlantic; others, such as the Swire Deep, east of the Philippine Islands and the Bartlett Trough, south of Cuba, are long, narrow and steep-sided *troughs.*

The ocean floor also rises in elevated tracts, known as *swells,* where they are broad and gentle, and *ridges,* where they are narrow and steep-sided. One of the best known of these large elevated portions of the sea bottom is the North Atlantic Ridge, an irregular mountain range extending in a north-south line for 9,000 miles through the middle of the Atlantic Basin.

Seamounts. The tops of oceanic mountains which do not reach the surface are called *seamounts.* Some of these may never have risen to sea level. Others were formerly islands but now have sunk as much as a mile below the sea surface. Those of the latter group have flat tops or are bordered by flat benches that were planed off by waves. As further evidence that these flat seamounts have subsided, dredgings from them show rounded pebbles, similar to materials in streams and on beaches, and dead reef coral, which must have grown in shallow water.

Fracture Zones. In recent years a number of great fractures, or fissures, in the sea floor have been charted. Maurice Ewing and Bruce Heezen, in the Schooner *Vema,* by using echo soundings and seismographs, have traced a fracture zone for 4,500 miles. It is marked by a trench which averages one mile deep and 20 miles wide and coincides along its length with an active earthquake zone. This branching rift system extends through the North and South Atlantic, around the southern tip of Africa and into the Indian Ocean, where branches extend into the Arabian Sea, the Red Sea, and the rift valleys of East Africa. In the eastern Pacific the work of H. W. Menard and others discloses four subparallel, east-west fracture zones. The explanations for these great fracture zones are still in the hypothetical stage.

Sedimentation. The ocean bottom is a major site of accumulation of sediment. Most of the sediment is derived from the lands and a small percentage comes from extraterrestrial sources. Of the sediment derived from the lands much is washed in by streams, some is blown by the wind, some is dumped by melting glaciers and their icebergs, and some is gained by the attack of waves on shorelines.

In the sea the sediment is transported and sorted by currents. As a general rule the coarsest and heaviest sediment is left near shore, while the finer material is carried farther out and settles in deeper and quieter water. Most of the land-derived sediment settles on the continental shelf, but, because of the location and strength of certain *turbitity currents*, some of it may be carried far to sea.

On the bottom of the abyss much of the sediment is extremely fine-grained; such material is derived from cosmic dust, from wind-blown material, and from planktonic organisms. Where this material is predominantly inorganic, it usually has a reddish color and is called red clay. Where it consists predominately of organic fragments, it is called *ooze*. Depending on the nature of the organic particles, it is designated by such terms as *foraminiferal ooze, radiolarian ooze,* and *diatomaceous ooze.*

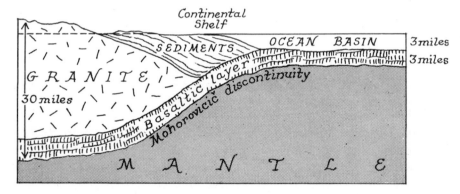

FIG. 16-2. The material beneath the continents and the ocean basins, as interpreted from geophysical exploration.

Origin of the Ocean Basins. The question naturally arises: Why do the ocean basins stand at a lower level than the continental masses? It has long been suspected that the ocean basins are underlaid by heavier rock than that which makes up the continents. Thus the greater attraction of gravity on these heavier rocks pulls the oceanic areas down and thereby crowds the continents upward. Geophysical investigation of the nature of the material beneath the ocean floor confirms this belief.

GENERAL CHARACTERISTICS OF OCEAN WATER

Composition. Water is often called the universal solvent. It is therefore not surprising to find great quantities of mineral matter, or salts, as well as gases, in solution in the ocean. Analyses show that 32 of the elements are dissolved in sea water, many of which, however, such as silver and gold, are present only in minute quantities. It has been calculated that if the 3.5 pounds of mineral matter dissolved in each 100 pounds of ocean water were deposited on the bottom, they would cover the entire ocean floor to a depth of 175 feet.

Dittmar, who analyzed seventy-seven samples obtained on the Challenger Expedition, found the average proportions of the more common salts in sea water to be as follows:

Salts in Ocean Water	Per Cent
Sodium chloride, common salt (NaCl)	77.758
Magnesium chloride ($MgCl_2$)	10.878
Magnesium sulphate, Epsom salt ($MgSO_4$)	4.737
Calcium sulphate, gypsum ($CaSO_4$)	3.600
Potassium sulphate (K_2SO_4)	2.465
Calcium carbonate ($CaCO_3$)	0.345
Magnesium bromide ($MgBr_2$)	0.217
	100.000

The salinity of the ocean is not uniformly distributed. Because of the low rate of evaporation and also because the water from melting ice does not contain dissolved mineral matter, the polar waters have the lowest salinity. Another belt of less than average salinity is the humid Equatorial Rain Belt. By the same token, the subtropical belts of low precipitation and high rate of evaporation are more than normally saline. Around the mouths of large rivers, such as the Amazon and the Mississippi, salinity is extremely low; in partly enclosed seas in dry regions, such as the Red Sea, it is exceptionally high.

In addition to the solids, sea water also contains dissolved oxygen, nitrogen, and carbon dioxide, doubtless absorbed from the atmosphere. These gases, as well as the dissolved mineral matter, are essential to the life in the ocean.

It is commonly agreed that most of the dissolved salts have been leached from the lands and carried in by streams, although some of them, are probably furnished by submarine volcanic eruptions. Furthermore, it is highly probable that the original ocean contained an appreciable amount of dissolved salts. In view of these circumstances, any estimate of the age of the ocean based on the rate of contribution of salts by streams cannot be entirely reliable.

Temperature. Since the ocean is warmed by the heat of the sun, the distribution of its surface temperature is closely related to the intensity and effectiveness of solar radiation. At the Equator the average surface temperature is about 80°F.; from the Equator poleward there is a gradual decrease in temperature to about 30°F. in high latitudes. The circulation of ocean currents disturbs the uniformity of this general decrease in temperature with increase in latitude.

Because of the high specific heat and turbulence of sea water, the diurnal range of temperature at the surface is small, in most places less than 1°F. The maximum temperature usually occurs in the early afternoon and the minimum shortly before sunrise. In the overlying air the diurnal range is considerably greater. The annual range of temperature of the surface water is also markedly less than that of the air above.

Sea water of normal salinity freezes at about 28.6°F. Where the salinity is lower, the freezing point is higher. In high latitudes, especially in bays where the salt content is low, the average winter temperature drops below the freezing point and sea ice forms. The wind and tides smash this ice into rough, hummocky sheets and blocks. Such a mass of broken ice is called *pack ice*. Pack ice is an almost permanent feature around the continent of Antarctica and is formed each winter in Hudson Bay, the Gulf of St. Lawrence, the Baltic Sea, and in other regions of high latitude.

Except in polar waters, the temperature of the ocean water decreases with depth. At the Equator in the central Pacific, where the surface temperature is 82°F., temperature at 600 feet is only 52°F.; a few hundred fathoms still farther down it drops below 40°F. Thus, even in the tropics the high temperature is confined to a shallow surface layer. In polar regions there is a temperature inversion from about 29.5°F. at the surface to 32° or 33°F. at 3,000 feet, and thereafter a slow decrease to the bottom. It has been calculated that at least 80 per cent of the water in the ocean has a temperature below 40°F. Furthermore, very little sunlight penetrates below 100 fathoms.

LIFE IN THE OCEAN

Organisms that live in the sea are abundant and varied, and include both plants and animals. If we group them according to their general habitats, we find three categories—*plankton, nekton,* and *benthos.* The plankton consists of floating forms, mostly microscopic in size, which drift passively with currents and tides and are universal in distribution. Among the most common organisms in this category are the *diatoms, Radiolaria,* and *Foraminifera.* Since this floating life is a source of food for many of the other marine organisms it is sometimes called the "pasture of the sea." The nekton comprises the swimming organisms such as fishes, whales, and seals, and the benthos lives on the bottom. Some of the latter, such as corals and crinoids, are attached, whereas others, such as the clams, snails, and starfish, are able to crawl about from place to place. Although the great majority of forms in the benthos are limited to shallow water, some forms are found on even the deepest bottoms.

MOVEMENTS OF THE OCEAN WATER

The sea is a restless body of water. Perhaps one of its greatest movements is that of the cold water which sinks in high latitudes and creeps Equatorward along the ocean floor. The various surface movements of the ocean water are impelled by a number of forces, some of them very complex in their interactions. These movements may be simply classified as (1) waves, (2) currents, and (3) tides.

Waves. Anyone who has visited the seashore or made an ocean voyage is familiar with the common waves generated by the wind. In each wave the water particles, set in motion by the friction of the wind, rotate at the same time that the rollers move continuously in one direction. The size of the waves depends on the wind's velocity and its fetch, or distance which it blows over the water. Some waves have been observed that were as much as 60 feet from trough to crest. As it approaches the shore the bottom of a wave drags on the ocean floor, and retards its rotary motion. If the sea bottom slopes gradually, the wave will break some distance from shore, forming an offshore line of *breakers*, from which the surf rushes onto the beach. On cliffed shores, however, the waves will break directly against the cliff at the shoreline, because the water is deep right up to the shore.

Another less common type of wave is caused by submarine earthquakes and volcanic eruptions which displace thousands of tons of sea water. Because of their extraordinary size, these waves are sometimes very destructive when they break on low-lying, densely populated coasts. One such wave drowned about 40,000 people on the island of Java in 1883. Waves of this kind are popularly called *tidal waves*, but since they are in no way related to the ordinary tides, the Japanese *tsunami* or the English *sea wave* is a more appropriate term.

Currents. *Local or Shore Currents.* The relatively small currents restricted to coastal regions are of several different kinds. The *undertow* is surf water returning to the sea along the bottom and beneath the incoming waves. Where waves strike the shoreline at an oblique angle, a *longshore* current running more or less parallel to the shoreline will be produced in addition to the undertow. *Offshore* currents are found at the mouths of rivers where great quantities of fresh water are moving out to sea. Local winds and differences in the rate of evaporation may cause other minor currents.

Ocean Currents. In each of the three great oceans, Atlantic, Pacific, and Indian, there are two large gyrals, called *ocean currents*, one in the North and the other in the South. Perhaps the most basic cause for

FIG. 16-3. The broad sandy strand of Daytona Beach, Florida, at low tide — a shoreline of emergence. *(Daytona Beach Chamber of Commerce)*

these great ocean currents is the difference in surface temperature which causes tropical waters to expand, rise, and move poleward at the surface, while cold polar waters sink and move Equatorward at depth. Were there no winds, no land areas, and no rotation, the surface movement of water would everywhere be poleward. In turning the movement to other directions the planetary winds are most important. The westerly winds in middle latitudes drag the surface water eastward, while the trade winds in low latitudes move it westward. This couple produces a gyral, clockwise in the Northern Hemisphere and counterclockwise in the Southern Hemisphere. The rotation of the earth, which deflects moving bodies to the right in the Northern Hemisphere and to the left in the Southern Hemisphere, may have some direct effect on the currents. The distribution and shapes of land masses provide restricting boundaries for the movement of the currents. (See Fig. 7-3.)

Each of these currents is known by different names in different parts of its course. In the North Atlantic the *North Equatorial Current* moves westward in the path of the northeast trade winds. On approaching South America the land masses as well as the rotation of the earth deflect the current northward and it becomes the *Gulf Stream*. In the zone of the westerly winds it is the *West Wind Drift* moving eastward. On approaching Europe it divides, part of it being deflected northward along the coast of Europe as the *North Atlantic Drift* and part of it southward around northwest Africa as the *Canaries Current*.

In the South Atlantic the current is similar to that in the North Atlantic, except that the motion is counterclockwise instead of clockwise.

FIG. 16-4. Cobble beach north of Gloucester, Massachusetts — a shoreline of submergence. (*U. S. Geological Survey*)

The Pacific and Indian oceans likewise have two great currents each, one in the north and one in the south. Those in the Pacific are much larger than those in the Atlantic, those in the Indian Ocean somewhat smaller.

The ocean currents extend to a depth of not more than 1,500 feet and move at the rate of only a few miles per hour. As indicated earlier, they have tremendously important effects on the climates of adjacent lands. They are also important in distributing floating life, or plankton.

Tides. The periodic rise and fall of the ocean surface caused by gravitational attraction of the moon and of the sun on the earth is the tide. In most places the period between high tides is 12 hours and 26 minutes; but at some places the interval varies considerably from this normal. In the open ocean the tidal range, or difference between high and low tide, is not more than two feet; but on approaching the shore, the height of the tide is increased by the shallowing of the bottom. Along most coasts the range is from 3 to 10 feet; at the heads of funnel-shaped bays, such as the Bay of Fundy in Nova Scotia, the range may be 50 feet or more.

The rise and fall of the tide is usually gradual, the rise coming as a series of waves, each breaking higher on the strand than the preceding one. On entering some river mouths and narrowing bays, however, the tide comes in as a rapidly moving wall of water known as a *bore*. The bore is especially pronounced in the Severn and Amazon rivers and at many places along the coast of China.

Along irregular coasts the tidal range may be notably different in

253

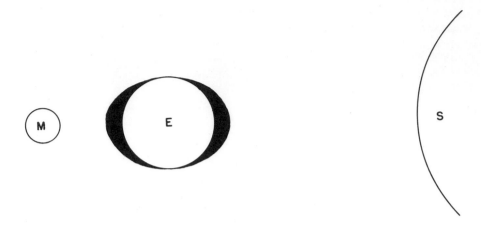

SPRING TIDE

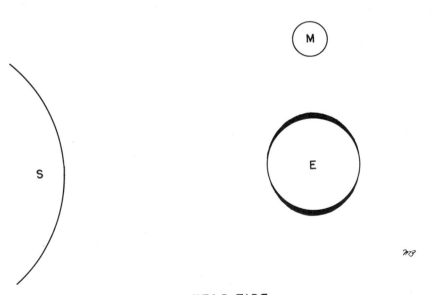

NEAP TIDE

FIG. 16-5. Diagram showing the relative positions of the sun (S), moon (M) and earth (E) at spring tide and neap tide. The solid black represents the tidal bulges, greatly exaggerated.

adjacent bays. If there is a narrow connecting strait between two such bays a rapid current or *race* will pass through the strait. Such a race, when strongly developed, as it is at Hell Gate between New York Bay and Long Island Sound, is a hazard to navigation.

The area along the shore which is covered by high tide and exposed at low tide is known as the *strand*. Its width depends both on the range of the tide and the slope of the land. Where the shoreline consists of vertical cliffs the width of the strand is zero; along some low and gently sloping coasts, on the other hand, the strand is a mile or more in width. Broad strands, often with sandy beaches, are common along the Coastal Plain from New York southward.

The Cause of Tides. Although the full explanation of the tides involves the use of complex mathematical and physical formulae, a reasonably satisfactory explanation can be stated in simple terms. We may first consider the tide caused by the moon.

In order to explain the tides it is necessary to review two important laws, namely, the law of *attraction* or gravity between heavenly bodies and *centrifugal force*. Bodies attract each other in proportion to their masses and inversely as the squares of their distances from each other. A body with twice the mass of another has twice the attractive force at the same distance. If one of two bodies of the same mass is twice as far from a third body as the other is, its attractive force on the third body is only one-fourth that of the other. On rotating and revolving bodies centrifugal force acts in the opposite direction to gravity. It pushes outward from the axis of rotation and also from the center of revolution.

The earth and the moon attract each other and would come together if it were not for the centrifugal force of revolution. They revolve around a common center which is the center of gravity of both the earth and the moon. Since the mass of the earth is about 80 times that of the moon, the center of gravity of the two bodies is 1,000 miles below the surface of the earth and 3,000 miles from its center. In revolving about this common center of gravity the center of the earth describes a circle with a radius of 3,000 miles, while the center of the moon describes a circle about the same point with a radius of 237,000 miles.

The distance between the earth and the moon is determined by the balance between their gravitational attractions for each other on the one hand and their centrifugal forces on the other. At the center of the earth and at the center of the moon this balance is perfect. On the side of the earth nearest the moon, however, the attraction of the moon is greater than it is at the center of the earth, and the earth tends to bulge toward the moon. On the side of the earth away from the moon the pull of the moon, weaker than it is at the center of the earth, is overbalanced by the centrifugal force, and the earth tends to bulge out on this side also. Thus it can be seen that the tide-producing force is the differential attraction of the moon: at the center of the earth the attraction is equal to the centrifugal force; on the near side of the earth the attraction is greater, on the far side less than the centrifugal force.

The solid portion of the earth, being essentially rigid so that one part does not move freely over other parts, is distorted very little by the tide-producing force. The surface waters, however, respond rather freely by bulging out on opposite sides of the earth. These bulges are the high tides and between them are the low tides.

Tides are produced by the sun in the same manner as by the moon; but the solar tides are only about one-third as great as the lunar tides. Because of its great mass the sun attracts the earth with about 175 times the force that the moon does, in spite of the fact that the sun is many times as far distant. Thus it is evident that tides are not produced by and proportional to strength of gravity alone, but by *differential* pull. In the case of the moon the tide-producing force is the difference between the pull of the moon on the center and on the near and the far sides of the earth. From center to center the distance between the earth and the moon is about 240,000 miles. From the near side of the earth the distance to the center of the moon is 236,000 miles and from the far side it is 244,000 miles. The tide-producing force on either side of the earth is then the result of a difference in distance of 4,000 miles. The tide-producing force of the sun is also due to its differential pull on the center and the near and far sides of the earth. But 4,000 miles is a much smaller fraction of 93 million miles than it is of 240,000 miles. Therefore, the differential pull of the sun is much less than the differential pull of the moon.

Spring and Neap Tides. At the times of new moon and full moon the sun and the moon are pulling on the earth in the same line. The lunar and solar tides are then combined, the high tides are higher and the low tides lower than at other times. These are known as the *spring tides.* During the first and the third quarters of the moon, the sun and the moon are pulling on the earth at right angles to each other. The tidal range at these times is much less than at other times. These are the *neap tides.* Thus during each lunar month there are two periods of spring tides and two of neap tides.

EROSION AND DEPOSITION BY WAVES AND CURRENTS

Waves and currents, and to some extent the tides, are constantly at work on the land along the shoreline. The power of the waves is enormous, especially in times of storm, when they often destroy breakwaters and other structures. Along some shores the sea is cutting back and encroaching upon the land, while in other places, especially near river mouths, the land is being built out into the sea.

Sea Cliffs, Wave-Cut Benches, and Wave-Built Terraces. On coasts where the waves beat against the shore, the land is gradually worn back by the grinding action of the tossing water and its load of rock fragments. In this way a niche is formed at the level of wave action which undermines the overhanging rock until it slides or falls into the sea, there to provide more tools for further wave erosion. Where the rock is strong a more or less vertical cliff, known as a sea cliff, results. Such wave-cut cliffs are found at many places along the New England Coast, along the Pacific Coast of North America and on the western coast of Europe.

FIG. 16-6. Rugged, cliffed shoreline of Peru, near Huarmey. *(Photo by Lt. George R. Johnson)*

As the sea cliff retreats, a wave-cut bench, or platform, develops at the lower limit of wave erosion. Sand and other detritus, shifted seaward across this bench to the offshore edge, drops below the reach of the waves and builds up a wave-built terrace. Many bold coasts are dangerous to navigation because they are bordered by a belt of shallow water underlain by such wave-cut and wave-built features.

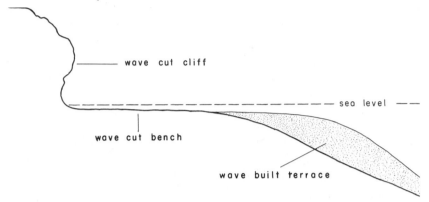

FIG. 16-7. Diagrammatic section through a typical wave-cut cliff, bench and terrace along a shoreline subjected to wave attack.

Sea Caves and Stacks. Waves, like other agents of erosion, wear away weak rocks faster than resistant ones. Where rocky coasts are traversed by bands of weak rocks or zones of closely spaced joints, waves often erode pronounced indentations in the form of caves or of long, narrow inlets. Waves, cutting into a weak zone from the opposite sides of a rocky promontory sometimes leave a portion of the promontory isolated from the mainland as a small island or stack.

Bars. While some shore regions are being cut away by marine erosion, others are being built up by the waves and currents, which deposit sediment supplied in part by the streams flowing into the sea and in part by the activity of waves on the shoreline. In many cases the sediment, consisting of gravel, sand, or silt, accumulates in distinctive forms, known as bars. According to their shape and position, bars are given various specific names.

The *offshore bar,* or barrier beach, is a long, low ridge parallel to the shore and separated from it by a shallow *lagoon.* These bars are formed in front of the line of breakers where the waves break in shallow water some distance from shore. Offshore bars are common along the Atlantic Coast from New Jersey southward. Atlantic City is located on one of them. The south shore of Long Island is also bordered by offshore bars.

Where the shoreline is marked by deep embayments, longshore currents may build a finger-shaped bar out from a headland into the deeper

FIG. 16-8. Sea caves near La Jolla, Calif. *(Photo by Arnold, U. S. Geological Survey)*

FIG. 16-9. Stacks on the shore of Flower Pot Island in Georgian Bay. *(Geological Survey of Canada)*

water of the bay. Such a bar is called a *spit*. Sandy Hook, a bar extending several miles into Outer New York Bay from the New Jersey mainland, is a good example.

Bay bars, as the name indicates, are located in bays. According to their positions within the bays they are designated more specifically as bay-mouth, bay-head, bay-side, and mid-bay bars.

Frequently a bar will form in the sheltered water between the mainland and a nearby island. If the bar extends entirely across, the island becomes land-tied, and, together with the connecting bar, is called a *tombolo*. These tombolos are common along the New England Coast, and also along the coast of Italy, whence the name comes. The Rock of Gibraltar and the bar connecting it to the coast of Spain is a tombolo.

Beaches. On the beach or strand along the shore, either erosion or deposition may be taking place. If erosion is active the beach is narrow, steep, and often rocky. Where deposition is taking place, the composition and size of the beach material depends on the nature of its source and on the strength of the outgoing tide and undertow. On *pebble beaches* only the coarse fragments are allowed to remain; where the pebbles are flat and overlapping they form a *shingle beach*. In well-protected areas where both the undertow and the outgoing tide are weak, *mud beaches* may be found. According to the popular usage of the term, however, the typical beach is a *sandy beach*.

TYPES OF SHORELINES

Changes in the level of the land or of the sea produce certain easily recognized features of erosion and deposition along the shoreline where land and sea meet. These features are so distinctive that three of the four main types of shorelines are made by elevation and subsidence of the land.

It should be kept in mind that in most cases a rise in sea level has the same effect as a subsidence of the land, and that a depression of sea level is equal to a rise of the land. In cases where it is not possible to determine which moved, the land or the sea, it is customary to consider the changes in relative level as movements of the land.

Four main types of shorelines are recognized. The first type is produced by subsidence of the coastal region and is termed a *shoreline of submergence*. The second is the result of a partial emergence of the sea bottom and is therefore a *shoreline of emergence*. *Neutral shorelines*, the third type, show no evidence of either uplift or subsidence of the land; while the fourth type, the *compound shorelines*, combines the features of two or more of the preceding types.

Shoreline of Submergence. The subsidence of the coastal land brings the sea in contact with a surface that has been molded by streams,

FIG. 16-10. Numerous islands, peninsulas, and embayments characterize the youthful, submerged shoreline of Maine. *(American Museum of Natural History)*

glaciers, and other subaerial agents. The sea enters and drowns the lower courses of the streams, so that they become estuaries or embayments of the sea. Other drowned low-lying areas form smaller bays, coves, and sounds. The divides become peninsulas, promontories, or capes; isolated hills become islands. Such a shoreline is long and very irregular, and its deep indentations often make good harbors. The sea bottom offshore is apt to be irregular, with the original inequalities of the drowned surface. The coast of New England is a good example of a shoreline of submergence.

The above features are typical of the early stages of a shoreline where the coast was hilly before submergence. Marine erosion, like stream erosion, follows a more or less regular sequence known as a *cycle*. The exposed headlands and islands of the submerged coast soon become cliffed and cut back by wave attack. Wave-cut benches and wave-built terraces develop. Numerous spits, tombolos, and bay bars form in the slack waters. The bays slowly become filled with sediment. While the headlands are being cut back and the embayments built out, the shoreline is in the youthful stage. When the shoreline has been shortened and smoothed as much as possible, maturity is attained. After maturity is reached the shoreline may be cut back slowly; the wave-cut bench becomes wider and the force of the waves becomes weaker. Eventually a state of equilibrium is reached; the shoreline becomes stationary. This is old age.

Shoreline of Emergence. Emergence of a portion of the sea bottom that has been smoothed by the accumulation of sediments exposes a nearly flat coastal plain of marine deposits. The previous shoreline is now some distance inland. Between it and the new shore lies a relatively smooth, gently sloping surface. Offshore the water deepens gradually. Where the waves break, some distance from shore, an offshore bar is soon built up, separated by a lagoon from the shore. The shoreline of Texas is a good example of this, the youthful stage of an emergent coastline. As the offshore bar is gradually pushed toward the shore by the beating of the waves, the lagoon becomes filled with sediment washed in from the land and by vegetation growing in the shallow water. At maturity the lagoon disappears and the former offshore bar coincides with the shoreline. After maturity is attained the shoreline may be cut back and a cliffed shore and wave-cut bench formed. Except for the presence of the coastal plain, the shoreline of emergence is similar, from this stage onward, to the shoreline of submergence.

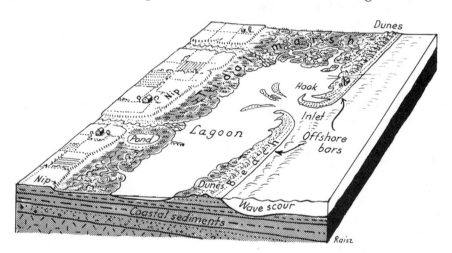

FIG. 16-11. Typical features on a shoreline of emergence in the youthful stage of development. As maturity arrives the offshore bar is pushed toward the shore and the lagoon is filled; then the beach coincides with the mainland shore.

Neutral Shoreline. The neutral shoreline owes its features neither to elevation nor to submergence of the land, but rather to the building of the land out into the sea. The shorelines of volcanoes rising from the sea bottom belong to this class. Deltas deposited at the mouths of streams, outwash material from glaciers, and coral reefs also have neutral shorelines.

Compound Shorelines. Many shorelines have had complex histories. In

FIG. 16-12. Daytona Beach, Fla. Some of the offshore bars of the Atlantic Coast are broad and heavily populated. Well-known localities are Daytona Beach, Palm Beach, and Miami Beach in Florida, and Atlantic City in New Jersey. (*U. S. Geological Survey*)

most cases, however, the features of one type predominate, and the shoreline is classified according to these dominant features. In some cases the features of two or more types are equally prominent or so nearly balanced that the shoreline is designated as compound. A good example of such a shore is the Chesapeake Bay region. Here a flat coastal plain indicates emergence, at the same time that the drowned rivers resulting from submergence form the pronounced embayments of Hampton Roads and Chesapeake Bay. The evidence here indicates that an emergence which produced the coastal plain preceded a later submergence which drowned the broad rivers.

ISLANDS

Three types of oceanic islands may be recognized. These are (1) continental, (2) orogenic, and (3) volcanic. Most continental islands are

263

located on the continental shelf. Structurally parts of the continents, they are separated from them by shallow water, so that a slight rise of the land or a fall of sea level would unite them to the mainland. The British Isles are a good example of this type of island. The shallow English Channel and the Strait of Dover were formerly a stream valley that was drowned by a rise of sea level. Some islands of continental make-up, such as Madagascar, are separated from the mainland by deep water. According to one theory such islands were separated from their parent continents by the sinking of long narrow strips of land between the two. According to another theory the islands are fragments that have broken off and drifted away from the continents.

Orogenic islands are the tops of mountains which rise from the ocean floor in long, arc-shaped chains. The Japanese Islands, the Philippines, the East Indies and the West Indies are examples. Although volcanoes are found on many orogenic islands, the principal structure, that of mountains, distinguishes them from the purely volcanic islands.

Most of the mid-ocean islands are the tops of volcanoes which have been built up from the sea floor. The Hawaiian and other mid-Pacific islands belong to this group. In many cases the volcanic activity is extinct or has been dormant so long that the surface has become covered with coral-reef material, and the islands have become the so-called coral islands.

CORAL REEFS

Corals are a relatively low order of marine animals, belonging to the *Phylum Coelenterata*. A coral consists of two parts: (1) the polyp, or soft body, and (2) the corallum, which the polyp builds by taking calcium carbonate from solution and depositing it around the soft body as anchorage and protective skeleton. In many cases corals live in colonies, the skeleton of one joining with those of its neighbors. When the polyps die and decay, or are devoured, there is left a stony base on which young polyps lodge, attach themselves, and build their own skeletons. Thus coral reefs grow. Other organisms also grow on coral reefs and in some cases outnumber the corals.

The reef-building corals thrive best within rather narrow limits of environmental conditions. In their growth they are practically limited to water of normal ocean salinity that is 40 fathoms (240 feet) or less in depth. The optimum temperature is between 68°F. and 78°F. The water must be relatively free from clastic sediments, which usually means that the adjacent land has low relief. Furthermore, the water must be in motion, for they depend on it to bring them food.

The ocean temperatures favorable to the growth of reef-building corals are now practically limited to areas within 30° of the Equator.

Fossil coral reefs, however, are found in much higher latitudes. This is one reason for assuming that climatic zones have not always had their present distribution.

Suggestions for Further Reading

DARWIN, Charles, in Mather and Mason's *Sourcebook in Geology* (New York, McGraw-Hill, 1939).

EWING, Maurice, *Bulletin American Museum of Natural History* (1952), Vol. 99, p. 87.

HAMILTON, Edwin L., "The Last Geographic Frontier: the Sea Floor," *The Scientific Monthly*, Vol. 85, No. 6, December, 1957.

KUENEN, P. H., *Marine Geology* (New York, Wiley, 1950).

KUENEN, P. H., *Realms of Water* (New York, Wiley, 1956).

LOBECK, A. K., *Geomorphology* (New York, McGraw-Hill, 1939).

SHEPARD, F. P., *Submarine Geology* (New York, Harper, 1948).

— 17 —

Minerals
and Their Properties

COMPOSITION OF MINERALS

$\mathbf{M}$INERALS ARE the building blocks of the solid earth. To be a mineral a substance must be a naturally occurring, inorganic solid having a definite chemical composition and a set of physical properties characteristic of it alone. There are more than 1,700 known minerals, only a few score of which are abundant or common. Even though they are the building blocks of the lithosphere and are themselves units, minerals are not, in most cases, simple, or elementary substances. Before proceeding further with a description of minerals, some discussion of elements and atoms appears essential.

Chemical Elements. All matter of which we have knowledge is made up of chemical elements and their compounds. While some of the elements, such as oxygen, aluminum, and iron, are common and familiar to all of us, others are so rare that even many chemists have never seen them. Some of the elements are active, that is, they will readily combine with other elements to form compounds. On the other hand some elements, such as helium, neon, and argon, are so inert that they are never found in the combined state. At ordinary temperatures most of the elements are solid, two are liquid and several are gaseous.

Ninety-two elements are known to exist in nature and a few others have been produced artificially. It has been learned and still is being learned that some of the substances formerly considered as unchangeable units (elements) of matter are undergoing change. The so-called elements that exhibit this change are said to be radioactive. The nature and results of radioactivity now constitute an important field of research. The discoveries made so far have profoundly influenced not only the

266

sciences but also other fields of human activity and promise to have even greater influence in the future.

The table below from a report by Clark and Washington, based on chemical analyses of several thousand rock specimens from various parts of the world, gives the percentages in which 20 of the most common elements are found in the accessible portion of the solid earth.

The Twenty Most Common Elements in the Earth's Solid Crust

Element	Percentage
Oxygen (O)	46.71
Silicon (Si)	27.69
Aluminum (Al)	8.07
Iron (Fe)	5.05
Calcium (Ca)	3.65
Sodium (Na)	2.75
Potassium (K)	2.58
Magnesium (Mg)	2.08
Titanium (Ti)	0.62
Hydrogen (H)	0.14
Phosphorus (P)	0.13
Carbon (C)	0.094
Manganese (Mn)	0.09
Sulfur (S)	0.08
Barium (Ba)	0.05
Chlorine (Cl)	0.045
Chromium (Cr)	0.035
Fluorine (F)	0.029
Zirconium (Zr)	0.025
Nickel (Ni)	0.019
All others	0.063
	100.000

Atoms. Before the isolation of radium in 1898 it was believed that the atom was the smallest unit of an element and was absolutely unchangeable. The discovery that radium and some other elements are constantly disintegrating and giving off atoms of helium upset this belief. Soon there evolved the *electron theory*, which assumes that atoms themselves are made up of smaller particles called *electrons, neutrons, protons,* and other particles. The protons are electrically positive, the electrons negative. Neutrons are electrically neutral; it is possible that they are in reality formed by the close union of an electron and a proton, the electrical charges of which exactly balance each other. The nucleus of an atom is made up of protons, or positive particles, and neutrons, or neutral particles. Outside of the nucleus and revolving around it like planets around the sun are enough electrons to balance the unsatisfied positive particles in the nucleus. An atom is far too small to be seen by any means yet devised; and, since the atom in turn consists of still smaller particles, the minuteness of the electrons and protons is incomprehensible. Nevertheless, minerals and other matter are made of them.

Compounds. A few minerals such as native gold (Au) and diamond (C) consist of single elements. They are aggregates of uncombined atoms. The great majority of minerals, however, are chemical compounds, consisting of the atoms of two or more elements combined as molecules. The compound has properties that are different from those of any of its constituent elements. For example, ordinary table salt, which is the mineral halite, is composed of the soft, silvery metal, sodium, and the green, poisonous gas, chlorine.

As a rule the combination of elements in a compound is in definite proportions of the atoms of each, so that the composition of the substance can be expressed by a chemical formula. Halite, a compound consisting of one part each of sodium and chlorine, is indicated by the formula NaCl. The composition of quartz, which

FIG. 17-1. James Dwight Dana (1813-1895), leading American mineralogist of his time. Author of more than 200 books and papers. His *Manual of Mineralogy* is still a standard reference book. (*Columbia University Dept. of Geology*)

is one part of silicon to two parts of oxygen, is designated by SiO_2. In corundum there are two parts of aluminum to three parts of oxygen, and the formula is written Al_2O_3.

HOW TO STUDY MINERALS

The complete study of minerals requires careful tests of their (1) physical properties, (2) chemical properties, (3) optical properties as studied with the petrographic microscope, and (4) their atomic structure as revealed by the X-ray. Discussion here will be limited almost

entirely to the physical properties, as chemical and optical characteristics are best treated in more advanced textbooks of mineralogy. The
identification of minerals from their physical properties requires the
keen and careful observation which is the basis of all scientific work.
If the student has not already cultivated this ability, he should do so as
soon as possible.

The equipment need not be elaborate for the beginner. A knife or
small steel file, a porcelain streak plate, a small horseshoe magnet, and
a pocket lens with a magnification of from 6 to 10 times are all that
are necessary.

PHYSICAL PROPERTIES OF MINERALS

Shape or Form. Minerals grow as long as conditions are favorable for
growth, and there are no such things as infant minerals, youthful minerals, or adult minerals. Specimens of a given mineral may vary from
microscopic size up to several feet in diameter. While size is not
important in the case of common minerals, it is worth consideration in
the case of rare minerals such as the diamond and emerald, which are
not expected to occur in enormous sizes.

Shape, however, is important. Nearly all minerals are crystalline, that
is, the atoms of which they are composed are arranged in a precise and
orderly pattern. Under favorable conditions of growth, this internal
symmetry will be expressed externally as a *crystal* form. The crystal
habit of any given mineral is more or less distinctive and is a very
important criterion of mineral identification. The systematic study of
crystal forms is the science of *crystallography*. Several weeks of intensive
work are required in order to become familiar with the various forms of
crystals. In the descriptions of individual minerals below a few common
crystal forms will be mentioned.

Because of crowding or other unfavorable conditions, minerals in most
cases do not exhibit definite crystal forms. For these cases there are
certain descriptive or structural terms which are often useful in mineral
identification. *Colloform* minerals appear to have solidified from jelly
and are often wavy or banded; *earthy* minerals are made up of very
fine, loosely compacted particles; *granular* ones consist of irregular grains;
a few minerals sometimes occur in small spheres that resemble fish roe
and are called *oolitic*; the *botryoidal* form, like a bunch of grapes, is
assumed by some; and a *fibrous* or thread-like structure is typical of a few
others. If a mineral exhibits neither crystal form nor any of the other more
definite shapes or structures, the term *massive* is commonly used in
describing it.

Color. For some minerals color is a definitive property; for others it has little significance as a means of identification. A given mineral may occur in a variety of colors and several different minerals may show about the same color. If all minerals occurred as absolutely pure chemical compounds or elements, the use of color in their identification would be much more reliable. One of the causes of variation in color in a particular mineral is the presence of pigments or impurities in its composition. Although these pigments usually occur only in small quantities, sometimes so small that they are not recognized in an ordinary chemical analysis, they color a mineral in somewhat the same manner as a tiny drop of dye colors a tub of water. Another complication is the discoloration produced on the surface of minerals by the processes of chemical weathering. This difficulty can be removed, however, by examining a fresh surface.

In spite of the apparent difficulties, color is an important property to the trained observer. Even though a given mineral does occur in a variety of colors, the range of those colors is more or less limited. And, different minerals of the same color are often distinguished by differences in the shades of that color. Thus, the green of different minerals may be an apple green, a lettuce green, an asparagus green, an olive green, or a pistachio green.

Luster. The luster of a mineral is the appearance of its surface in reflected light. This property is independent of color, for minerals of the same color may have different lusters and minerals of the same luster may have different colors. Lusters of minerals are commonly indicated as (1) *metallic* and (2) *nonmetallic*. In either group the luster may be bright or dull, as bright metallic and dull metallic. More specific varieties of nonmetallic luster are designated by the descriptive terms *glassy (vitreous), earthy, resinous, pearly, silky, greasy,* and *adamantine* (a brilliant luster like that of diamond).

Weight or Specific Gravity. The weight of a mineral depends on the weight and the spacing of the atoms of which it is composed. If it consists of heavy atoms close together the mineral is very heavy; on the other hand, if it consists of light atoms spaced far apart it is very light. The specific gravity of a mineral is its weight as compared with the weight of an equal volume of water. Minerals range in specific gravity from less than one (ice) to about 20 (iridosmine); however, most of them lie between 2 and 4. Mineralogists have various instruments for determining accurately the specific gravity of minerals, and this property is often important for the purpose of identification. If one does not have access to an instrument that measures specific gravity precisely he can nevertheless, with a little practice, make a fairly satisfactory estimate by hefting the mineral in the hand. In this manner he can at least distinguish marked differences in the weight of minerals.

Cleavage. Some minerals have a tendency to break readily along certain parallel planes, producing relatively smooth surfaces and fragments of distinctive shapes. This cleavage habit is of great help in the identification of minerals. The number of cleavage planes and the angles between them are constant for a given mineral. For example, mica has cleavage in only one direction; halite cleaves in three planes at right angles to each other, so as to form rectangular fragments; sphalerite cleaves in six directions, with angles of 90° and 120° between the cleavage faces. The ease of breakage and the degree of perfection in the cleavage of a mineral is designated by such terms as *perfect, distinct,* and *indistinct.* In a mass of fine grains, such as rock gypsum, cleavage may not be evident, for the mineral cleavage applies to each grain and the grains may be oriented in various directions.

Fracture. A number of minerals that do not have cleavage, break or *fracture* in a more or less distinctive way. Quartz, the broken surface of which often resembles the curved surface of a shell, possesses *conchoidal* fracture. Broken copper usually has a rough, jagged, or *hackly* surface, and fibrous amphibole a *splintery* one. Most other minerals have a rough or *uneven* fracture that is of no particular value in identification. As in cleavage, the fracture of a mineral applies to individual units. A granular mass, such as olivine, will show a rough, or uneven, surface when broken, whereas each broken grain shows conchoidal fracture.

Hardness. The resistance of a smooth surface of a mineral to abrasion is called its hardness. This property of a mineral is fairly constant and is an important criterion in identification. The hardness of a mineral is determined by scratching it with the sharp point of another mineral or with an instrument of known hardness and comparing it with a standard scale of 10 minerals, arranged in order of increasing hardness, as follows:

Scale of Hardness

1.	Talc	6.	Feldspar
2.	Gypsum	7.	Quartz
3.	Calcite	8.	Topaz
4.	Fluorite	9.	Corundum
5.	Apatite	10.	Diamond

In the above scale any mineral of higher number will scratch those of lower number. Care should be taken to distinguish a scratch, which is permanent, from a "chalk" mark, which can be rubbed off. Minerals that are very brittle or are weathered on the surface may show an apparent hardness lower than the true hardness.

If the student knows that his fingernail has a hardness of 2.5, a copper penny 3.5 and a knife blade 5.5, he will find these materials very useful in determining the hardness of a great many minerals.

Streak. The streak of a mineral, the color of its fine powder, is usually obtained by pulverizing the mineral on a piece of unglazed porcelain, or by scratching the mineral with a knife or file. The streak often differs markedly from the color of the unpowdered mineral. For example, black hematite has a red streak. Also, the streak of a given mineral is nearly always the same even though the body color varies. Thus the different colored fluorites, yellow, green, violet, blue, brown, black, and colorless, all have a white streak.

Other Properties. Among the properties that are more limited in their application we may list the following:

Magnetism. Some of the iron-bearing minerals, especially magnetite, are attracted by a magnet. The lodestone variety of magnetite will itself act as a magnet.

Striations. The presence and pattern of fine parallel lines on crystal faces and on cleavage planes often help in identification. The prism faces of quartz crystals are usually marked by horizontal striations, whereas those of topaz crystals are vertically striated. Labradorite feldspar often has visible striations on the cleavage surfaces.

Taste. Minerals that are soluble in water often have a distinctive taste. Halite has a salty taste.

Feel. The soapy feel is characteristic of talc; their cold feel distinguishes gems from glass.

Change of colors. Opal, diamond, and some other minerals display various colors when viewed from different directions.

Reaction with hydrochloric acid. This chemical test is here noted because of its importance in distinguishing calcite from other carbonate minerals. Calcite will effervesce in cold hydrochloric acid; to produce this effect on the other carbonates the acid must be heated.

DESCRIPTIONS OF MINERALS

The minerals described below include the most common rock-makers and a few of the common ores. Diamond and topaz, which are neither rock-makers nor ores, are also included because they are in the scale of hardness. In the descriptions no attempt is made to list all of the physical properties of each mineral. Instead, only those that are especially pronounced or are most useful for rapid determination are given. The student should compare these descriptions with as many different samples of each mineral as possible. The chemical formulae for the minerals are listed primarily for reference.

NATIVE COPPER, Cu

   Form: Usually in irregular masses
   Color: Copper red, surface often tarnished black or green or blue
   Luster: Metallic

Specific gravity: 8.8
Hardness: 2.5 to 3
Streak: Copper red
Malleability: Can be rolled or hammered into thin sheets
Uses: One of our most useful and important metals for wire, roofing, and
    many other uses

DIAMOND, C

Form: Usually found in octahedral crystals; a black massive variety called
    carbonado is found in Brazil.
Color: Colorless, light yellow, brown are the most common colors, although
    other colors are occasionally found.
Luster: Adamantine when polished; greasy when unpolished
Hardness: 10; much harder than any other substance
Play of colors: When cut into a gem with many facets the diamond shows
    a striking play of colors.
Uses: Gems, abrasives, cutting tools, dies for wire drawing

GRAPHITE, C (Black lead, Plumbago)

Form: Scales, grains, compact masses
Color: Black or dark gray
Luster: Metallic to earthy
Cleavage: Good in one plane
Hardness: 1 to 2
Streak: Dark gray
Feel: Greasy
Uses: Mixed with clay to make "lead" pencils; lubricants, paints, foundry
    linings, crucibles

QUARTZ, SiO_2—Quartz is perhaps the most widely distributed mineral. A few
    of its properties are listed here and other properties are indicated
    in the description of the varieties.

Form: Commonly in hexagonal crystals with pyramidal ends. The rec-
    tangular faces of the crystals are usually striated crosswise. Also
    occurs in irregular grains or masses.
Luster: Vitreous to greasy
Cleavage: None or very poor
Fracture: Conchoidal to subconchoidal
Hardness: 7
Streak: White
Varieties of Quartz: The following list includes the most common varieties
    of quartz.

Rock crystal. Colorless, glassy, commonly in crystals
Smoky quartz. Crystals or masses of smoky yellow, brown or black color.
    Smokiness probably due to some carbon compound

FIG. 17-2. Native copper in irregularly branching masses. *(American Museum of Natural History)*

FIG. 17-3. Quartz crystals. Note the pyramidal crystal ends and the transverse striations on the crystal faces. *(American Museum of Natural History)*

Amethyst. Like rock crystal except that it has a purple or violet color. Becomes golden-brown when heated

Rose quartz. Rose-pink color, usually massive in form. The color becomes paler on long exposure to light.

Citrine quartz. Pale yellow, glassy luster. Also called false topaz and Spanish topaz

Milky quartz. Milky-white color, usually massive, sometimes in crystals

Chalcedony. Microcrystalline; waxy luster, often botryoidal or concretionary, white or bluish-gray in color

Agate. A banded or vari-colored chalcedony

Jasper. A red chalcedony colored by the admixture of iron oxide

Flint. Smoky-gray to nearly black or brown nodules, usually found in chalk beds. Has good conchoidal fracture. To the unaided eye it appears to be amorphous. When examined microscopically, it is usually found to be very finely crystalline. A similar substance less homogeneous, occurring in the older rocks, is known as *chert*.

Opal. An amorphous hydrated variety. Occurs as crusts and cavity fillings. Softer and lighter in weight than other varieties of quartz. The forms that have the scintillating brilliance, known as opalescence, are prized as gems.

Quartz sand and gravel. More or less rounded fragments of any of the varieties of quartz. Because of its widespread occurrence and its resistance to weathering, quartz is by far the most common constituent of sand and gravel.

Uses: Gems, optical instruments, radio receivers, glass, wood filler, concrete

CORUNDUM, Al_2O_3

Form: Hexagonal crystals or granular masses
Color: Brown, blue, red, green, yellow, gray
Luster: Adamantine or vitreous
Specific gravity: About 4
Cleavage: 3 directions nearly at right angles, sometimes indistinct
Hardness: 9
Varieties:

Ordinary corundum, also called adamantine spar. Occurs in coarse crystals or masses of dull adamantine luster and gray or brown color

Emery. Consists of opaque, dark gray, granular corundum intimately mixed with magnetite

Ruby. Transparent to translucent corundum with a rich red color

Sapphire. Like ruby, is transparent or translucent and includes all of the colors except the deep red

Uses: Gems, abrasives

MAGNETITE, Fe_3O_4

Form: Common in octahedral crystals and in granular masses
Color: Black

FIG. 17-4. Agate. *(American Museum of Natural History)*

FIG. 17-5. Octahedral crystals of magnetite. *(American Museum of Natural History)*

FIG. 17-6. Stalactitic form of limonite. *(Photo by the author)*

FIG. 17-7. Calcite, var. dogtooth spar. *(American Museum of Natural History)*

Luster: Metallic
Specific gravity: Heavy, about 5
Hardness: 5.5 to 6.5
Streak: Black
Magnetism: Strongly attracted by a magnet. The variety called *lodestone* is itself a magnet.
Use: As an ore of iron

HEMATITE, Fe_2O_3

Form: Granular, micaceous, earthy, oolitic, reniform
Color: Steel gray, iron black, red
Luster: Brilliant metallic, earthy
Specific gravity: 4.5 to 5
Streak: Reddish brown or brownish red
Varieties: The gray to black brilliant metallic variety is called *specular iron* or *micaceous hematite*. *Red hematite* has a dull metallic or an earthy luster. *Oolitic hematite* occurs in small red concretions resembling fish roe.
Uses: The most important iron ore in the United States; also used as a pigment in paint and as rouge

LIMONITE, $2Fe_2O_3.3H_2O$

Form: Earthy, botryoidal, concretionary, stalactitic
Color: Brown, yellow, nearly black
Luster: Dull earthy, silky, varnish-like
Hardness: 5 to 5.5
Streak: Yellowish-brown. When mixed with hematite, it is reddish-brown.
Uses: Minor ore of iron; pigment

BAUXITE, $Al_2O_3.2H_2O$

Forms: Soft, earthy, clay-like masses and in aggregates of pea-like concretions
Color: White, gray, yellow, brown, red
Luster: Dull earthy
Hardness: 1 to 3
Streak: Like the color
Uses: Ore of aluminum

CALCITE, $CaCO_3$

Hardness: 3
Streak: White
Cleavage: Perfect in three directions not at right angles, yielding rhombohedral fragments
Effervescence: Cold acid causes rapid effervescence by the liberation of carbon dioxide.
Color: Calcite is commonly white, yellowish or colorless, but it occurs in a great many colors.

FIG. 17-8. Pyrite, aggregate of cubic crystals. *(American Museum of Natural History)*

FIG. 17-9. Galena. *(American Museum of Natural History)*

FIG. 17-10. Cubical crystals of fluorite. *(American Museum of Natural History)*

FIG. 17-11. Fluorite cleaved into an octahedron. *(American Museum of Natural History)*

Varieties: Among the crystalline varieties are *Iceland spar,* colorless and transparent and exhibiting strong double refraction; *dogtooth spar,* crystals which somewhat resemble canine teeth in shape and *travertine,* banded crystalline deposits from springs, streams, and dripping water. *Chalk, marl* and other noncrystalline forms of calcium carbonate are commonly considered as varieties of calcite.

Uses: Calcite is the chief constituent of limestone and marble. These rocks are used in making lime, plaster and cement, as building stones and as a flux in the smelting of iron ores. Iceland spar has a very important technical use as a light polarizer in petrographic microscopes.

DOLOMITE, $CaMgCO_3$

Form: Rhombohedral crystals and granular masses

Color: White, gray, pink

Luster: Vitreous or pearly

Cleavage: Rhombohedral like calcite

Hardness: 3.5

Streak: White

Uses: Building stone (much marble consists of dolomite), agricultural lime, source of magnesia. Dolomite is distinguishable from calcite by its slightly greater hardness and by the fact that it does not effervesce readily in cold acid.

PYRITE, FeS_2 (Fool's Gold, Iron Pyrites)

Forms: Cubes, octahedrons, pyritohedrons (crystals with 12 faces, each face bounded by 5 sides), granular and compact masses

Color: Pale brass-yellow

Luster: Metallic

Specific gravity: 5

Hardness: 6

Streak: Greenish-black

Uses: Rarely used as a source of iron; gold is sometimes present as an impurity in sufficient quantity to make it a valuable gold ore; most important use is in the manufacture of sulphuric acid

CHALCOPYRITE, $CuFeS_2$ (Copper Pyrites, Yellow Copper Ore)

Forms: Usually massive; sometimes in wedge-shaped, four-sided crystals

Color: Bright brass-yellow, often tarnished blue, purple, or black on the surface

Luster: Metallic

Specific gravity: 4.2

Hardness: 3.5 to 4

Streak: Greenish-black

Use: An important ore of copper

GALENA, PbS (Lead glance)

Forms: Cubic crystals, granular masses
Color: Lead-gray
Luster: Metallic
Specific gravity: 7.5
Cleavage: Cubic—3 directions at right angles
Hardness: 2.5
Streak: Lead-gray
Uses: Most common lead ore

SPHALERITE, ZnS (Zinc blende, Black Jack)

Forms: 12-sided crystals, granular and cleavable masses
Color: Brown, yellow, black
Luster: Resinous or waxy
Cleavage: Cleaves in six directions producing 12-sided forms
Hardness: 3.5 to 4
Streak: White, pale brown or yellowish
Uses: Most common zinc ore

GYPSUM, $CaSO_4.2H_2O$

Hardness: 2
Streak: White
Varieties:

> Selenite. Usually occurs in transparent colorless crystals with perfect cleavage in one direction and imperfect cleavage in two other directions. Cleavage pieces are rhombic in shape and flexible, but not elastic. The luster is pearly.
> Satin spar. The fine fibrous variety with a silky or satiny luster and usually white color
> Alabaster. Fine grained and compact or massive. It is commonly used for statuary and other carvings.
> Rock gypsum, or plaster stone. Similar to alabaster except that it has a dull stony luster and often contains noticeable impurities. Its most common use is in the production of plaster of Paris. Some of the so-called chalk of the classroom is made of gypsum.

APATITE, $Ca_5F(PO_4)_3$ (Phosphate rock)

Forms: Often occurs in 6-sided crystals, sometimes in granular masses with no crystal form evident
Hardness: 5
Luster: Vitreous to resinous
Streak: White
Color: Usually green or brown
Cleavage: Poor in one direction

FLUORITE, CaF_2 (Fluor spar)

> *Hardness:* 4
> *Luster:* Vitreous
> *Color:* Colorless, violet, green, yellow
> *Streak:* White
> *Cleavage:* Octahedral, that is, four directions which produce an 8-sided form
> *Crystal form:* Usually cubical
> *Use:* The most important use of fluorite is as a flux in reducing metals in open hearth furnaces. It is also used in making hydrofluoric acid, in cheap jewelry, and for electrodes in some arc lamps.

HALITE, NaCl (Rock salt, Common salt)

> *Form:* Cubic crystals or granular
> *Color:* Colorless or white when pure. Impurities may give it shades of gray, yellow, red, or purple.
> *Luster:* Vitreous
> *Cleavage:* Three directions at right angles
> *Hardness:* 2.5
> *Streak:* White
> *Taste:* Salty
> *Feel:* Wet or greasy
> *Solubility:* Readily soluble in water
> *Uses:* An essential food and a food preservative; many uses in the chemical industries

FELDSPAR. The name feldspar is applied to a family of closely related minerals which are very common in the rocks of the earth, especially in igneous and metamorphic rocks. While the advanced student of mineralogy is able to distinguish between the several different members of this family, the beginner will not find it easy to do so. Because of the difficulty of distinguishing the many varieties of feldspar, it is customary to simplify their study by dividing them into the two groups, *orthoclase* and *plagioclase*.

> ORTHOCLASE, $KAlSi_3O_8$
> > *Color:* White, gray, pink, bluish-green, colorless
> > *Luster:* Vitreous or pearly
> > *Cleavage:* Two good cleavages at right angles
> > *Hardness:* 6
> > *Streak:* White
>
> PLAGIOCLASE. The composition of plagioclase is similar to that of orthoclase except that sodium and/or calcium take the place of potassium.
> > *Color:* Light to dark gray, white, gray-green
> > *Luster:* Vitreous or pearly
> > *Cleavage:* Two cleavages nearly at right angles, one of them usually better than the other
> > *Hardness:* 6
> > *Streak:* White

Other properties: Fine parallel striations are commonly, though not always, found on the most prominent cleavage plane. Some varieties show a play of colors when rotated in light.

Uses of feldspar: Widely used in making porcelain, pottery, glass and scouring powder. Some varieties are used as gems.

MUSCOVITE. White mica, or isinglass, a complex silicate[1] of potassium and aluminum

Form: Thin scales or scaly sheets
Color: Colorless, gray, light brown
Luster: Pearly on the flat surfaces
Cleavage: Perfect in one direction so that it can be easily split into very thin sheets.
Hardness: 2 to 2½
Other properties: Tough, flexible and elastic
Uses: Insulating material in electrical apparatus; when ground it is used in roofing, in rubber tires and as "snow" in motion pictures

BIOTITE. (Black mica), a complex silicate of aluminum, iron, magnesium and potassium. Except for the black color, the physical properties of biotite are like those of muscovite. Biotite has very little commercial use.

HORNBLENDE. (Amphibole), a complex silicate of aluminum, calcium, magnesium and iron

Form: Usually occurs as prism-shaped pieces with ragged ends
Color: Black, dark green
Luster: Silky to dull vitreous
Cleavage: Two directions with angles of about 125° and 55°
Hardness: 5.5
Streak: White or greenish-gray

AUGITE (Pyroxene). In chemical composition and also in physical properties augite is very much like hornblende. These two minerals are difficult to distinguish from each other in hand specimens of rocks. As a rule hornblende has a higher luster, better cleavage and occurs in longer and thinner grains. Perhaps the most valuable feature in distinguishing them is the difference in the angles between their cleavage planes. In hornblende the cleavage angles are 125° and 55°, whereas in augite they are 86° and 94°, or nearly right angles. Both of these minerals can be distinguished from biotite by their greater hardness and by the fact that they cannot be split into thin elastic sheets.

OLIVINE. $(Mg, Fe)_2SiO_4$

Form: Usually in irregular grains or granular masses
Color: Olive green, yellowish-green, brownish-green

---

[1] A silicate consists of silicon and oxygen combined with one or more of the metallic elements.

Luster: Vitreous
Fracture: Conchoidal
Hardness: 6.5 to 7
Use: Transparent specimens are used as gems

GARNET. The different varieties of garnet differ somewhat in composition. The most common one is a silicate of aluminum and iron.

Form: Commonly in good crystals of 12 or 24 faces
Color: Deep red is the most common color, but it is also found in a variety of other colors.
Luster: Vitreous, resinous
Specific gravity: Noticeably heavier than many of the common minerals
Hardness: 6.5 to 7.5
Uses: Good lustrous garnets are used as gems. The principal use of ordinary garnet is in making sand paper and other abrasives.

TOPAZ $(AlF)_2SiO_4$

Form: Occurs in prismatic crystals that are usually vertically striated and also in irregular masses and as pebbles
Color: Colorless, yellow, pale blue, white
Luster: Vitreous
Cleavage: Good in one direction, transverse to the length of the crystal
Specific gravity: About 3.5, noticeably heavier than quartz
Hardness: 8
Uses: Gems

KAOLINITE, $H_4Al_2Si_2O_9$ (Kaolin, China clay)

Form: Compact and clay-like or loose and mealy masses
Color: White when pure; may be stained almost any color, especially yellow, brown, red
Luster: Dull earthy
Other properties: Soft, crumbly, plastic when wet
Uses: Brick, tile, crockery, china, paper filler; an important constituent of soil

SERPENTINE. A hydrous silicate of magnesium

Form: Fine granular masses; sometimes fibrous
Color: Green
Luster: Greasy, waxy, earthy, silky
Streak: White
Hardness: 2.5 to 3
Uses: Building and decorative stone, small carvings; fibrous variety (asbestos) used as heat insulating material

TALC, $H_2Mg_3Si_4O_{12}$

Hardness: 1 (the pure laminated variety)
Luster: Pearly, greasy or waxy

Feel: Soapy or greasy

Color: White, sea green, gray

Varieties: Pure talc usually occurs in thin plates which are flexible but not elastic. The massive compact variety, usually with admixture of other minerals which make it harder than one, is called *steatite* or *soapstone*.

Uses: Paper filler, in paints, laboratory tables and sinks, toilet powder

CHLORITE. A complex silicate of aluminum, magnesium and iron with water.

Form: Usually occurs in thin flakes or scales like mica. In some cases the flakes are so small that their aggregate appears massive.

Color: Green

Luster: Pearly to earthy

Cleavage: Perfect in one direction

Hardness: About 2

Flexibility: Chlorite flakes are flexible but not elastic.

TOURMALINE. A very complex silicate containing, perhaps, a greater variety of chemical elements than any other mineral. As some of these elements are interchangeable, tourmaline may be regarded as a series of isomorphous minerals rather than a single species with definite chemical composition.

Form: Crystals usually have trigonal cross section and crystal faces are striated lengthwise.

Color: Black is the most common color. This variety is called schorl. Other colors may be red, yellow, brown, green, blue, and colorless. Some crystals show sharp bands of different colors.

Luster: The black variety has the luster and color of coal. Other varieties are vitreous.

Hardness: About 7

Other properties: Pyroelectrical and piezoelectrical

Uses: Colored varieties, other than black, are used as gems. Plates cut transverse to the principal axis of the crystal are used in depth-sounding apparatus.

THE MOST COMMON MINERALS

The student should make a special effort to become familiar with the several varieties of quartz, feldspar, and calcite, for these three minerals occur in far greater abundance in the rocks of the earth than all other minerals combined. Quartz can be readily distinguished from the other two by its superior hardness and its lack of cleavage. Calcite is much softer than feldspar and can be readily scratched with a knife. Furthermore, calcite has rhombohedral cleavage, whereas feldspar has only two cleavage planes and they are at right angles or nearly so. Calcite will effervesce in diluted acid, whereas feldspar will not.

Suggestions for Further Reading

ENGLISH, George Letchworth, *Getting Acquainted with Minerals* (New York, McGraw-Hill, 1958).

FENTON, Carroll Lane, and FENTON, Mildred Adams, *The Rock Book* (New York, Doubleday, 1940).

GEORGE, Russell D., *Minerals and Rocks* (New York, D. Appleton-Century Company, Inc., 1943).

LOOMIS, Frederick Brewster, *Field Book of Common Rocks and Minerals* (New York, Putnam, 1948).

PIRSSON, Louis V., *Rocks and Minerals*, 3rd edition revised by KNOPF, Adolph (New York, Wiley, 1953).

POUGH, Frederick H., *A Field Guide to Rocks and Minerals* (Boston, Houghton Mifflin, 1953).

WINCHELL, Alexander N., *Elements of Mineralogy* (Englewood Cliffs, N. J., Prentice-Hall, 1942).

— 18 —

Volcanism

ALL THE PHENOMENA associated with the movement of hot molten and vaporous matter are included in the broad term *volcanism,* or igneous action. This great process, or group of associated processes, is one of the most important of the constructional, or earth-building, activities. *Extrusive* phases of igneous action are immediately evident at the surface; *intrusive* volcanism is deep-seated.

EXTRUSIVE VOLCANISM

Volcanoes. A volcano is an opening in the earth through which heated matter rises to the surface and around which it builds a more or less cone-shaped hill. The opening, or vent, through which the hot material rises is the *crater.* In addition to the centrally situated main crater, volcanoes may have one or more subsidiary craters on the flanks of the cone. In some volcanoes, Vesuvius for example, the main crater has been enlarged into a giant crater, or *caldera* by the collapse of the top of the cone or by a severe explosion which blew the top away. Subsequent eruptions have built up a smaller cone within the caldera of the larger and older one.

Number and Distribution of Volcanoes. Although an exact tally has never been made, it is quite certain that the number of volcanoes on the earth runs to several thousand, of which only four or five hundred are now active. It is customary to classify as active those volcanoes that have erupted within the experience of man; the others are considered extinct. This distinction between active and extinct volcanoes is not rigid, for a volcano may lie dormant for many centuries and then resume activity.

Volcanoes are commonly associated with mountain-making and earthquakes in regions of weakness in the earth's crust. Here the rocks are folded, fractured and otherwise deformed by stresses from within. Perhaps 90 per cent of the active and recently extinct volcanoes are

FIG. 18-1. Looking down into the crater of the Peruvian volcano, El Misti. *(Photo by Lt. George R. Johnson, American Geographical Society)*

located in two long, narrow, mountainous belts adjacent to deep ocean basins. Outside of these belts the only volcanic area of any great importance is Iceland, with its twenty-five or more active volcanoes.

One of the great belts, or series of belts, of active and recently extinct volcanoes is the so-called Pacific Girdle of Fire that forms an intermittent ring around the Pacific Ocean Basin. Among the active volcanoes on the eastern border of the Pacific are Wrangell and Katmai in Alaska; Lassen in California, the only active volcano in the United States; Popocatepetl and Orizaba in Mexico, Sangay and Cotopaxi (19,613 ft.), the highest active volcano in the world, in Ecuador. Many other active ones as well as hundreds now extinct are located in this mountain belt extending from Cape Horn to the Aleutians. On the western side of the Pacific, too, there are numerous volcanoes, both active and extinct, in Kamchatka, Japan, the Philippines, East Indies, and New Zealand. Among those of special interest are Kluchevskaya (16,130 ft.) in Kamchatka, the highest active volcano in the Eastern Hemisphere; Fujiyama, the sacred volcano of Japan; and Mayon, a beautifully symmetrical cone in the Philippines.

Another great interrupted ring of volcanoes can be traced around the

287

FIG. 18-2. Kiska volcano is one of the many that have risen from the sea floor in the Aleutian Island chain. *(Official U. S. Navy Photo)*

FIG. 18-3. The crater of Kilimanjaro, Tanganyika. Rising to an altitude of 19,324 feet, it is filled with snow—though it lies almost on the equator. *(Photo by Mary Light, American Geographical Society)*

earth more or less parallel with the Equator and for the most part north of it. In the Atlantic portion of this belt are Mont Pelée and the other volcanoes of the West Indies and the volcanic archipelagos of the Azores, the Canaries, and the Cape Verde Islands. Vesuvius, Etna, Stromboli, and Vulcano are well-known examples in the Mediterranean region. Along the Red Sea there are several extinct volcanoes; the town of Aden is built in the crater of one of them. To the south, on the Equator, is the great extinct cone of Kenya. East of the Indian Ocean, in the East Indies, are Krakatoa in the Strait of Sunda, Papayandang on Java, and numerous others. Continuing eastward across the Pacific there are many groups of volcanic islands rising from the deep ocean floor. Of these the Hawaiian group is the largest. The Hawaiian Islands consist of a dozen or more large volcanic cones, of which only Mauna Loa, Kilauea, and Hualalai are now active.

Materials Erupted by Volcanoes. Solids, liquids, and gases are ejected from volcanic vents. In the case of solids, the material may have been liquid in the throat of the volcano and solidified after being thrown into the air, or it may have been solid matter that was fragmented by the eruption. Large solid particles are known as *volcanic bombs*, the intermediate ones, which are the size of walnuts or other small nuts, are *lapilli*, and the fine material is *ash* or dust. Much of the solid matter falls to the ground nearby and builds up a cone around the crater; in some cases, however, the ash may be thrown up to great heights and carried by the wind some hundreds or thousands of miles from its place of origin. The liquid erupted from the volcanoes consists of molten rock matter called *lava*. Among the gases emitted are water vapor, carbon dioxide, carbon monoxide, sulphur dioxide, and chlorine.

Kinds of Cones. The shape of a volcanic cone depends mainly on the material of which it is composed. The accumulation of solid fragments around the orifice produces a *cinder* cone, the sides of which slope very steeply, usually between 30° and 45°. On the other hand, liquid matter will flow away from the crater and form a broad gently sloping *lava* cone. Some cones consisting solely of lava have slope angles of less than 10°. The cones of many volcanoes are built up by alternate eruptions of fragmental and liquid matter. Such *composite* cones are intermediate in steepness between the pure cinder and the pure lava cones.

Types of Volcanoes. Studies show that volcanoes display a great variety in their characteristics. No two are exactly alike in their behavior. But if we put them into groups on the basis of closely similar characteristics, we may recognize (1) the explosive type, (2) the quiet type, and (3) the intermediate type.

Explosive type. In volcanoes of this type the eruption is very violent and of short duration, and the ejected matter consists mainly of solids and gases. The solid matter is apt to be highly siliceous in composition

FIG. 18-4. Volcanic bombs often have ear-like projections and rinds that resemble bread crusts. (*U. S. Geological Survey*)

and is often blown full of holes or even blown to bits by the rapid escape of imprisoned gases. Around the crater the rough, jagged particles pile up at a steep angle and form a cinder cone.

Cinder Cone

Lava Cone

Composite Cone

FIG. 18-5. Types of volcanic cones. The low, flat cone is made up entirely of superposed layers of lava; the steep-sided cinder cone is built up of angular fragments erupted from the vent in violent explosions; the composite cone, the most common type, consists of alternating layers of lava and cinders.

One of the most violent volcanic eruptions on record was that of Krakatoa in the Strait of Sunda, between Java and Sumatra. With the exception of some mild earth tremors and one or two small eruptions, the volcano had been dormant for about 200 years and its slopes were well clothed with vegetation. On August 27, 1883, four terrific explosions took place. More than half of the island volcano was blown away. The top, which had stood 1,500 feet above the sea, was blown off down to a depth of 1,000 feet below sea level. Ash was thrown into the air to an estimated height of seventeen miles and carried by air currents to all parts of the earth. It fell in notable quantities on the streets and buildings of western Europe, 11,000 miles away. Much of the finer dust remained suspended in the air for several months and colored brilliantly the sunrise and sunset in all parts of the world. Great waves fifty feet high were generated in the ocean and propagated halfway around the earth. A number of nearby coastal towns and villages were destroyed, and 36,000 people lost their lives. The actual sounds of the explosions of this volcano were heard nearly 3,000 miles away.

Mont Pelée, on the island of Martinique, in the West Indies, is another example of the explosive type of volcano. After.some quaking and intermittent ejection of ash for several days, a devastating eruption took place on May 8, 1902. A great mass of incandescent smoke, ash, and dense gases rushed from the crater and swept westward across the city of St. Pierre. The entire city was burned and its ruins buried beneath a blanket of ash; none of its 40,000 inhabitants escaped. The hot cloud continued across the harbor and destroyed all of the ships, save one. After the expulsion of ash and gases, molten matter welled up in the crater and solidified as it rose, until a spine projected several hundred feet above the throat of the volcano.

Quiet type. At the other extreme are the volcanoes which erupt with very little violence. Molten lava, boiling and sputtering in the crater, frequently rises and flows over the rim or bursts through a fissure in the side of the cone. Very little solid or gaseous matter is ejected. The lava, basic in composition and of a high degree of fluidity, builds up lava cones which commonly have a slope of 10° or less.

The volcanoes which constitute the Hawaiian Islands are good examples of the quiet type. These islands consist of a number of volcanoes which have been built up from the ocean floor by repeated eruptions. Mauna Kea, the highest of these volcanoes, rises from a depth of 18,000 feet below sea level to a height of 13,784 feet above sea level. Measured from the broad ocean floor on which it rests, this volcano is the highest mountain in the world. Yet its slope is very gentle, for its base is more than 100 miles in diameter. Although the bulk of this volcano consists of lava, there are several small cinder cones on its upper slopes.

Of the Hawaiian volcanoes, Mauna Loa and Kilauea are the only ones which have shown much activity in historic times. Their frequent flows have been in regions of sparse population and consequently have resulted in little loss of life and property. In 1936 a flow from Mauna Loa was directed toward a populous place, but was diverted from its course by aërial bombing.

Intermediate type. Most of the volcanoes of the world are intermediate between the purely explosive and the purely quiet types. This group embraces a wide range of characteristics, approaching the quiet type on the one hand and the explosive type on the other. Explosive eruptions of fragmental matter alternating with quiet eruptions of liquid lava build up a composite cone of intermediate steepness. Not only is the cone intermediate in form and general make-up, but the chemical composition of the lava too is usually between the acidic and the basic extremes.

Vesuvius, on the border of the Bay of Naples in Italy, one of the best known volcanoes in the world, is typical of the intermediate type. This volcano consists of a cone within a cone. Within the outer cone with its large caldera of prehistoric origin is a smaller cone built up by the later eruptions of historic time. After the formation of the prehistoric cone and before the Christian era, Vesuvius had lain dormant for several centuries, and its slopes were deeply weathered and intensively culti- vated. Few people recognized the volcanic origin of the mountain. But in the year 63 A.D. the volcanic energy began to assert itself in the form of earthquakes, which grew in frequency and intensity until finally in 79 an eruption occurred which destroyed the towns of Herculaneum, Pompeii, and Strabiae. Excellent accounts of this eruption are found in letters of the younger Pliny, written at the time, and in Bulwer-Lytton's well-known tale, *The Last Days of Pompeii.*

From 79 to 1631 Vesuvius exhibited only occasional and mild activity. In 1631 a violent eruption caused the loss of 18,000 lives. From that time to the present the volcano has not been quiet for any great length of time. Every few weeks or few months or few years it has erupted, sometimes ejecting only ash and gases and sometimes liquid lava.

New Volcanoes. While volcanoes become extinct and are destroyed by the processes of erosion, new ones come into being. The birth of a new volcano is, however, not a phenomenon of frequent occurrence. Within historic time man has had the opportunity of observing the early activity of only a few. Among these we may mention Graham's Island and Parícutin. Graham's Island resulted from an eruption in the Mediterranean between Sicily and Africa in the year 1831. Where there had previously been water at least 600 feet deep a cinder cone was thrown up to a height of 200 feet above sea level. This island of loose fragments was eroded so rapidly by the waves, that it was reduced to a shoal within the short period of three months.

Parícutin, in the Mexican state of Michoacán, 200 miles west of Mexico City, has been observed in its early stages by more geologists than has any other volcano. Earthquakes began to occur in the vicinity on February 11, 1943, and daily increased in frequency until about 300 were reported to have occurred on February 19. Eruptions started the next day in the middle of a plowed field. Within four months a cinder cone composed entirely of fragments had risen to a height of 1,200 feet. Lava flows then began to appear, some pouring over the rim of the crater and some bursting through the sides of the cone. Within seven months

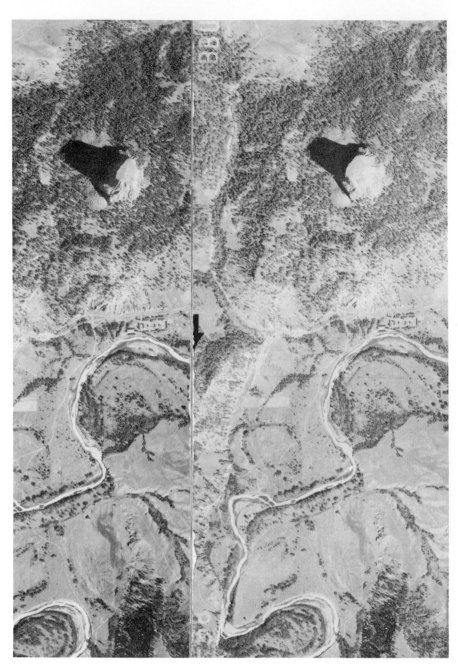

FIG. 18-6. Stereo-pair, or stereogram, of Devils Tower and vicinity, Wyo. Devils Tower has been interpreted by some as a volcanic plug and by others as the steeply-rising upper portion of a laccolith. This stereogram can best be viewed with a stereoscope of 2½-inch base line.

FIG. 18-8. Church tower projecting above lava flow from Paricutin. Smaller buildings in the village were covered. Surface of the flow consists of large, rough blocks.

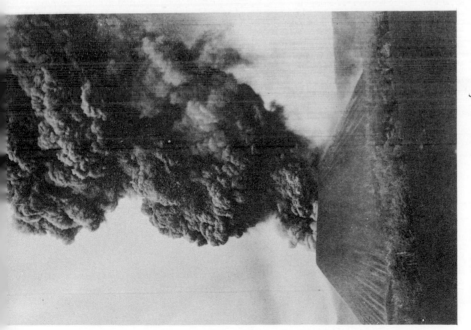

FIG. 18-7. The Mexican volcano, Parícutin, a few months after its birth in February, 1943. (*American Museum of Natural History*)

the cone had grown to 1,500 feet. In 6 years it was 3,000 feet. The periods between eruptions have become longer and the eruptions less violent. At the time of this writing there is only an occasional mild outburst.

Fissure Eruptions. Another form of extrusive igneous activity is that of fissure eruptions. In this case the lava pours forth quietly from cracks and spreads in sheet-like layers over the surface. Instead of forming distinct cones, flows from neighboring fissures tend to merge and cover a large area.

Old lava flows are recognized in many parts of the world. In the Columbia Plateau of northwestern United States an area of about 200,000 square miles consists of rocks formed by the solidification of successive flows of basic lava from many fissures. In the walls of the Snake River Canyon this lava is exposed in a thickness of as much as 3,000 feet. In the Deccan Plateau of south central India an area equally as large consists of similar flows of basic lava. Smaller lava flows are found in many localities; for example, the Watchung Ridges of New Jersey and the Saltonstall Mountain in Connecticut consist of old lava flows. Modern fissure eruptions are not of common occurrence, but a number of examples are found in Iceland.

Hot Springs, Geysers, Fumaroles. Hot springs and geysers are found mainly in volcanic regions or in regions that have experienced recent igneous activity. Some of the water and steam that comes to the surface in this way is probably derived from the molten igneous matter, but most of it is ordinary ground water that has been heated by contact with or nearness to the hot material.

Fumaroles are vents from which gases issue. They are found in nearly all volcanic regions and also in some places where no other volcanic phenomena are evident at the surface. Steam is the most common gas expelled by fumaroles, although sulphur gases and carbon dioxide are usually present. The steam from some fumaroles has a temperature much above that of boiling water. In the volcanic area of Tuscany, near Rome, and at The Geysers, near San Francisco, the steam from fumaroles has been harnessed for the generation of power.

INTRUSIVE VOLCANISM

Hot molten matter poured out on the surface is known as lava. The same material beneath the surface is called *magma*. Not all of the magma which originates within the earth is extruded to the surface. In fact, most of it cools and solidifies underground. Although we cannot observe the underground movement of molten matter while it is in progress, we can see the forms which have resulted from the cooling and solidification of the magma after they are exposed to view by subsequent

FIG. 18-9. Lava sheets with vertical shrinkage cracks, Yellowstone Park.
(Photo by C. H. Tozier, Harvard University Dept. of Geology)

FIG. 18-10. The canyon of the Snake River in Idaho exposes the successive lava flows which make up the Columbia Plateau. *(Photo by Russell, U. S. Geological Survey)*

erosion. The intrusive igneous masses which solidify beneath the surface are named and distinguished from each other on the bases of shape and relationship to the surrounding rocks.

Forms of Intrusives. The following are the most common forms:

Necks. When a volcano becomes extinct the magma solidifies in the conduit which leads up to the crater and forms a more or less cylindrical plug or neck. This neck is usually more resistant to erosion than the lava and ash and is left standing after the surrounding material has been carried away. Shiprock, near Farmington, New Mexico, is one of the many good examples of volcanic necks found in that region.

Dikes. Dikes are thin, tabular masses, ranging from a fraction of an inch to several hundred feet in thickness, that fill fissures in other rocks. In some cases they occupy the fissures that lead to surface flows; in others, they did not reach the surface and are exposed only after erosion of the overlying rocks.

Dikes are found in all kinds of rocks—igneous, sedimentary, and metamorphic—and in all parts of the world. In some localities they are the only evidence of igneous activity. Sometimes a dike is more resistant to erosion than the enclosing rock and is left as a wall or ridge when the surrounding material is worn down; at other times the reverse is

FIG. 18-11. The forms in which igneous rocks occur.

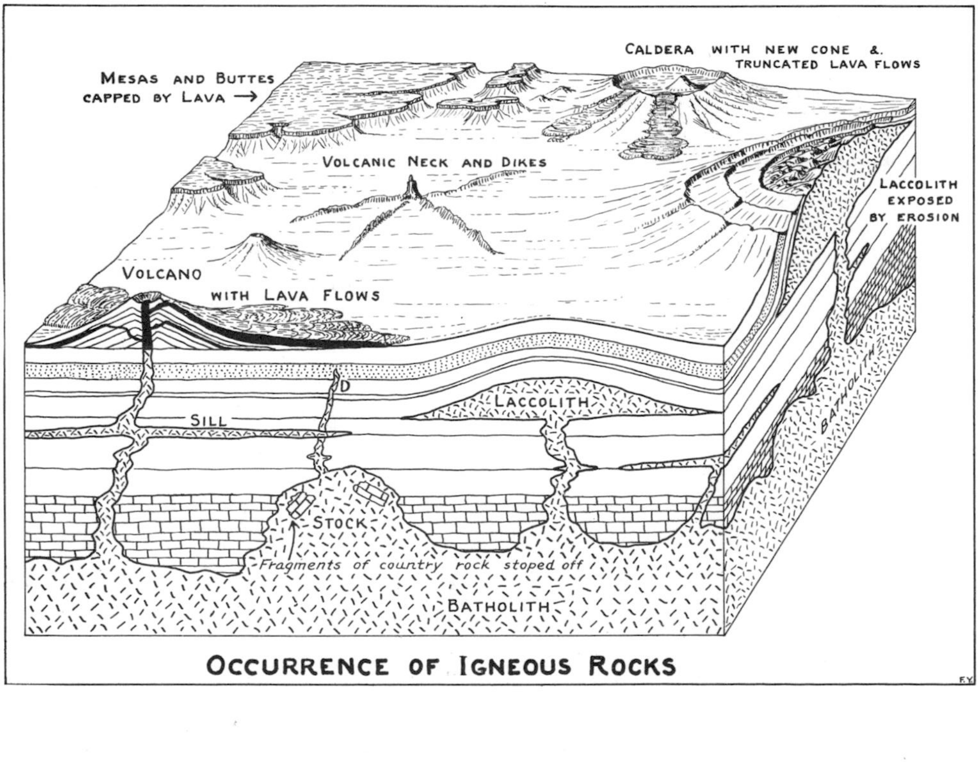

OCCURRENCE OF IGNEOUS ROCKS

true and the dike is marked by a trench or ditch on the surface.

Sills. Sills, like dikes, are thin, tabular forms. They differ from dikes in that they are parallel to the beds of rock which they intrude, whereas dikes cut across the bedding planes. It is correct to say that sills are horizontal only if the enclosing rock beds are horizontal. Inasmuch as sills occur as layers which have been injected between beds of other rocks, they are most commonly found in sedimentary rocks. The west side of the Hudson Valley from New York City to Haverstraw—the Palisades of the Hudson—is the edge of a thick sill which extends westward from the river for an unknown distance. Other examples are found in Connecticut, Massachusetts, New Jersey, and elsewhere.

Laccoliths. Where the magma is intruded rapidly between layers of other rocks, or is so viscous that it does not spread rapidly, the overlying

FIG. 18-12. Weavers Needle, a volcanic plug in Tonto National Forest, Ariz. *(U. S. Forest Service)*

FIG. 18-13. Small dikes cutting across beds of sedimentary rocks, Sacramento Valley, Calif. *(Photo by Diller, U. S. Geological Survey)*

strata are arched up and the intrusion becomes a lens-shaped laccolith, more or less circular in ground plan, thick in the middle and thinning toward the margins. Some laccoliths are of large size, being as much as a mile in thickness and several miles in diameter. Many examples are found in the western United States, especially in southern Utah and in west-central Montana.

There are, of course, all gradations from laccoliths to sills, depending on the degree of flatness of the intrusion. There are also combined forms, such as the local thickening of a sill into a laccolith. Furthermore, in the mountains of New England, the Highlands of the Hudson and other ancient metamorphic regions, some igneous intrusions are difficult to classify, for they have been mashed and sheared into such complex forms that their original relationships are obscured.

Batholiths. The largest and deepest of the igneous intrusions are the huge batholiths that extend downward to the basaltic substratum. The upper surface of a batholith is commonly irregular or undulating, with dome-like cupolas, or *stocks*, projecting upward from the main body. Many of the dikes, sills, laccoliths, volcanoes, and surface flows are apparently the offshoots from batholithic masses.

Since batholiths solidify at great depth beneath the surface, they are exposed only in those regions which have suffered great uplift and deep erosion of the covering material. Many of the large mountains that have been subjected to long erosion exhibit batholithic cores. In the Rocky Mountain Front Range in Colorado, for example, the batholith exposed in the central part of the mountain is flanked by the upturned, eroded edges of the layers of sedimentary rock which formerly covered the intrusion. The core of the Sierra Nevada consists of a batholith some 400 miles long; and a still larger batholith constitutes the mountains of Idaho.

CAUSES OF IGNEOUS ACTIVITY

Any explanation of the causes of igneous activity must be based in part on inference, for the depths of the earth cannot be observed directly. We know the melting temperature of rocks at the surface and under moderate pressures, but we cannot duplicate the enormous pressure that exists miles below the surface. We have a fair knowledge of the rate of temperature increase for depths of a mile or two, but beyond that we must rely on inference. We can measure the temperature and examine the composition of igneous matter when it comes to the surface, but we do not know how much it has cooled and how much it has mixed with other material since leaving its source. Inasmuch as inference thus necessarily enters into an explanation of volcanism, there is a lack of agreement among authorities.

One point on which authorities differ is that of the origin of the heat. Some say that the heat of the interior of the earth is largely original, or residual, from the time the earth was pulled away from the sun. Others believe that most or all of the original heat has been lost and that the present high temperature is the result of con.pression, chemical reorganization, and radioactivity within the earth. But, whatever its cause, the interior of the earth is hot, at least in parts.

At depths of several miles it is probable that the temperature is high enough to melt all rocks at surface pressure. But the enormous pressure at that depth prevents the rocks from expanding to the liquid state. Perhaps a delicate balance between the effects of temperature and those of pressure is normally maintained. In certain places, however, the pressure may be decreased by the up-arching of the overlying rocks or by the erosion of some of the overlying load; or, an excessive amount of heat may accumulate in local areas. The temperature then becomes the dominating influence and local bodies of magma are formed. Once a magma pocket forms it tends to move outward toward the surface where the pressure is less, partly by melting its way and partly by following the fissures and other openings. Most of its driving force is spent before reaching the surface and it may solidify in the various intrusive forms described above. If the impelling force is especially strong, however, some of the molten matter may drive through to the surface and burst forth as volcanoes and fissure eruptions.

Suggestions for Further Reading

HINDS, Norman E. A., *Geomorphology* (Englewood Cliffs, N. J., Prentice-Hall, 1943).

JAGGAR, T. A., *Volcanoes Declare War* (Honolulu, Hawaii, Paradise of the Pacific, 1945).

JOHNSON, Gaylord, *The Story of Earthquakes and Volcanoes* (New York, Messner, 1938).

LOBECK, A. K., *Geomorphology* (New York, McGraw-Hill, 1939).

THORNBURY, William D., *Principles of Geomorphology* (New York, Wiley, 1954).

VON ENGELN, O. D., *Geomorphology* (New York, Macmillan, 1942).

── 19 ──

Igneous Rocks

Two main methods are employed in the study of rocks, the megascopic and the microscopic. For microscopic study a rock slice is mounted on glass, ground to a thickness of .03 millimeters and capped with a cover glass to make a *slide*. When such slides are placed under the petrographic microscope, the identity of the minerals, the minute structures and many other important features become evident to the trained observer.

For megascopic study some hand specimens, a pocket lens, knife blade and, most of all, a keen eye and an inquiring mind are the only essential equipment. In addition, the student should observe the occurrence and relationships of rocks in nature and read what other people have written about them.

BASES FOR CLASSIFYING IGNEOUS ROCKS

Composition. Igneous rocks are formed by the solidification of molten matter originating within the earth. Some of the magma is erupted to the surface, forming the extrusive rocks; some cools and solidifies beneath the surface, forming the intrusive, or plutonic, rocks.

The molten matter, or magma, from which igneous rocks are formed is of complex and variable composition. Igneous rocks of various types from many parts of the world have been fused and subjected to chemical analysis. These analyses show that in a typical sample more than 99 per cent of the magma consists of the elements oxygen, silicon, aluminum, iron, calcium, sodium, potassium, magnesium, hydrogen, titanium, phosphorus, and carbon, combined in the form of oxides and intimately mixed together. Perhaps it would be better to say that each oxide is dissolved in the others. From numerous analyses it has been calculated that the average percentage composition of all igneous rocks in terms of oxides is as follows:

SiO_2,	59.12	Na_2O,	3.84
Al_2O_3,	15.34	K_2O,	3.13
Fe_2O_3,	3.08	H_2O,	1.15
FeO,	3.80	CO_2,	0.102
MgO,	3.49	TiO_2,	1.05
CaO,	5.08	P_2O_5	0.299
	others,	0.395	

The remaining fraction of a per cent may include small amounts of a great many elements.

If a mass of magma or lava does not cool too rapidly, the constituent materials crystallize out of the liquid to form the mineral grains of igneous rocks. Because different crystals grow simultaneously, each is crowded by its neighbors and good shapes are rare. The resulting rock is a mass of interlocking, irregular crystals, each of which has the internal structure which is true of its kind, even though the external form may be difficult to recognize as a crystal.

The most common, or essential, minerals of igneous rocks are the feldspars (orthoclase and plagioclase), quartz, the micas (muscovite and biotite), hornblende, augite or some other pyroxene, and olivine. Corundum and magnetite are occasionally found in considerable quantity. Other minerals are of more limited occurrence.

Although some of the oxides named above form minerals by themselves, most of the common igneous rock minerals are formed by a combination of two or more oxides. Quartz is a simple oxide of silicon, SiO_2; corundum is an aluminum oxide, Al_2O_3; magnetite is formed by the union of two iron oxides, FeO and Fe_2O_3, into Fe_3O_4. The other more complex igneous minerals named are called silicates because they consist of SiO_2 (silica) in combination with other constituents. Orthoclase, for example, consists of $K_2O.Al_2O_3.6\ SiO_2$. Most of the other common silicates are even more complex than orthoclase.

Texture. By texture is meant the *size* of the grains. The most important factor in determining the size of the mineral grains in an igneous rock is the rate of cooling of the material as it solidifies. Each mineral crystallizes within a certain range of temperatures; and the longer the cooling mass remains within the limits of that range, the larger the crystals grow. It is evident that the rate of cooling depends on the size, shape, and position of the igneous body as a whole. Lava poured out on the surface in thin sheets or thrown into the air in finely divided particles will cool very rapidly. On the other hand, a large magmatic mass which solidifies deep beneath the surface loses heat very slowly.

Five kinds of texture may be distinguished in igneous rocks. At one

FIG. 19-1. Phenocrysts of feldspar in a dark, fine-grained matrix — an example of porphyritic texture. *(American Museum of Natural History)*

FIG. 19-2. Vesicular lava from San Francisco Mountain, Ariz. *(American Museum of Natural History)*

FIG. 19-3. Massive granite, consisting of light-colored feldspar, colorless or greyish quartz and black hornblende. *(Harvard University Dept. of Geology)*

FIG. 19-4. Graphic granite, a pegmatite fabric. Large books of mica as well as good crystals of tourmaline, fluorite and other minerals may be found in pegmatites. *(American Museum of Natural History)*

extreme are certain lavas which have chilled so rapidly that no grains at all are evident. The rock is a homogenous natural glass that shows no differentiation into mineral grains. This is the *glassy* texture. In those lavas and small intrusive bodies which have cooled somewhat more slowly, but still at a fairly rapid rate, crystallization takes place for a relatively short time and all grains are so small that it is difficult or impossible to distinguish them without the microscope. This may be called *fine* texture. In some rocks certain minerals grow into large and prominent grains, while others remain small and more or less indistinguishable. Thus there are two distinct sizes of grain in the same rock. Such a rock, with phenocrysts, or large grains, in a matrix, or ground mass, of smaller grains, has *porphyritic* texture. In large intrusions cooling is a slow process, and all of the grains grow to a more or less uniformly large size. Since this *coarse* equigranular texture is typical of granite, it is often called the granitoid texture. Finally, there are the extreme cases of magmas kept fluid for so long a time by a high content of volatile matter that mineral grains grow to dimensions of several inches or even a few feet. A rock with such large grains has *pegmatitic* texture.

Fabric. The fabric of an igneous rock is determined by the physical state and arrangement of the materials that solidified from the magma to form the rock. Each of the many different fabrics is an important clue in deciphering rock history. Although students of petrology have identified a great many fabrics, both megascopic and microscopic, we shall here limit ourselves to only a few terms which can be readily observed in hand specimens. Most igneous rocks are either *crystalline,* composed of crystals, or *amorphous,* composed of glass. Some are composed partly of crystals and partly of glass. Many of the crystalline rocks show no particular pattern in the arrangement of their mineral grains; they are said to have a *massive* fabric. In some rocks certain of the minerals are strung out in wavy, parallel streaks or lines, as if the molten matter had been slowly moving in one direction as the minerals crystallized. This arrangement gives the rock a *linear,* or flow, fabric. In certain kinds of granite one finds a *graphic* arrangement, formed by an intergrowth of quartz and feldspar in which the quartz grains resemble ancient cuneiform characters used in writing. Amorphous igneous rocks may be *compact,* as obsidian; *vesicular,* or full of tube-like holes made by expanding gases, as pumice; or *fragmental,* as tuff, which is composed of volcanic ash.

The above fabrics may be tabulated as follows:

	massive		compact
Crystalline	linear	Amorphous	vesicular
	graphic		fragmental

CLASSIFICATION AND DESCRIPTION
OF IGNEOUS ROCKS

Classification. Variations in fabric, in texture, and in composition result in a great many kinds of igneous rocks. A scheme of classification whereby similar kinds are grouped together greatly facilitates the study of rocks. For a detailed study by those who have access to all methods of investigation an elaborate and detailed table of classification is desirable, but for a brief study of hand specimens by beginning students, a simple grouping such as that given below is all that is necessary.

We shall make two groups on the basis of fabric: (1) crystalline igneous rocks and (2) amorphous igneous rocks. The crystalline rocks in turn are arranged in groups on the basis of composition, from the acid rocks at the left of the table to the basic rocks at the right. The composition groups are further divided on the basis of texture, from the coarse at the top to the fine at the bottom. Inasmuch as no minerals are distinguishable in the amorphous rocks, the varieties are differentiated on such features as color, compactness, vesicularity, and size of fragments.

Table of Igneous Rocks

	CRYSTALLINE			
	Acid	*Intermediate*		*Basic*
Textures	Orthoclase Quartz Mica and/or Hornblende	Orthoclase Mica and/or Hornblende	Plagioclase Biotite and/or Hornblende	Augite Plagioclase Olivine Biotite
Coarse	Granite	Syenite	Diorite	Gabbro
Porphyritic	Rhyolite (Quartz) Porphyry	Trachyte Porphyry	Andesite Porphyry	Basalt Porphyry
Fine	Felsite		Basalt	
	Rhyolite	Trachyte	Andesite	Basalt

AMORPHOUS

Compact: Obsidian
Vesicular: Pumice—light color, small vesicles
Scoria—dark color, large vesicles
Fragmental: Tuff—fine texture
Agglomerate—coarse texture

Descriptions of Common Types. *Granite-rhyolite Group.* Granite, the most common coarse-textured igneous rock, is widespread in the form of large intrusions in eastern Canada, in New England, in the Appalachians, in the Rockies, and in other parts of the world where deep erosion has removed the overlying cover. Orthoclase is the predominant mineral, and quartz is always prominent. In addition to these two minerals at least one other is always present, but the third mineral is variable. In some granites it is biotite, in others it is hornblende, and in still others it is muscovite or, more rarely, augite. The fabric is generally massive, the minerals occurring as interlocking, irregular crystals, but linear and graphic fabrics are sometimes found. Inasmuch as orthoclase is the most abundant mineral in granite, the color of the rock is determined largely by the light-gray or pink color of that mineral. Granite is a very important stone for monuments and heavy construction and has long been quarried at various localities in New England and in the southern Appalachians.

Rhyolite is made up of the same minerals as granite, but the texture is usually so fine that it can be identified only with the microscope. As is indicated by this fine texture, rhyolite occurs as extrusions and as small intrusions, in the western United States and in some other regions of volcanic activity.

Rhyolite porphyry is like rhyolite and granite in composition. It is mixed in texture, some of the grains being comparable in size to those in granite and the others to those in the ordinary rhyolite. Hand specimens of this rock are recognized by identifying the large grains (phenocrysts) and assuming that the small grains are of the same minerals as the phenocrysts. If quartz grains are especially prominent as phenocrysts the rock is sometimes called a quartz porphyry.

Syenite-Trachyte Group. Generally speaking, the syenite-trachyte group is like the granite-rhyolite group in composition, except for the absence of quartz. This group contains only orthoclase and one or more of the dark minerals, hornblende, augite, and biotite. This group of rocks is much less abundant than the granite-rhyolite group.

Diorite-Andesite Group. This group is like the syenite-trachyte group in composition, except that plagioclase takes the place of orthoclase. The distinction of rocks in the two groups is therefore a matter of identifying the feldspar. This is not always an easy matter in hand specimens. In many cases, however, plagioclase can be recognized by striations on the cleavage faces or by the angle between the cleavage planes. Then, too, the dark minerals are more prominent in a diorite than they are in a syenite. Andesite, the fine-textured rock in this group, is so named from its widespread occurrence in the Andes Mountains of South America.

Gabbro-Basalt Group. In this group plagioclase and augite or some

FIG. 19-5. Syenite has more of the dark-colored minerals and less quartz than granite. *(American Museum of Natural History)*

FIG. 19-6. Obsidian, showing glassy texture and excellent conchoidal fracture. *(American Museum of Natural History)*

FIG. 19-7. Scoria from Kilauea, Hawaii. Pumice differs from scoria in having lighter color and smaller vesicles. *(American Museum of Natural History)*

309

other pyroxene are the chief minerals; biotite, olivine, and magnetite may also be present. In the typical gabbro, plagioclase and augite are more or less equally represented. At one extreme are rocks consisting almost entirely of plagioclase, known as *anorthosite*; at the other extreme is *pyroxenite*, consisting almost entirely of pyroxene. *Peridotite* is a special variety of gabbro consisting mainly of olivine. Since the dark minerals are prominent in this group and even the plagioclase may be dark colored, the rocks have a dark gray, dark green, or black color.

Basalt, the fine-textured equivalent of gabbro, is the most abundant of the extrusive rocks. The great lava flows of the Columbia Plateau in the northwestern United States and those of the Deccan Plateau in India as well as the volcanic masses of the Hawaiian Islands consists mainly of basalt. In addition, numerous dikes, sills and smaller lava flows of basalt are found in many parts of the world.

Felsite and Basalt. Because of the difficulty or impossibility of identifying the minerals in the fine-textured rocks, the distinction between the different types is often uncertain. For this reason a grouping is often made on the basis of color. The light-colored rocks, those of almost any shade except dark gray, dark green, and black, are given the noncommittal name of felsite; dark ones are called basalt. Under this grouping the term felsite includes rhyolite, trachyte and lighter shades of andesite, and basalt includes not only true basalt but also the dark shade of andesite.

Amorphous Igneous Rocks. Obsidian is natural glass, lava that has solidified so rapidly that the minerals did not crystallize. Chemical analysis shows that most obsidian has the same composition as granite. If the material had cooled slowly the rocks would consist of orthoclase, quartz, and one or more of the dark minerals. In spite of its acid composition most obsidian is dark colored or black because of the presence of a small amount of dark material or of embryonic crystals uniformly distributed through the glass. Obsidian, as well as pumice and scoria, often forms as a crust on the surface of lava flows.

Pumice is a glass with the same chemical composition as obsidian. It differs from obsidian in that it is full of holes. Expansion of gases in the magma puffed it up into a frothy foam and quick chilling preserved the porous condition. *Scoria* is like pumice except that the composition is more basic, the vesicles, or holes, are larger and the color is darker.

Tuff consists of compacted volcanic ash. *Agglomerate* is made up of larger angular fragments of lava.

JOINTS IN IGNEOUS ROCKS

Hot molten matter must necessarily contract on cooling and solidifying. All igneous rocks have cracks, or joints, because the only method

FIG. 19-8. Columnar joining in basalt, Orange, N. J. *(Photo by Iddings, U. S. Geological Survey)*

FIG. 19-9. Columnar joining in the basalt of the Giants Causeway, Northern Ireland. *(Harvard University Dept. of Geology)*

by which the igneous masses can accommodate themselves to contraction is by forming such cracks. We shall see later that all other rocks also have joints. The arrangement and spacing of the joints depend, among other things, on the rate of cooling and on the size and shape of the mass. In flat sills, dikes, and some surface flows columnar jointing is typical. The main joints, vertical to the largest cooling surfaces and polygonal in pattern, divide the mass into columns or palisades, such as those seen on the west side of the Hudson River at New York City. Thick masses, such as laccoliths and batholiths, are commonly cut into rough rectangular prisms by joints in three planes, more or less at right angles to each other. The prominence and the spacing of joints play an important part not only in the weathering of rocks but also in quarrying operations.

Suggestions for Further Reading

FENTON, Carroll Lane, and FENTON, Mildred Adams, *The Rock Book* (New York, Doubleday, 1940).

GEORGE, Russell D., *Minerals and Rocks* (New York, D. Appleton-Century Company, 1943).

KEMP, James Furman, *Handbook of Rocks*, 6th edition revised by GROUT, Frank F. (Princeton, N. J., Van Nostrand, 1940).

LOOMIS, Frederick Brewster, *Field Book of Common Rocks and Minerals* (New York, Putnam, 1948).

PIRSSON, Louis V., *Rocks and Minerals*, 3rd edition revised by KNOPF, Adolph (New York, Wiley, 1953).

POUGH, Frederick H., *A Field Guide to Rocks and Minerals* (Boston, Houghton Mifflin, 1953).

SPOCK, Leslie E., *Guide to the Study of Rocks* (New York, Harper, 1953).

— 20 —

Sedimentary Rocks

THE SEDIMENTARY ROCKS consist of (1) broken, worn and altered fragments of pre-existing rocks, (2) material precipitated from solution by water, and (3) organic remains. Although more than 70 per cent of the rocks at the surface are sedimentary in origin, they form only a thin veneer on the underlying basement of igneous and metamorphic rocks.

Mechanical Sediments. The fragments of other rocks result from weathering and erosion. These particles of various sizes—boulders, pebbles (gravel), sand, silt, and clay—that are mechanically transported and deposited by wind, water, and ice are termed mechanical sediments. Since quartz occurs in considerable quantity in the primary rocks and is resistant to both chemical and mechanical destruction, it is not surprising to find it as the most common constituent of sand and gravel. Clay, which is kaolin mixed with impurities, is also abundant in the mechanical sediments, being derived from the weathering of feldspar and other primary silicate minerals.

Chemical Sediments. When the surface and ground waters have dissolved so much material that they become saturated, they may precipitate part of their load and deposit it as chemical sediments. Calcium carbonate is perhaps the most widespread chemical sediment; calcium sulphate (gypsum), sodium chloride (salt), silica, and some iron compounds, such as hematite, are also common.

Organic Sediments. The organic sediments consist of shells and other hard parts of plants and animals which remain after the more perishable parts of organisms have been destroyed. Among the organic accumulations the most common are the calcareous and siliceous skeletons of water-living plants and animals and the woody tissues of land plants.

FORMATION OF ROCKS FROM SEDIMENT

Places of Deposition. Most of the sediment derived from the lands is deposited around the borders of the continents in the shallow shelf seas. Streams carry their loads of rock fragments into the ocean where they are distributed by the waves and currents. Glaciers and the wind also contribute their quotas to the sediment which is accumulating on the bottom of the sea. The ocean is not only a great reservoir for the deposition of mechanical sediments; certain portions of it are also the sites of chemical precipitation. In some lagoons, bays, and in other arms of the sea the material in solution becomes so concentrated that part of it is precipitated on the bottom. Furthermore, the ocean is the dwelling place of myriads of organisms that use the mineral matter dissolved in the water to construct hard parts that either strengthen, support, or protect their otherwise flabby bodies. These hard structures do not decay upon the death of the animal or plant, and consequently they may make large accumulations of organic sediment in many localities. For example, the Great Barrier Reef off northeastern Australia, composed almost exclusively of the remains of organisms, is 1,400 miles long, 30 miles wide and several hundred feet thick. To all sediments, whether mechanical, chemical, or organic, that are laid down in ocean water, the name *marine* is given.

A considerable quantity of sediment is deposited, if only temporarily, in various types of localities on the lands. Streams leave portions of their loads on their deltas and floodplains and in other lowland areas. The wind piles up sand in deserts and along some seacoasts and deposits fine silt as loess over wide areas. In the cold regions of high latitudes and high altitudes, glaciers drop their load of debris, as they did in the past when they invaded large areas that now have temperate climates. Lakes are settling basins for sediment which is carried into them by streams and other agents; ground water precipitates material in caverns and around some springs; and in swamps, such as the Everglades and the Great Dismal Swamp, great quantities of partly decayed vegetable matter accumulate. Sediments, such as those above, that are deposited on land or in fresh water are often called *continental*.

The student who becomes familiar with the various characteristics of sediments deposited in different environments can interpret much of the past history of the earth by examination of the sedimentary rocks. These rocks contain clues which enable the experienced observer to identify the agent of deposition, and to deduce the type of locality, the climate, the topography, and many other facts concerning the environment in which the sediment was deposited.

Methods of Consolidation. Sediments may be consolidated into rock by (1) cementation, (2) compaction, or (3) crystallization. Coarse, porous sediments, such as sand, gravel, and shell fragments, may be bound together by the deposition of cement between the grains by water percolating through the porous material. Silica, calcium carbonate, and iron oxide are the most common cements, although others are sometimes found. In the case of clay and other fine or colloidal materials there is no need of a cement, for such finely divided sediments are in themselves cohesive and become hard on drying. As more and more sediment is laid down, water is driven out of the lower layers by the weight of the overburden. Material precipitated from solution often forms interlocking crystals like those in an igneous rock and therefore requires no cement; or it may precipitate and harden in an amorphous gel.

PRINCIPAL MINERALS IN SEDIMENTARY ROCKS

Three minerals and their varieties make up the greater part of the sedimentary rocks. Quartz in the form of worn and broken grains is the most widespread of all the minerals composing this class of rocks. In fact, most of the pebbles and sand grains which make up the coarser mechanical sediments consist of this mineral. Quartz also occurs as crystalline and noncrystalline silica in the form of flint, chert, opal, and chalcedony. Kaolin, too, is a common sediment, rarely seen as the pure white mineral, but usually as clay stained gray, black, red, brown, yellow, or some other color by the admixture of impurities. Calcite, or calcium carbonate, is another important sedimentary mineral. It occurs in a variety of forms including distinct crystals, fine clay-like lime mud, shells of animals and other organic structures.

Among the sedimentary minerals of lesser abundance are gypsum, halite, limonite, and red hematite. To this list should be added carbonaceous matter. Although it does not satisfy the strict definition of a mineral, this vegetable matter is the chief constituent of peat and coal.

SPECIAL FEATURES OF SEDIMENTARY ROCKS

Bedding. One of the outstanding characteristics of sedimentary rocks seen in the field is their arrangement into layers, or beds. For this reason they are referred to as stratified rocks. The beds are of various thicknesses, from a fraction of an inch up to several feet and the layers are distinguished from each other by differences in texture, differences in composition, or both.

The stratified arrangement of the rocks is a natural result of the

FIG. 20-1. View from Bright Angel Point, North Rim, Grand Canyon National Park, showing flat-lying sedimentary beds. Looking south down Bright Angel Canyon and toward San Francisco Peaks, faintly visible on the distant horizon. *(Union Pacific Railroad)*

unstable conditions under which the sediment was deposited. Changes in the velocity of streams, currents, and winds during deposition will cause variations in the texture of the sediments; changes in the direction of these depositing agents may cause them to carry and lay down material different in composition from that which they previously deposited. Other factors, such as diastrophism and climatic changes, also play a part in creating variations in the nature of the sediments that accumulate in a given locality.

Colors. The most abundant minerals in the sedimentary rocks—quartz, kaolin, and calcite—are white or colorless when pure. Yet one finds rocks that consist mainly of these minerals occurring in a great variety of colors. In addition to white, which is expectable, red, brown, yellow, gray, and black are common. This means that the chief minerals are often stained by traces of impurities.

Iron oxides are perhaps the chief coloring agents. They impart various shades of red, brown, and yellow, the particular shade of red, brown, or yellow apparently depending on how much water is combined with the iron oxide. The dehydrated oxide, hematite (Fe_2O_3), has a deep red color. Oxides of other metallic elements, such as copper and manganese, also contribute to the colors of sediments. The former often displays a blue-green color or an iridescent tarnish, the latter acts as a pink or deep black pigment.

Most of the shades of gray and black so common in sedimentary rocks, especially in shales, are due to the admixture of various amounts of carbon derived from the organic matter in the sediment. In coal the carbon is, of course, highly concentrated.

Ripple Marks. It is not uncommon to find the top surface of a sedimentary stratum marked by parallel ridges and furrows which resemble the ripples on the surface of a pool of water. These ripple marks, most common in sandstones, are formed in sediments deposited where waves and currents drag the bottom. The wind blowing over the surface of sand dunes also makes ripples.

FIG. 20-2. Ripple marks on sandstone, Shoshone Reservation, Wyo. *(Photo by Darton, U. S. Geological Survey)*

FIG. 20-3. Mud cracks in river silt drying and
shrinking after a flood, Licking Creek, Ky.
(Photo by Mansfield, U. S. Geological Survey)

FIG. 20-4. Large concretions in sandstone, Los Angeles, Calif. *(Photo by Arnold, U. S.
Geological Survey)*

Mud Cracks. The surface of fine sediment that has been exposed to the drying action of sun and air after the subsidence of a flood or the drying up of a pond often exhibits shrinkage cracks that break up the caked surface of the mud into polygonal blocks. Perhaps the most favorable places for the development of this phenomenon are the flat floors of arid interior basins. After a heavy downpour of rain such flats are covered by shallow lakes in which sediment washed down from the surrounding uplands is deposited. During the long periods between the infrequent rains the water evaporates and the mud and silt of the lake floor shrink, crack, and harden on losing moisture to the air. Before the next rain the wind may fill the cracks with sand and thus preserve them as casts. This process may be repeated many times and a thick succession of strata, each with its top surface marked by sand-filled mud cracks, may be laid down.

Concretions. Certain inclusions in sedimentary rocks that are formed during or after the deposition of the sediment are known as concretions. Ordinarily they differ in composition from the main body of the rock and are formed from one or more of the minor constituents. In moving through a sedimentary bed the ground water may dissolve a minor constituent out of a large area of rock and redeposit the accumulated material in concentrated form around certain nuclei. Flint and chert concretions are usually found in chalk and other limestone; calcite, limonite, and pyrite as well as other concretions of different compositions occur in sandstones and shales.

The inclusions range in size from a fraction of an inch to several feet in diameter. Their shapes, too, are variable; some are spherical, others flat, elongate, irregular, compound, or fantastic. Some concretions are formed by the precipitation of material around fossils as nuclei. In such cases the form of the concretion is influenced by the shape of the enclosed fossil. Other concretions enclose inorganic nuclei such as grains of sand; in still others no definite nucleus is apparent.

Although concretions generally comprise only a minor constituent of a rock bed, some sedimentary rocks are composed almost exclusively of them. This, for example, is true of oolitic limestone and oolitic hematite.

Fossils. Sedimentary rocks are often called the fossiliferous, or fossil-bearing rocks, because they frequently preserve the remains of plants and animals that were buried by the deposition of the sediment. Igneous rocks, except volcanic ash, contain no fossils. The material of which they are made came from the interior of the earth where there is no life, and the lava poured out on the surface is so hot that any organisms it may cover are destroyed. But volcanic ash, considered by some as a sedimentary rock, may cool to such a degree before falling that it will preserve rather than destroy the remains of organisms. Many of the metamorphic rocks derived from sedimentary rocks originally contained fossils, but these were destroyed by the processes of metamorphism. Thus we see that fossils are practically limited to the sedimentary rocks.

RELATIVE AGES OF SEDIMENTARY STRATA

In any undisturbed series of sedimentary strata the beds succeed each other in the order of their ages, the oldest at the bottom and the youngest at the top. It could not be otherwise, for sediments can be deposited only on the top surface of something that antedates the time of their deposition. This fact is called the *principle of superposition* and is of great importance in deciphering the history of the earth.

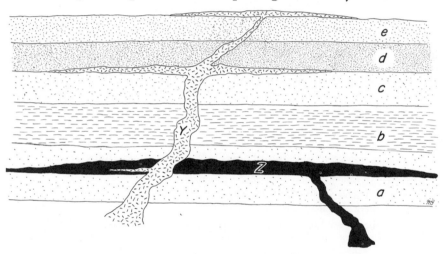

FIG. 20-5. Relative ages of sedimentary and igneous rocks. The sedimentary strata, a, b, c, d, and e, are successively younger from a to e. Igneous intrusion Z is younger than a and possibly younger than the other sedimentary beds as well. Intrusion Y, which cuts through all the others and spreads out on the surface as an extrusion, is youngest of all.

Extrusive igneous rocks, or surface flows, also conform to this principle of superposition, but the law does not hold for the intrusive igneous forms. For example, a sill which is intruded between two strata is younger than the overlying as well as the underlying bed.

CLASSIFICATION OF SEDIMENTARY ROCKS

Because of the various and often complex modes of origin of the sedimentary rocks, no simple scheme of classification yet devised is perfect. A division into three groups—mechanical, chemical, and organic —is probably most satisfactory. It should be kept in mind, however, that some rocks are the result of more than one process. For example, a sandstone, listed as a mechanical sediment, owes its induration to the chemical precipitation of cement between the grains. In the table below, those rocks included in the mechanical group consist mainly of sediment that was transported and deposited by mechanical means; in the chemical group are the chemicals precipitated from solution apparently without the aid of organisms; and the organic group includes those rocks that consist mainly of the preserved parts or structures of plants and animals.

Table of Common Sedimentary Rocks

Mechanical	Chemical	Organic
Conglomerate	Limestone (some)	Limestone (most)
Sandstone	Travertine and tufa	Coquina
Siltstone	Oolitic limestone	Reef limestone
Shale (Mudstone)	Gypsum	Chalk
Limestone (some)	Rock Salt	Peat
	Chert, Flint, Geyserite	Coal
	Iron ore (some)*	

* Some iron ores are of igneous origin.

DESCRIPTIONS OF THE COMMON SEDIMENTARY ROCKS

Conglomerate. Conglomerate consists of gravel mixed with sand and bound together by cement. In most cases the pebbles are made of quartz, but they may consist of the worn fragments of other minerals and rocks. In the typical conglomerate the pebbles are well rounded, an indication that they have traveled far or that they have been shifted back and forth for a long time. A special variety of conglomerate, known as *breccia*, contains angular pebbles.

Sandstone. As the name implies, sandstone consists of cemented sand grains. Most sands are quartz fragments, but magnetite, olivine, garnet, calcite, gypsum and other sands also occur. The color of a sandstone depends not only on the composition of the sand grains, but also on the kind of cement. In the white and light-colored rocks the cement is usually either silica or calcium carbonate, but in the red, brown, and yellow varieties it is iron oxide. In the case of sandstones in which more or less clay is mixed with the sand, color depends mainly on that of the admixed clay. *Arkose* is a special variety of sandstone, or conglomerate,

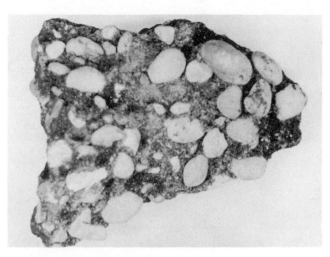

FIG. 20-6. Conglomerate, or pudding stone, consisting of rounded pebbles in a finer matrix. *(Photo by the author)*

FIG. 20-7. Closely folded thin-bedded crystalline limestone and shale of the McKenzie formation. *(American Museum of Natural History)*

FIG. 20-8. Coquina, a mass of cemented shell fragments. *(Harvard University Dept. of Geology)*

FIG. 20-9. Oolitic limestone consists of small concretions resembling fish roe. *(American Museum of Natural History)*

which contains feldspar fragments, and perhaps mica flakes, in addition
to quartz.

Shale (Mudstone). Shale is hardened mud, the finest mechanical or
clastic sediment. The material of which it is made is mostly clay (kaolin), usually mixed with extremely fine sand (silt), organic matter, iron
oxide, or other impurities. Inasmuch as clay is cohesive and becomes
hard merely on drying, no cement is necessary. Most shales are thinly
bedded and will split easily along the bedding planes. Red, brown, and
yellow shales owe their color to iron oxides, while those of black color
contain organic matter. Some black shales include so much oily matter
that they are the source rocks of petroleum; others grade into beds
of coal.

Siltstone. This rock is intermediate in texture between sandstone and
shale. It consists of fine sand with some clay. There are all gradations
between sandstone and shale, such as shaly sandstone and sandy shale.
Siltstone includes most of these gradations.

Limestone. A rock composed mainly of the mineral calcite (calcium
carbonate) is a limestone. There are many varieties. Most limestones
consist of materials that were once the skeletal parts of living organisms.
Many groups of plants and animals living in the sea—molluscs, corals,
and foraminifera—extract calcium carbonate from the water and use it
to build their shells or other hard structures. In addition to limestones
of organic origin there are some which are direct chemical precipitates
and others that are at least partly of mechanical origin.

Coquina. This term is applied to a limestone composed of coarse
shells and shell fragments. Such deposits are now accumulating in places
off the coast of Florida and older coquinas are known from various
parts of the world.

Reef Limestone. Coral reefs are now common in the shallow waters
of tropical and subtropical seas, the largest reef known being the Great
Barrier Reef of Australia. Not only corals but lime-secreting algae and
other organisms contribute to the building of reefs. The pores and other
open spaces in the network of skeletons become filled with limy sediment and the reef becomes cemented into a compact rock mass. Ancient
reef limestones are found in Kentucky, Michigan, and in other places
now far distant from the sea.

Chalk. Chalk is a fine-grained, soft and porous variety of limestone
consisting of the microscopic shells of foraminifera, the pulverized
fragments of other shells, and other calcareous matter cemented together with a calcareous cement. The color is usually white, as it is in
the chalk of the white cliffs of Dover in England, but it may be stained
yellowish or gray by impurities. Concretions of flint are frequently associated with chalk.

Travertine and Tufa. Travertine is a crystalline, usually banded, variety of limestone formed by the precipitation of calcium carbonate from solution. This precipitation commonly takes place in caves and around springs, especially near hot springs. Travertine which takes a good polish and in which the banded structure is accentuated by varied tinting from metallic oxides is called "Mexican onyx." Large deposits of travertine are found in Yellowstone Park, in southern California, and near Tivoli in Italy.

Calcium carbonate precipitated in a porous, loose, or moss-like form is called calcareous tufa. Deposits of this kind are found around some springs and shrinking lakes.

Oolitic Limestone. Some limestones are composed of small concretions resembling fish roe. In the center of each rounded concretion there is ordinarily a tiny sand grain. It is believed that the concretions were formed around sand grains in bodies of water which held calcium carbonate in solution and sand grains in suspension, each sand grain serving as a nucleus around which the lime was precipitated until the grain grew large enough to sink to the bottom. On the bottom the particles were cemented together by more calcium carbonate precipitated between the grains. Extensive beds of oolitic limestone are found in England. The famous Indiana limestone, widely used as a building stone in this country, consists largely of oolites.

Compact Limestone. Extensive beds of extremely fine-grained, compact limestone are found on all continents. Because of its many variations in color, in its content of impurities, and in other properties it is designated by various specific names. Although the color is most commonly gray, it occurs in a great many tints and shades of that color. *Dolomitic limestone* contains a considerable amount of magnesium carbonate in addition to the calcium carbonate; *hydraulic limestone,* or *cement rock,* is mixed with clay; *cherty limestone* contains nodules or beds of chert. Exceptionally fine-grained limestone suitable for making printing blocks is called *lithographic limestone.*

Authorities do not all agree on the method of origin of compact limestones. Probably chemical precipitation plays the dominant role; however, some of the material no doubt consists of mechanically deposited lime mud. And perhaps much of the original calcium carbonate is derived from organic remains, whether by mechanical abrasion or by solution.

Sedimentary Rocks of Lesser Abundance. Sandstones, shales, and limestones constitute the great bulk of the sedimentary rocks. Those briefly described below are much less abundant, but are of interest because of their economic value as well as their historical importance.

The rock *gypsum,* consisting of the mineral of the same name, is precipitated in lakes and in arms of the sea after the water has become saturated by long evaporation in an arid climate. Some caves also contain deposits of gypsum. *Rock salt* consists of the mineral halite. Like gypsum, it is precipitated after long evaporation of sea and lake water. The occurrence of beds of salt and gypsum in such humid regions as New York, Ohio, and Michigan is evidence that the climate of those regions has changed since the beds were deposited.

Chert and *flint* are crypto-crystalline varieties of silicon dioxide (silica). Chert and flint are precipitated by the ground water either as irregular nodules or as beds replacing other soluble rock, such as limestone. *Geyserite* is a variety of opal, precipitated as a more or less porous deposit around some hot springs and geysers.

Limonite and *hematite* sometimes occur, either separately or mixed together, in sufficient abundance to be called rocks and in a form concentrated enough to make them valuable iron ores. These rocks may be readily identified by properties listed in their descriptions as minerals. Limonite and most hematite ore precipitates from water either underground or on the surface in swamps, lakes and seas. Some hema-

FIG. 20-10. Joints in limestone. Sedimentary rocks are generally traversed by two main sets of joints which, together with the bedding planes, divide the rock into prismatic blocks. **Deans Mills, N. Y.** *(New York State Museum).*

tite occurs in the form of oolites identical in structure with those of oolitic limestone.

Coal is a familiar and widely used commodity. It is formed by the accumulation and partial decay of swamp plants and is preserved by a covering of other sediments. *Peat, lignite, bituminous coal* and *anthracite* represent successive stages in the formation of coal, from the original cellulose making up the plant to the almost pure carbon from which most of the volatile constituents have been driven off.

Suggestions for Further Reading

FENTON, Carroll Lane, and FENTON, Mildred Adams, *The Rock Book* (New York, Doubleday, 1940).

GEORGE, Russell D., *Minerals and Rocks* (New York, D. Appleton-Century Company, Inc., 1943).

KEMP, James Furman, *Handbook of Rocks*, 6th edition revised by GROUT, Frank F. (Princeton, N. J., Van Nostrand, 1940).

LOOMIS, Frederick Brewster, *Field Book of Common Rocks and Minerals* (New York, Putnam, 1948).

PIRSSON, Louis V., *Rocks and Minerals*, 3rd edition revised by KNOPF, Adolph (New York, Wiley, 1953).

POUGH, Frederick H., *A Field Guide to Rocks and Minerals* (Boston, Houghton Mifflin, 1953).

SPOCK, Leslie E., *Guide to the Study of Rocks* (New York, Harper, 1953).

— 21 —

Metamorphism
and Metamorphic Rocks

METAMORPHISM

Both igneous and sedimentary rocks are subject to changes under two distinct sets of conditions. Those that are exposed at the surface are broken down by the processes of weathering and erosion. Others are deeply buried or may be otherwise subjected to high temperature and great pressure. Under the latter conditions they undergo the changes which are included in the term *metamorphism,* and the originally igneous or sedimentary rocks affected by these changes become metamorphic rocks.

Agents or Forces of Metamorphism. *High temperature, great pressure, movement* of the lithosphere and the circulation of *hot liquids and gases* are the chief causes of metamorphic changes. These agents may act separately, but in most cases two or more of them act together.

The heat which causes metamorphism may come from hot igneous masses, or it may be the normal heat which prevails at depth, or it may be caused by the friction of movement of solid rock masses. Hot liquids and gases, carrying materials which form new minerals, emanate from igneous intrusions and penetrate the surrounding rocks. The composition of the rock is thus changed by the addition of magmatic material. Changes brought about in pre-existing rocks by the heat and the liquids and gases from nearby hot igneous masses are included in the term *contact metamorphism.*

Pressure is of two kinds. *Static* or balanced pressure is due solely to the weight of the overlying load of rock or sediment and increases with depth. *Dynamic* or unbalanced pressure causes and accompanies the various movements of the lithosphere. As a result of unbalanced pressure the rocks are subjected to enormous stress. The strata are folded, crumpled and crushed, stretched in some places and mashed together in others. Minerals are sheared and flattened; old compounds are broken down and combined into new minerals.

Not only the emanations from magmatic sources, but hot solutions formed locally by the high temperature of deep burial and the friction of movement are also important factors in recrystallization and in other alterations of rocks.

Kinds of Changes. By the processes of metamorphism rocks are changed in *texture*, in *fabric*, in *structure*, and in *composition*. In some cases only one of these changes is apparent; for example, slate is made from shale by the development of slaty cleavage—a structural change. In other cases two types of change are prominent, such as the change in both texture and structure in the formation of marble from limestone. In many rocks, however, several kinds of change are evident; thus a garnetiferous mica schist differs in texture, in fabric, in structure, and in composition from the original shale from which it was formed.

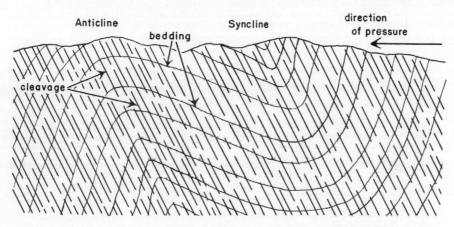

FIG. 21-1. Relation of slaty cleavage planes to bedding planes.

Relative Effects on Igneous and Sedimentary Rocks. As a rule, the igneous rocks are less susceptible to metamorphic changes than are the sedimentary rocks. One reason for this is that the igneous rocks were originally formed at high temperatures and often also under great pressure. They are therefore not easily affected by these metamorphic forces. In addition, the igneous rocks, especially the intrusive ones, often occur in large masses of great thickness and are not easily deformed by pressure and movement. Furthermore, the massive igneous rocks do not possess the bedding planes, so characteristic of sedimentary beds, along which solutions might easily travel.

FIG. 21-2. Banded metamorphic rock, Mitchell County, N. C. *(Photo by Keith, U. S. Geological Survey)*

FIG. 21-3. Crumpled, schistose metamorphic rock, Yukon Region, Alaska. *(Photo by Schrader, U. S. Geological Survey)*

FIG. 21-4. Slaty cleavage cutting across folded beds, Slatington, Pa.
(Photo by Hardin, U. S. Geological Survey)

FIG. 21-5. Intricately folded metamorphic rock, near Philadelphia.
(Photo by Hardin, U. S. Geological Survey)

METAMORPHIC ROCKS

Fabrics and Structures. The most striking and characteristic structural fabric of the metamorphic rocks is *foliation*. As the name implies, foliated rocks are made up of leaf-like layers, and their constituent minerals are flattened and oriented parallel with the folia. There are three kinds of foliation. In some rocks the folia are of different colors, that is, light and dark minerals are segregated in alternating layers which give the rock a *banded* pattern. This is the fabric of gneiss. The name *schistose* is applied to those foliated rocks which consist mainly of one mineral, especially if that mineral is one of flat habit, such as mica. Since there is only one principal mineral, color banding is not apparent. Such a rock is called a *schist*. Fine-grained foliated rocks, such as slate, which can be split into smooth, thin, flat sheets are said to have *slaty cleavage*. The cleavage planes in slate do not represent the original bedding planes of the shale from which slate is formed. The cleavage is a metamorphic structure produced by compression and usually cuts across the original bedding planes, often obliterating them.

In addition to the development of banding, or schistosity, or slaty cleavage, the foliated rocks are often closely folded, mashed, injected by igneous material, and crumpled into intricate and complex patterns. Movement while the rocks were under high temperature and high pressure is necessary to produce these structures.

Not all metamorphic rocks have a foliated fabric. Some are massive like the igneous rocks, but can be distinguished from them on the basis of composition. Serpentine, for example, may be massive; nevertheless, its composition is proof that it has been metamorphosed.

Minerals of Metamorphic Rocks. Some of the minerals common in igneous and sedimentary rocks are widespread also in metamorphic rocks. Calcite and dolomite occur in the sedimentary limestones and also in the metamorphic marbles. Feldspar, mica, hornblende, and pyroxene are common to both the igneous and the metamorphic rocks, and quartz is widespread in all three groups.

Other common minerals are either limited entirely to the metamorphic rocks or else occur so sparingly in other rocks that they are termed metamorphic minerals. Among these are graphite, garnet, serpentine, and talc. In addition to the common minerals, many kinds of the rarer species are found in metamorphic rocks.

Grades of Metamorphism. Some of the minerals in metamorphic rocks together with the structures are indicators of the grade, or intensity, of metamorphism. In the case of a shale (argillaceous rock) subjected to dynamic pressure, the rock is folded and the flat scales of clay minerals are oriented in the direction parallel to the axial planes of the folds. This orientation produces the slaty cleavage structure of a *slate*.

In this process some of the original shale material may recrystallize in the form of microscopic mica and chlorite, and these scaly minerals will be arranged in the same parallel planes.

With continued, and perhaps increased, pressure and temperature the continued growth of the flat crystals changes the slate to a rock that is coarse enough to be called a *phyllite*. At this stage the cleavage (foliation) is not so smoothe as it is in the slate stage, being somewhat crenulated. The cleavage surfaces have a silky sheen, due to the tiny flakes of mica.

With time and increasing intensity of the metamorphic conditions the mica flakes grow larger and other minerals develop. When the mica flakes have grown large enough to be distinguished individually, the rock is called a *schist*. Quartz, garnet, and other grains may be present. In a still higher grade of metamorphism, at a higher temperature, staurolite and kyanite crystals are formed.

Table of Metamorphic Rocks

Name	Fabric	Composition	Derived from
Slate	Slaty cleavage	Minerals not distinguishable	Shale
Phyllite	Slaty cleavage or schistose	Fine-grained light mica	Shale and fine-grained igneous rocks
Schist	Schistose	One principal mineral Varieties of schist are named according to the principal mineral	Shale and fine-grained igneous rocks
Gneiss	Banded	Like the coarse igneous rocks	Coarse-grained sedimentary and igneous rocks
Quartzite ..	Massive	Quartz	Sandstone
Marble	Massive	Calcite or dolomite	Limestone
Serpentine ..	Massive	Serpentine	Basic igneous rocks
Soapstone ..	Massive	Talc	Basic igneous rocks

DESCRIPTIONS OF METAMORPHIC ROCKS

Slate. Slate closely resembles shale, from which it is derived by low-grade metamorphism. Like shale, slate is so fine in texture that the

FIG. 21-6. Complex metamorphic rock which was injected by dark bands of igneous intrusions. The intrusions have been fractured and faulted, and the fractures are filled with white quartz veins. *(U. S. Geological Survey)*

mineral grains are not distinguishable with the naked eye. Technically, an important difference between shale and slate is that the latter has slaty cleavage produced by dynamic metamorphism. In the field this slaty cleavage usually can be readily distinguished from the bedding plane parting of shale. In laboratory hand-specimens this distinction is not so obvious, but the slate can be identified by its higher luster, greater degree of compactness and the smoother appearance of the cleavage surface as compared to the bedding plane surface.

The most common colors of slate are gray, black, and red. The gray and black colors are due to the metamorphism into graphite of the carbonaceous material in the original rock. Various shades of red result from the presence of metallic oxides.

Slate is used commercially for roofing, blackboards, and other purposes. Large quarries are located in northeastern New York, western Vermont, and eastern Pennsylvania.

Phyllite. Phyllite is intermediate between and grades into slate and schist, being coarser than the former and finer than the latter. It has a silky, glimmering luster which is due to the presence of small flakes of lustrous mica. Phyllite represents a degree of metamorphism less intense than is necessary to form schist. Probably most phyllite is formed from shale, but some is the result of the metamorphism of lava.

Schist. Schist is a foliated metamorphic rock consisting mainly of one mineral. The folia are irregular in thickness and are usually bent and crumpled. Varieties are named according to the predominant mineral. Mica schist is the most common but hornblende schist, chlorite schist, talc schist, graphite schist, and others also occur. The mineral grains are larger than those in phyllite and usually can be identified with the unaided eye. Schist represents an advanced stage of metamorphism of shale or, sometimes, of fine-grained igneous rocks.

Gneiss. Gneiss is a coarse-grained, banded metamorphic rock in which the bands are commonly folded and contorted in a complex manner and are of unlike mineral composition. A typical gneiss consists of the same feldspar, quartz, and mica that make up a granite, but, unlike granite, gneiss has the dark mica segregated in distinct layers which alternate with the light-colored layers of feldspar and quartz. Some gneisses are the product of the metamorphism of sediments, such as impure sandstone; others result from the alteration of feldspathic igneous rocks. In one interesting variety of gneiss, known as injection gneiss, the banding is caused by the injection (intrusion) of thin sills of igneous matter between the folia of a schist.

Quartzite. Quartzite is a metamorphosed sandstone. When metamorphism is complete the silica cement and the sand grains of the original sandstone are crystallized together into a completely crystalline, homogeneous mass of quartz. There are, of course, various degrees of metamorphism and consequently all gradations from simple sandstone to completely recrystallized quartzite. White when pure, the latter, like sandstone, may be stained red, yellow, or other colors by the presence of impurities.

Marble. Marble is a crystalline calcareous rock which is the metamorphosed equivalent of limestone. The principal mineral is either calcite or dolomite, and the texture ranges from fine to coarse. As a rule the bedding planes and other sedimentary structures are destroyed during metamorphism and the resulting rock is massive in character.

Pure marble is white, but impurities may give it a great variety of colors. Carbonaceous material altered to graphite gives gray and black colors; red, brown and yellow tones are caused by oxides of iron; green shades may be due to chlorite or serpentine. In some cases the impurities are uniformly distributed through the rock; in others they occur as spots, streaks, or bands.

Because of its many pleasing colors and the relative ease with which it can be cut and shaped, marble is in great demand for building, monumental, and ornamental purposes. In this country the principal producing area lies in a belt extending from Vermont southwestward to Alabama; there are especially large quarries in western Vermont, eastern Tennessee, and northwestern Georgia. In Europe well-known types of marble are produced in Belgium, France, Greece, and Italy. The fine-grained, white statuary marble of the Carrara district in Italy, for example, is famous throughout the world.

Serpentine. Serpentine rock consists mainly of the mineral serpentine, usually mixed with some accessory minerals such as pyroxene, olivine, magnetite, calcite, and dolomite. The rock is green in color, soft and greasy to the feel and usually massive in structure. Serpentine is believed to be the product of hydrothermal metamorphism, that is, it is the result of hot solutions hydrating the magnesium silicates of deeply buried masses of basic igneous rocks and changing them to serpentine. The pleasing appearance of its various shades of green and the ease with which this stone can be cut make serpentine highly desirable for interior decoration and ornaments. A variety containing streaks or spots of calcite or dolomite is known as *verde antique.*

Soapstone. This rock, also known as *steatite,* is composed essentially of the mineral talc, although chlorite, mica, pyrite, dolomite, and other minerals generally occur as accessories. The rock is commonly white, bluish gray, pale green, or dark in color; it has a greasy feel and is soft enough to be easily cut with a knife. Like serpentine, soapstone is a product of hydrothermal metamorphism. It is widely used for table tops, sinks, tanks, ornaments, and other purposes. Soapstone occurs at a number of localities in the belt of metamorphic rocks which extends from Vermont to Alabama, one of the largest quarries being at Schuyler, Virginia.

THE ROCK CYCLE

In the preceding discussions we have seen that rocks change as their environment changes. Each rock type is the result of the elements of the environment acting on the materials at hand. When igneous rocks are exposed at the surface, they are attacked by the processes of weathering and broken down into the materials which form the sedimentary rocks. On deep burial the sediments are changed by the processes of metamorphism into complex metamorphic rocks. If these metamorphic rocks are subjected to sufficiently high temperature, they melt and become magma. On cooling, the magma forms igneous rock. Thus the cycle from igneous rock to sedimentary rock to metamorphic rock and back to igneous rock again is completed, a sequence of events which has perhaps taken place many times in the past.

Suggestions for Further Reading

FENTON, Carroll Lane, and FENTON, Mildred Adams, *The Rock Book* (New York, Doubleday, 1940).

GEORGE, Russell D., *Minerals and Rocks* (New York, D. Appleton-Century Company, 1943).

KEMP, James Furman, *Handbook of Rocks*, 6th edition revised by GROUT, Frank F. (Princeton, N. J., Van Nostrand, 1940).

LOOMIS, Frederick Brewster, *Field Book of Common Rocks and Minerals* (New York, Putnam, 1948).

PIRSSON, Louis V., *Rocks and Minerals*, 3rd edition revised by KNOPF, Adolph (New York, Wiley, 1953).

POUGH, Frederick H., *A Field Guide to Rocks and Minerals* (Boston, Houghton Mifflin, 1953).

SPOCK, Leslie E., *Guide to the Study of Rocks* (New York, Harper, 1953).

— 22 —

Movements and Structures of the Lithosphere

LET US NOW go into the field and observe the larger structural characteristics of rocks and their relations to each other, and at the same time infer some of the types of movement that produce these structures.

MOVEMENTS OF THE LITHOSPHERE

Vertical Movements: Uplift and Subsidence. That the lands have changed their positions relative to sea level and also that different parts of the lands have changed their relative elevations is proved by abundant evidence. Some of these changes in level are of recent occurrence, while others took place long ago. For example, the flat Atlantic and Gulf Coastal Plain, from New York City southward, was covered by the sea not long ago, that is, within the last 30 million years. Uplift of a few hundred feet has exposed a broad stretch of the sea bottom covered with marine sediments containing the fossils of marine organisms. Portions of the Pacific Coast also show evidences of recent uplift, but because of the mountainous nature of the shoreline, these uplifts are recorded as wave-cut cliffs and benches that are now well above sea level. Underneath the Mississippi Valley and the Appalachian Plateau, too, are rocks that were deposited millions of years ago on the bottom of the sea. And in the Rocky Mountains and in the Alps marine sediments are found at elevations of more than 10,000 feet above sea level.

At the present time Scandinavia seems to be rising at the rate of one to three feet a century. At this rate the amount of uplift would be about 20,000 feet in a million years. Of course, erosion is always active on newly exposed surfaces, so that the net elevation is always less than the total amount of the upward movement. Furthermore, we cannot predict how long the uplift will continue.

Evidences of subsidence are not easily examined because they are covered by the sea. A number of localities, however, show unmistakable signs that subsidence has taken place. The rugged New England Coast with its islands, shoals, and drowned rivers is the product of the sinking of the land. Subsidence, too, has isolated the British Isles from continental Europe, and geologically-recent flooding of former lowlands has produced the North and the Baltic seas.

In a number of places, changes in level within historic times have been recorded. On the island of Capri off the coast of Italy a cool sea cave known as the Blue Grotto was used as a retreat by the ancient Romans. An opening which they cut in the roof in order to admit more light is now partly submerged. At Jamestown, Virginia the remains of the foundation of the fort built by the settlers in the early seventeenth century are now covered by a few feet of water. Columns of the temple of Jupiter Serapis at Pozzuoli, Italy, erected by the early Romans, show that after the temple was built the land subsided about twenty feet and then rose again.

Horizontal Movements: Compression and Tension. In addition to the vertical movements of the lithosphere there are primarily lateral movements of the earth's crust which involve compression and tension. In fact, it is probable that all earth movements have their tensional and compressional components. The principal evidences of this stretching and crushing are found in the structure of the rocks, especially in folds and faults.

Causes of Earth Movements. We may here add a few remarks to the general discussion of earth movements in their relation to gradation, to volcanism, and to isostasy, given in Chapter 4. It is generally believed that the interior of the earth is shrinking. This shrinkage may be due to the loss of heat or to the reorganization of molecules under great pressure or to both of these causes. As the inner portion of the earth becomes smaller the outer portion must shorten its circumference to fit the shrunken interior. Shortening of the circumference is accomplished by wrinkling or folding of the more pliable rocks and breaking or faulting of the brittle ones.

In conformity with this general line of reasoning, the continental and the oceanic segments of the earth may be said to act as great wedges. Both probably move downward toward the center of the earth. Being larger and composed of heavier material, the oceanic wedges move downward more and crowd the continental wedges between them. Large-scale buckling and fracturing of the continental margins thus takes

FIG. 22-1. Emerged strand lines on Mount Pelly, Victoria Island, Arctic Ocean. *(Geological Survey of Canada)*

place. The great oceanic and continental segments in turn consist of lesser segments, or wedges, which behave in a manner similar to the larger ones and thus cause lesser deformations within the continental and oceanic masses.

Some geologists question the shrinkage theory and ascribe crustal movements to convection currents beneath the crust. Related to this idea is the belief, strongly held by some, that the land masses are slowly drifting on a plastic substratum and that their forward margins become buckled by drag. Thus, the explanation of this important geological process is still unsettled.

INTERNAL STRUCTURES (FABRICS) OF ROCKS

All rocks have certain internal structures that reflect the conditions under which they were formed. Sedimentary rocks are commonly referred to as stratified, or bedded rocks, because they are arranged in layers, one above the other, varying in thickness from a fraction of an inch to many feet. Many igneous rocks, on the other hand, are more or less massive. This is true especially of the large intrusive masses.

340

FIG. 22-2. Ancient marine sedimentary strata elevated above the timber line in Glacier National Park. *(National Park Service)*

Some igneous rocks have a lineation or foliation which indicates movement in the molten mass as it solidified. The stratification of the sediments and the massiveness and lineation of the igneous rocks are primary structures.

Many of the metamorphic rocks have a foliated structure which resembles bedding in that it consists of layers. In these foliated rocks, however, the layers do not represent the original stratification, but are the product of the reorganization of the original rock in the processes of metamorphism. Such structure is secondary, inasmuch as it has been induced in a pre-existing rock.

In addition to internal structures (often called fabrics), rocks possess regional, or field, structures. Thus, for example, a massive rock may be faulted; a stratified rock may be titled, or folded, and perhaps faulted; and a foliated rock may possess one or more of these larger structures, formed by crustal movement.

REGIONAL STRUCTURES OF THE LITHOSPHERE

Measurement of Structure: Strike and Dip. These two terms are of the utmost importance in the measurement and description of rock structures. They are applied to the attitudes of beds of stratified rocks, to the foliation of metamorphic rocks, to the flow lines of igneous rocks and to fault planes and joints in all rocks. A convenient instrument for determining strike and dip is the Brunton pocket transit, which consists of a compass for measuring horizontal directions and a clinometer for reading vertical angles.

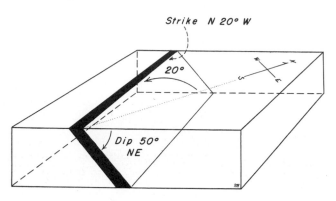

FIG. 22-3. Diagram illustrating dip and strike.

The term *strike* is used to designate the direction of the intersection of a plane, be it a stratum or fault plane, a joint or other surface, with the horizontal. The direction of this intersection is measured with a compass and usually expressed as a bearing, that is, in degrees, from north, as N. 30°E., or N. 40°W. *Dip* designates the angle at which a stratum or fault plane is inclined from the horizontal. It is measured at right angles to the strike. The student may gain facility in measuring strike and dip by practicing with a Brunton transit on various surfaces in the room. In making measurements in the field the beginning student will of course need the help of a more experienced person in identifying the structures.

Horizontal and Gently Tilted Strata. Movements which bring portions of the ocean floor above sea level expose the strata deposited there to examination, and the attitude of beds and other structures can then be measured. In some regions the rock layers are nearly horizontal over large areas, indicating that the movement has taken the form of a vertical or gently warping uplift. In perfectly horizontal beds the strike is in all directions and the dip is zero. But perfect horizontality does not exist over large areas; even in the regions of least disturbed rocks there are broad, gently dipping swells and sags.

In the Atlantic Coastal Plain the nearly horizontal rock strata dip

FIG. 22-4. Horizontal marine strata in the Del Carmin "Mountains," south of the border in the Big Bend National Park area. *(National Park Service)*

but a few degrees toward the sea. In such a region, where the rocks are nearly flat-lying and the surface of the ground, too, is nearly level, a single stratum makes the surface rock over a large area. Only in valleys where streams have cut through the top layer are the underlying beds exposed. In the Appalachian Plateau, the rock strata are also nearly horizontal. Here the streams have cut deep valleys and the eroded edges of many beds crop out in horizontal bands in the steep valley walls.

Dome and Basin Structures. In some places the rock strata dip away in all directions from a more or less circular center. Some of these domes contain cores of intrusive igneous rocks; others have been pushed up by salt plugs; in still others no intrusion is evident, but there may be a deep-seated one. The Henry Mountains of southern Utah are a group of domes in which laccoliths have arched up the overlying strata. A number of small domes, a mile or so in diameter, with salt cores are found in the Coastal Plain of Louisiana and Texas. In the Weald Dome of southeastern England no intrusion is visible.

In a basin, on the other hand, the dip of strata is toward the center from all sides rather than away from it in all directions. A large portion of the state of Michigan has a basin structure and the Paris Basin

343

FIG. 22-5. Symmetrical anticline, near Hancock, Md. *(Photo by Russell, U. S. Geological Survey)*

of France, with Paris at the center, is well known. Here the strata resemble a stack of saucers, each one smaller in surface area than the one next below, as a result of erosion.

Folded Structure. Consolidated rocks exposed at the surface are among the most rigid and unyielding objects that we know. Yet, although they were deposited in nearly horizontal layers, these rocks in many localities are buckled into a series of corrugations, or folds. Evidently the folding took place before the rocks were thoroughly consolidated, or else it occurred deep beneath the surface where they were in a plastic condition. In either case, the folding clearly resulted from lateral compression, for the horizontal distance between two points on a stratum is shortened. The initial cause for the compression may be gravitative stresses.

Folded strata are found in the Appalachian Mountains, in the Alps, the Himalayas, and in many other mountain regions. The circumference of the lithosphere has been shortened many miles by this folding. In fact, it has been calculated that if all of the folds in the Appalachian Mountains were flattened out, the distance across them would be increased by about forty miles. The foreshortening in the Alps and Himalayas is even greater, several score or hundreds of miles. Where

FIG. 22-6. Syncline, near Hancock, Md. *(Photo by Walcott, U. S. Geological Survey)*

the-folds are complex and combined with faulting they present many difficult problems to the field geologist.

Parts of a Fold. Folded strata consist of a series of alternating up-arches, or *anticlines*, and troughs, or *synclines*. In the anticline the form is convex upward and the strata dip away from the axis of the crest, while in the syncline the form is concave upward and the dip is toward the axis of the trough. Thus, in following a single stratum across a series of folds one finds that both the angle and direction of dip change each time an axis is crossed.

Kinds of Folds. Various terms are used to describe the many different varieties of folds. In a *symmetrical fold* the two limbs dip in opposite directions from the axis at the same angle. Apparently the compression, or resistance, from both sides was almost equal. In the *asymmetrical fold* the two limbs dip in opposite directions, but one is steeper than the other. Here there was evidently greater pressure, or less resistance, on one side. The *overturned fold* is one in which both limbs dip in the same direction, indicating overwhelming pressure from one side. Where such folds are so closely compressed that their limbs dip at the same angle they are called *isoclines*; they present structural problems by locally reversing the superposition of the beds.

Faults. Some rocks yield to stresses by bending or folding; others,

345

FIG. 22-7. Erosion of folded strata produces long ridges and valleys and the trellis drainage pattern. *(U. S. Air Force)*

where the pressure applied is too sudden or too great, or the resistance is high, are broken, and movement takes place by slipping along the fractures. Such a displacement of rock along a fracture is called a fault. Faults occur in all types of rocks, igneous, sedimentary, and metamorphic, but they are most easily recognized in sedimentary rocks where any displacement of the layers is readily detected.

Fault Terms. The plane of the fracture along which faulting has occurred is the *fault plane.* Fault planes occur in all positions from the vertical to the horizontal, nearly all of them being at some angle between these two extremes. The *strike* of a fault is measured in the same manner as the strike of a rock stratum; it is the horizontal direction of the fault plane. The inclination of the plane from the horizontal, measured at right angles to the strike, is the *dip.* The amount of movement along the fault plane is the *displacement.* Since most faults are inclined it is customary to speak of the rock above the fault plane as the *hanging wall* and that below as the *foot wall.* These are mining terms. In excavating a mineral vein along a fault the miner stands on the foot wall and the hanging wall is above his head.

Types of Faults. The most commonly used classification of faults is based on the direction of the relative movements along the fault plane. The *gravity fault,* sometimes called normal fault, is one in which the hanging wall has moved downward with respect to the foot wall. In the *thrust fault,* also called reverse fault, the hanging wall has moved up relative to the foot wall.

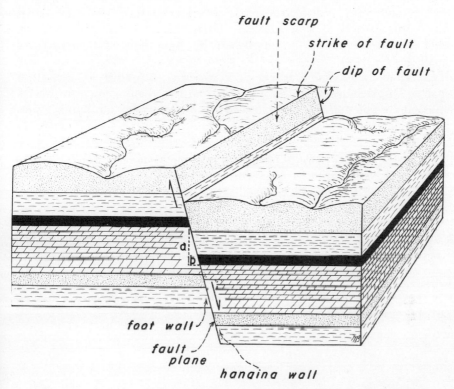

FIG. 22-8. **Normal fault.** Solid arrows show the direction of movement; a shows the vertical and b the horizontal displacement.

Low-angle thrust faults of great displacement are called *overthrusts.* If the movement of either wall was in a horizontal direction parallel to the plane of the fault, it is called a *strike slip fault.* The term *rift* is applied to these faults when they are of great length, such as the San Andreas Rift in California. A *tear fault* is a short fault, usually transverse between two long ones and crossing the main regional structure.

One finds in some regions that a relatively long and narrow block has dropped down between two faults. Such a down-dropped block is called a *graben.* The Rhine River, between the Vosges Mountains and the

Schwarzwald, Lake Tanganyika in Africa, and the Red and the Dead seas each occupies a graben. Blocks that have been raised between two faults are known as *horsts*. The faults bounding both grabens and horsts appear to be gravity faults.

Rate of Movements along Faults. Dislocations that have been observed along faults are from a fraction of an inch up to 30 or 40 feet at any one time. These sudden movements always produce earthquakes, but there are long intervals between them. On this basis it might be assumed that a fault with a displacement of several thousand feet was active for a long period of time, perhaps thousands of years, and that the total displacement was accomplished by hundreds or thousands of small, sudden slips.

Examples of Faults. Faulting is a widespread feature in the lithosphere. Displacements vary in amount from less than an inch to several miles and some faults can be traced along the strike for hundreds of miles. The Hurricane Fault, a gravity fault extending for 170 miles in

FIG. 22-9. A steeply-dipping normal fault in Chilhowee Mountain, Tenn. The left block has slid down with respect to the right, as shown by drag (the bending of the layers) and also by matching the layers on opposite sides of the fault. *(Photo by Keith, U. S. Geological Survey)*

Utah and Arizona, has a displacement of as much as 10,000 feet. Running along the east front of the Rocky Mountains in Montana, for a distance of probably 300 miles, is the Lewis overthrust in which rocks have been pushed 15 miles east of the original position. The San Andreas Rift in California is some 600 miles long, and displacement along the strike has probably amounted to 25 miles. Movement along this fault is still going on.

The Los Angeles water-supply aqueducts from the Sierra Nevada and

FIG. 22-10. Ebert Rim, near Valley Falls, Ore., a prominent, recent fault scarp. *(U. S. Forestry Service)*

from the Boulder Dam on the Colorado River cross a number of faults. Some of these are active at the present time, and extensive engineering precautions have been taken to guard against rupture of the water pipe lines and their supporting structures. The Catskill and Delaware aqueducts to New York City also cross some faults, but these faults are old and movement along them has apparently ceased.

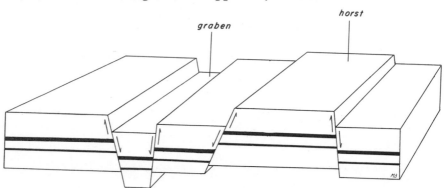

FIG. 22-11. Relationships of fault blocks in a graben and horst.

Joints. Joints are fractures which divide all rocks near the surface into angular blocks. In most cases they occur in two, or sometimes three sets, approximately at right angles to each other. In some lava flows, dikes, and sills, the joints, as indicated earlier, have a hexagonal pattern. The spacing of joints varies greatly, the distance between them being only a fraction of an inch in some places and many feet in others.

Origin of Joints. The origin of joint cracks in rocks has been the subject of much investigation, experimentation, and discussion. From this work there has emerged the general conclusion that some joints are *primary*, that is, are original features of the rock; others are *secondary*, that is, formed later. In the primary category may be cited the columnar jointing that is typical of dikes and sills. As igneous matter must contract when it cools and solidifies, the contraction is accommodated by shrinkage (tension) fractures. Sediments that were saturated with water should also shrink and crack when they are dried out, as witness the mud cracks on desert flats.

Secondary fractures are formed under the stresses of diastrophism. This group is most difficult to interpret in terms of the nature of the forces that cause them. Some of them are caused by tension (stretching); others are caused by the shearing action of torsion or a couple; still others by the shearing components of compression. Regardless of how they were formed, joints are a universal feature of all rocks.

Effects of Joints on Quarrying. Quarrying operations are greatly influenced by the joints in rocks. If these are too closely spaced, blocks

FIG. 22-12. Columnar joints in the Palisades sill, near Rockland
Lake, N. Y. *(Photo by the author)*

large enough for building purposes cannot be excavated. On the other
hand, the wide spacing of joints makes quarrying difficult and expensive.
The size limitations imposed on building stone by joints is illustrated
by the case of a New York architect who desired a piece of granite
sixty feet long for a monument. None of the quarries in New England
were able to supply a stone of this size.

Effects of Joints on Weathering and Erosion. Weathering and erosion
are also strongly guided by the orientation and spacing of joints. Where
joints are closely spaced the processes of weathering penetrate to great
depth. Streams carve out ravines and larger valleys where otherwise
resistant rock is weakened by numerous joints. In the Adirondack
Mountains and also in other regions of prominent joints, the stream valleys follow the joints in the same rectangular pattern. Many of the
angular mountains in Glacier National Park owe their shape to glacial
plucking of joint blocks, and in limestone regions many joints are
widened by solution into long valley sinks and tunnels.

Effects of Joints on Porosity. The porosity of a rock refers to the
amount of space available for the penetration of liquids and gases.
Joint cracks are important in this respect. In rocks that are otherwise
dense and relatively impervious, joints provide the main openings for
the circulation and accumulation of ground water. Also, commercial
quantities of oil and gas sometimes find lodgment in the cracks of
closely-jointed rocks.

351

FIG. 22-13. Unconformity in the Grand Canyon. The lower portion of the Canyon (the Inner Gorge) exposes ancient metamorphic rocks. The upper portion consists of flat-lying sedimentary beds.

Conformity and Unconformity. Beds of sediment deposited one upon another in unbroken succession are conformable. Each such bed has the same strike and dip as those above and below it. This uniformity indicates that the region remained relatively stable during the deposition of the series of strata.

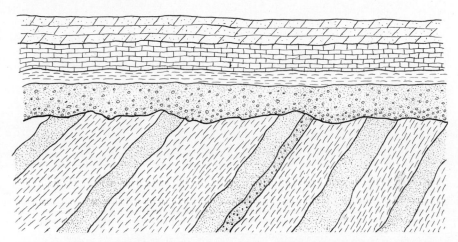

FIG. 22-14. **An unconformity.** The lower series of strata was tilted and eroded before deposition of the upper series. Other types of unconformity are illustrated in Chapter 26.

In contrast to the continuous succession of conformable strata, one often finds a series of beds with a certain attitude resting on another series with a different attitude. These two series are unconformable, and the surface separating them is an unconformity. In some cases the beds of the lower series are tilted at a steep angle or otherwise deformed, and the upper beds lie across their upturned and eroded edges. This condition shows that the lower series was tilted up and eroded before the upper series was deposited. The erosion interval constitutes a break in the sedimentary record. In other cases, the strata of the two series are parallel, but separated from each other by a surface that shows evidences of erosion. This would indicate an uplift sufficient to initiate erosion but no tilting, folding, or other deformation. Even though an unconformity indicates a break in the stratigraphic record, it is not without historical value, for it records, not sedimentation, but movements and erosion.

Suggestions for Further Reading

BILLINGS, Marland P., *Structural Geology* (Englewood Cliffs, N. J., Prentice-Hall, 1954).

DALY, R. A., *Strength and Structure of the Earth* (Englewood Cliffs, N. J., Prentice-Hall, 1950).

NEVIN, Charles Merrick, *Principles of Structural Geology*, 3rd edition (New York, Wiley, 1942).

WYLER, Rose and AMES, Gerald, *Restless Earth* (New York, Abelard-Schuman, 1954).

——— 23 ———

Earthquakes

E<small>ARTHQUAKES</small>, volcanic eruptions, violent storms and floods are the most terrifying and destructive of natural phenomena. Because they come without obvious warning and man's defense against them is often so ineffective, earthquakes, especially, arouse in him a realization of his own impotence in the face of the tremendous natural forces they represent. The scientific study of earth shocks enables him, however, to take measures which minimize their destructive effects and promises to lead to some degree of accuracy in predicting their occurrence. Great earthquakes that cause destruction to cities or towns occur on the average of from one to four times a year. Some 3,000 to 4,000 shocks perceptible to persons nearby occur each year. If we include all of the slight tremors, detected only by the most sensitive instruments, there are more than 100,000 annually. Indeed, our earth is a trembling one.

The study of earthquakes and related phenomena is known as the science of *seismology* (from *seismos*, the Greek word for earthquakes). One who is learned in the subject of earthquakes is a seismologist. *Seismic waves* are the vibrations which constitute an earthquake; they are detected and recorded by a *seismograph*; and the record of these waves is a *seismogram*.

CAUSES OF EARTHQUAKES

An earthquake is a trembling of the earth initiated by a sudden jar, or shock. The rocks vibrate in somewhat the same manner as a bar of steel or other rigid object will vibrate under the impact of a hammer blow.

Most of the shocks which cause the earth to tremble are associated with diastrophic movements. The sudden slipping of rocks along faults is doubtless the most important cause. In some cases the fault reaches the surface, and displacement of the ground, roads, and other objects

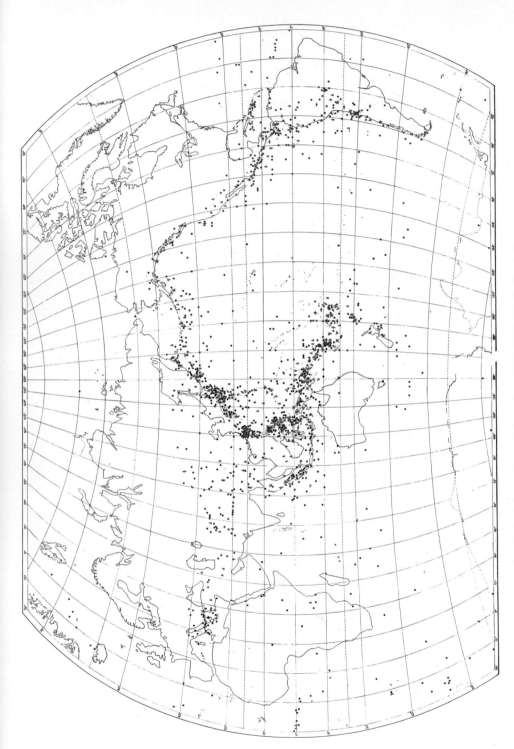

FIG. 23-1. Distribution of the major earthquakes, 1899-1923. Each black dot represents an epicenter with one or more occurrences during the 25-year period. (*American Museum of Natural History*)

can actually be observed. In other cases there are no surface indications of faulting, and one must infer either that the fault is deep seated or that the shock was due to some other cause.

In addition to faulting, which is probably the cause of all of the great earthquakes, volcanic explosions, the sudden injection of molten magma into fissures, the collapse of caverns, and landslides are among the lesser causes. Artificial earthquakes can even be set off by the explosion of gunpowder or dynamite in the ground.

DISTRIBUTION OF EARTHQUAKES

Like volcanoes, earthquakes occur most commonly in regions of unrest where mountain-making movements are taking place. These regions lie for the most part along those elevated margins of continents that are adjacent to great oceanic troughs. One such zone of crustal weakness borders the Pacific Ocean. Here are found the great earthquake regions of Chile, Peru, California, Alaska, Japan, and the Philippines. Another great belt extends from the Caribbean area eastward to the Himalaya Mountains and includes the Italian, Greek, Turkish, and Indian earthquake regions. About 90 per cent of the recorded shocks occur in the two belts named above.

On the other hand, the broad low interiors of continents are relatively free from earthquakes. Such regions are rarely affected by mountain-making movements and are considered stable. Only one series of violent shocks has been recorded for the interior of North America; they occurred in the vicinity of New Madrid, Missouri, in 1811-1812.

Submarine Earthquakes and Sea Waves. Earthquakes originate under the ocean as well as on the land. The movements associated with those quakes sometimes break submarine cables and communicate shocks to vessels on the surface. One of the most striking effects of the disturbance of the sea bottom is the displacement of ocean water above and the consequent formation of large sea waves, or *tsunami*. These waves have been known to reach a height of 90 feet and a length of 100 miles from crest to crest. They travel with great speed and for long distances. On reaching shore they sometimes wreak great damage. Much of the destruction of property and loss of life in the Lisbon earthquake of 1755 and the Japanese earthquake of 1923 was caused by tsunami.

NATURE OF EARTHQUAKES

Earthquake (Seismic) Waves. Waves are set in motion at the point of disturbance, called the *focus*, or center, and travel away through the rocks in all directions, decreasing in intensity with distance. Three types are recognized: primary, secondary, and long waves, designated as P,

S, and L respectively. The P-waves travel through the body of the earth at an average rate of about 5.5 miles per second; they are faster at depth than near the surface. The S-waves also go through the body of the earth, but at the slower rate of about 3 miles per second. They become absorbed when they reach depths below about 1,800 miles, an indication that the outer core of the earth may be fluid and hence unable to transmit this type of vibration. The L-waves follow the circumference of the earth and travel at a fairly constant rate of about 2.3 miles per second. Since these three types of waves travel at different rates, from a common source, it is obvious that the time intervals between their arrival at a given recording station will depend on the distance traveled. The P- and S-waves, which are of small amplitude and travel by a direct path through the earth, arrive first and constitute the first and second preliminary tremors, while the large amplitude L-waves that follow the circumference make the main shock.

Nature of Motion. In the passage of earthquake waves the ground actually vibrates, both horizontally and vertically. The amount of movement or size of the wave, known as the amplitude of vibration, is always small. Movement of a half inch is destructive and an amplitude of one inch is disastrous. The vibrations are not only small but are also of short duration, lasting from about five seconds in some cases up to as much as five minutes in others. One can usually hear accompanying the tremors a deep sound which resembles the low rumbling of thunder.

Intensity of Shocks. An earthquake is most intense, that is, the amplitude of vibration is greatest, at the point or line on the surface directly above the focus. This place of greatest intensity is called the *epicenter*. As distance from the epicenter increases, the intensity declines. Arbitrary scales have been devised to compare the intensities of different earthquakes and to classify the areas affected by any shock. The Rossi-Forel Scale, shown in abbreviated form below, is the one most commonly used until recently.

Rossi-Forel Scale of Intensities of Earthquake Shocks

1. *Microseismic.* Recorded only by the most sensitive seismographs
2. *Extremely feeble.* Recorded by seismographs of all kinds; felt by a few persons at rest
3. *Very feeble.* Direction or duration recorded on seismographs; felt by several persons at rest
4. *Feeble.* Felt by persons in motion; disturbance of easily movable objects; cracking of plaster
5. *Moderate intensity.* Felt by everyone; disturbance of furniture; ringing of some bells
6. *Fairly strong.* Awakening of those asleep; ringing of many bells; stopping of clocks; agitation of trees

7. *Strong shock*. Overturning of movable objects; fall of plaster; general panic, but without much damage
8. *Very strong*. Fall of chimneys; cracks in the walls of buildings
9. *Extremely strong*. Partial or total destruction of some buildings
10. *Extreme intensity*. Great disaster; ruins; disturbance of strata; fissures in the ground; landslides[1]

In recent years the scale devised in 1935 by C. F. Richter has come into common usage. Richter's Scale of Magnitude employs numbers, as does the Rossi-Forel Scale. The important difference is that Richter's Scale of Magnitude is based on instrumental records, rather than on subjective appraisals. He defines the magnitude of an earthquake in terms of the motions recorded by seismographs at specified distances from the disturbance. The energy released by an earthquake is expressed in terms of *ergs*. The energy released by an earthquake of magnitude 8.6, the largest recorded in recent years, is 3×10^{27} ergs, which is 3 million times the energy released by the first atomic bomb.

DETECTION AND RECORDING OF EARTHQUAKES

Seismographs and Seismograms. The essential feature of a seismograph is that one part of the instrument shall remain at rest, or nearly so, while the other part vibrates with the ground during an earthquake. The stationary part consists of a pendulum, which is commonly a heavy weight suspended by a wire so that the rapid movements of the ground scarcely affect it. The vibrating part of the instrument is rigidly attached to the bedrock and vibrates in unison with the ground. Mounted on this part is a revolving drum, driven by clockwork, which moves a strip of smoked paper beneath a stylus attached to the pendulum. The paper is marked in convenient units of time. When the earth is at rest the stylus traces a straight line. When earthquake waves reach the station the drum vibrates beneath the stylus and a wavy line, which is a seismogram, is drawn on the paper. Actual movements of the ground are magnified on the seismogram by means of a lever. In the more sensitive instruments designed in recent years, a beam of light reflected from a mirror traces the seismogram on photographic paper, or the differential movement of the two parts of the instrument is recorded electrically by means of an oscillograph. Thus the actual movement may be exaggerated to any desired degree as the record is traced.

Most seismographs consist of three recording units oriented in different directions, so that one of them detects motions in a north-south

[1] See United States Department of Commerce, Series 483 (Washington, D. C., 1930), p. 2.

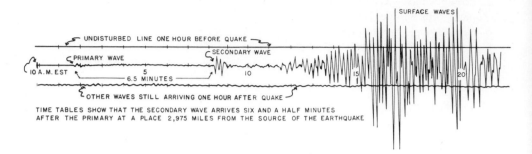

FIG. 23-2. Seismogram of a typical earthquake. The pattern of vibration and the time of arrival of the primary, secondary, and long (surface) waves are easily distinguished. *(Harvard University Seismograph Station)*

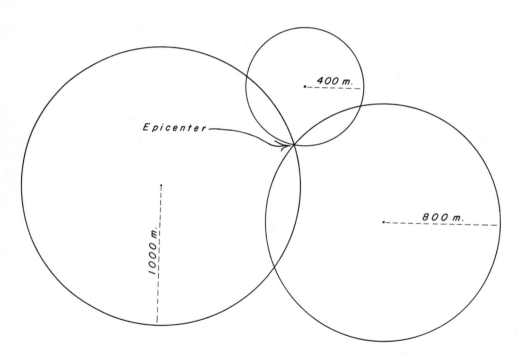

FIG. 23-3. Location of the epicenter of an earthquake when the distances from three recording stations are known.

direction, the second intercepts those in an east-west direction and the third registers vertical movements. Thus the three components of the wave motion are each recorded, and consequently its nature can be ascertained much more completely than it could if only one recording unit were used.

Location of Epicenter. As indicated above, the different types of earthquake waves travel at different rates and arrive at a given station with certain time intervals between them. Since the length of the intervals depends on the distance traveled and the speed of that travel is known, it is a fairly easy matter for the observer to calculate the *distance* to the epicenter. From one station alone the exact *direction* can be determined with less certainty than if the observer can get reports on the distance of the shock from two other stations. His task then is simple: three circles drawn with the three stations as centers and the respective distances as radii will intersect at the epicenter.

EFFECTS OF EARTHQUAKES

Destructive Effects. Loss of life and damage to property depend not only on the intensity of the earthquake, but to a larger degree on the density of population and concentration of the works of man in the region affected. One of our most violent earthquakes, that of New Madrid, Missouri, in 1811, caused only slight destruction because of the sparse population there, whereas the San Francisco earthquake of 1906, affecting a more densely populated area, resulted in much greater loss of life and destruction of a large part of the city.

It has been estimated that more than 6 million lives have been lost through earthquakes in the past 2,000 years, and property destruction in the same period probably runs into many billions of dollars. The number of persons killed within the time of a few minutes is sometimes astounding. Three hundred thousand people lost their lives in India in 1737; 100,000 in Sicily in 1908; 180,000 in China in 1920 and 200,000 in Japan in 1923.

A considerable portion of the death and destruction caused by earthquakes is the direct result of the shock, which shakes down the buildings and causes general chaos. But much greater destruction sometimes results from the fire, flood, famine, and disease which follow the shock. Water mains are broken, gas and electric lines are severed, stoves and lamps are overturned, and a general conflagration ensues. The destructiveness of fire following an earthquake is well illustrated by the fact that San Franciscans speak of their disaster of 1906 not as the great earthquake, but as "the great fire."

Preventive Measures. "Don't build your house on sand" is an adage which might well be remembered in earthquake regions. Both experience and reason show that loose materials, such as alluvium, till, loess, and fill, are shaken much more than solid bedrock. Large structures especially should be firmly footed on solid rock.

FIG. 23-4. Crack opened in unconsolidated material of the Kagoshima Plain in Japan at the time of an earthquake. *(American Museum of Natural History)*

A building erected in an earthquake region should be so firmly tied together that it will move as a unit and not shake apart during a shock. Ordinary brick buildings crumble down easily. Well-built wooden houses withstand the shock fairly well, but are susceptible to the fire that often follows. The modern steel and concrete structures are quite resistant both to shock and to fire, but even they will not withstand the most violent tremors. In the Japanese earthquake of 1923 about half

FIG. 23-5. Fence broken and offset several feet during the San Francisco earthquake of 1906. *(Photo by Gilbert, U. S. Geological Survey)*

of the modern steel and brick buildings in Tokyo were unharmed.

Geological Effects of Earthquakes. It should be emphasized again that the movement of the earth along faults which occurs at the time of earthquakes is the *cause* and not the result of the shocks. There are some minor surface features, however, which are the result of earthquakes. Where slopes are steep, strong earthquakes often cause landslides and avalanches. These landslides may divert streams to new courses or dam them up into lakes. In loose material, such as floodplain alluvium, the ground may be cracked or thrown into gentle waves by the compression attending the passage of the seismic waves. Disturbance of the ground water circulation is indicated by variation in the flow of springs, by the formation of new springs, and by changes of water level in wells. Compression of water-bearing sands beneath the surface may cause jets of water and sand to spout up for a time and to leave behind small, saucer-shaped craters when they subside.

EXAMPLES OF EARTHQUAKES

Lisbon, Portugal, 1755. On November 1, 1755, the greater part of the city of Lisbon was destroyed by earthquake shock, sea waves, and fire. The epicenter was submarine and some distance to the west of the city. Three great shocks came in rapid succession and reduced many of the houses to ruins. A sea wave 40 feet high soon followed and wrecked the shipping in the harbor. For hours afterward the sea continued to ebb and flow in great billows. Numerous fires broke out and completed the destruction. About 20,000 persons lost their lives and property damage amounted to about $100,000,000.

Comparison of the degree of destruction with the underlying rock formations shows an interesting relationship. Part of the city of Lisbon is built on unconsolidated sands and clays and the remainder is located on hard limestone and basalt. No building on the unconsolidated sediments escaped destruction or serious damage; most of those on the solid rocks were unharmed by the shocks. Thus the line between destruction and safety corresponded with the boundary between the loose and the solid rocks.

Sagami Bay, Japan, 1923. On September 1, 1923, earthquake, sea wave and fire leveled nearly all of Yokahama and a large part of Tokyo. Seismograph records show that the epicenter lay in Sagami Bay to the south of these two cities. As is the case in most earthquake disasters, the greater part of the destruction was due to the conflagration that followed the shock. Water mains were broken and the fire could not be extinguished. Some 200,000 lives were lost and property damage amounted to billions of dollars.

Surveys of the bottom of Sagami Bay before and after the earthquake show differences of several hundred feet in the depth of water. How much of this difference was due to actual movement along a fault and how much to warping or slumping is not known. On land the greatest vertical displacement took place to the north of the Bay, where an uplift of 6½ feet was measured. In addition to the vertical movements there were also horizontal displacements. Oshima Island, in the southern part of Sagami Bay, was shifted some 12 feet northward and the north shore of the bay moved almost the same amount eastward.

New Madrid, Missouri, 1811-1812. A series of earthquake shocks, which began in December, 1811 and continued well into the following year, affected the Mississippi Valley in the region of New Madrid, Missouri. Many fissures were formed in the floodplain deposits, some of them remaining open for years. It was said by observers that the ground rose and fell like low undulations in the sea. Parts of the floodplain subsided, and gave rise to lakes and marshes. The largest of these lakes is Reelfoot Lake in northwestern Tennessee, which is 18 miles long and has a maximum width of 3 miles. Inasmuch as this area was not then densely populated, the loss of life and property was small. Some people emigrated from the region as a result of the earthquakes and others were discouraged from settling there. But events of this kind soon lose their deterring effects; in a few years the region seemed to have returned to its normal habits and development.

It is believed that this particular earthquake resulted, not from mountain-building movements, but rather from the settling of the thick floodplain alluvium which had been deposited on an irregular floor. Whether faulting occurred in the consolidated rock beneath the floodplain is not known.

San Francisco, 1906. The greatest earthquake disaster to occur in the United States took place in San Francisco, California, in April, 1906. Some buildings were entirely destroyed, many others were damaged, and fires were started by the shock. Broken pipes cut off the water supply, none was available to fight the flames and a large part of the city was burned. Although the property damage was enormous, loss of life was small.

This earthquake was caused by movement along the great fault, known as the San Andreas Rift, which runs through San Francisco and extends for a long distance both to the north and south. With some exceptions, the intensity of the shock decreased uniformly with distance from the line of the fault. The exceptions to this uniform decrease occurred in areas of deep alluvium and on loose or "made" land. Such areas were disturbed much more than hard rock areas equally distant from the epicenter.

Movement along the San Andreas Rift was mainly horizontal, though there was some vertical displacement. Measurements show that the ground on the southwest side of the fault was moved northwestward about 2 feet in some localities and as much as 20 feet in others. Vertical displacement of this same side amounted to a maximum of 3 feet.

Undaunted by this great disaster, the people of San Francisco immediately began the work of rehabilitation. Valuable lessons in coping with the dangers of earthquake shock and its after effects had been learned, not only with regard to the location of buildings but also about the best types of construction. Areas of greatest danger were precisely located. New structures were built along more costly and substantial lines. Fortunately the city has experienced no serious shock since 1906 and may not for generations to come, but, in case there is a recurrence, San Francisco is well prepared to meet the situation.

THE INTERIOR OF THE EARTH AS
REVEALED BY SEISMIC WAVES

The velocity of seismic waves varies according to certain physical properties of the medium through which they travel. The velocity of a P-wave increases with the elasticity and density of the earth materials. The speed of the S-wave depends on the rigidity of its medium. This wave does not travel through liquid material. The surface separating zones in which wave velocities are different is called a *discontinuity*. Studies of the behavior of seismic waves, including the depths at which they are refracted and reflected as well as their velocities at different depths, have led seismologists to divide the earth from surface to center into three large zones, namely, *crust, mantle,* and *core.*

The crust of the earth comprises the outer 3 to 30 miles. Discontinuities, both large and small, are found within the crust. The most prominent and extensive of these is that which separates the granitic (sialic) layer of lighter rocks above from the basaltic (simatic) layer of heavier rocks below. The granitic layer, exclusive of the sedimentary cover, is about 30 miles thick under the continental masses and is very thin, and even absent in some places, beneath the ocean basins.

Beneath the crust, the mantle extends to a depth of 1,800 miles. In this zone the S-waves travel at higher velocities than in the crust, indicating a higher degree of rigidity. S-waves do not traverse the central part of the earth, which has a radius of about 2200 miles. This fact together with the behavior of the P-waves that traverse the core leads to the conclusion that the core of the earth consists of an *outer liquid zone,* which stops the S-waves, and an *inner solid zone,* through which the P-waves travel with greater velocity after they have passed through the liquid zone (See Fig. 4-1).

PREDICTION OF EARTHQUAKES

Anything approaching precise prediction as to the time and place of occurrence of earthquakes is scarcely more than a hope for the future. One hope in prediction lies in the study of foreshocks. This method is based on the premise that violent quakes are sometimes preceded by a relatively long period of foreshocks, or minor tremors. By locating the origin of the foreshocks the position of the fault along which larger movement might take place in the future can be determined. Another method of attack that has received some attention is based on the assumption that, before slipping takes place along a large fault, the ground on either side would show some distortion that might be detected by careful measurements.

Suggestions for Further Reading

BYERLY, Perry, *Seismology* (Englewood Cliffs, N. J., Prentice-Hall, 1942).

LEET, L. D., *Practical Seismology and Seismic Prospecting* (New York, D. Appleton-Century Company, Inc., 1938).

LEET, L. D., "Use and Abuse of Earth Waves," *American Scientist*, Vol. 45, No. 2, March, 1957.

LEET, L. D., *Causes of Catastrophe* (New York, McGraw-Hill, 1948).

LYNCH, Joseph, S. J., *Our Trembling Earth* (New York, Dodd, Mead, 1940).

WYLER, Rose and AMES, Gerald, *Restless Earth* (New York, Abelard-Schuman, 1954).

─ 24 ─

Landforms

EXPLANATORY DESCRIPTION

Constructional and destructional forces. The study of the origin and evolution of the surface features of the earth constitutes that branch of earth science known as *geomorphology*. In the development of the surface of the earth two fundamental types of processes are recognized. They are the constructional or up-building and the destructional or down-breaking forces. The constructional forces are diastrophism and volcanism. These forces originate within the earth; they set the stage and produce the structures on which the agents of destruction work. Uplift and subsidence, tilting and warping, folding and faulting, intrusion and extrusion of molten rock are all the work of these great constructional forces.

The agents of destruction are the wind, waves, streams, glaciers, and ground water. They are external forces which receive their energy from the sun rather than from within and operate on the surface of the earth. The great variety of landscape features which the earth exhibits is the result of the action of these destructional agents on the constructional landforms. Thus, the surface features in any region depend not only on the structure of the rocks but also on the agents of erosion active in that region.

Stages of Development. In explaining the development of landforms the stage of erosion must be emphasized. The agents of destruction work slowly, and landscapes change gradually as erosion proceeds. A newly uplifted region on which streams have been at work only for a relatively short time has a very different appearance from that of the same region after it has been eroded to the mature stage. And as time goes on and erosion continues without interruption, the characteristics of maturity will gradually change to those of old age.

Structure, Process and Stage. A description of a landform which includes the structure of the rocks, the process or agent of erosion and the stage of development of that process is an explanatory description. To one familiar with the characteristics of the different structures, processes, and stages, a few well-chosen explanatory terms are more meaningful than many pages of purely empirical description. Thus a brief statement such as: "a plateau of uniformly resistant beds in the mature stage of stream erosion," would convey to the student of landforms a picture of the essential characteristics of the region.

The description and explanation of landforms in terms of structure, process, and stage is a relatively recent development and has progressed most in this country. Through his investigations and writings in geomorphology, William Morris Davis (1850-1934) contributed more than any other man to the advancement of this branch of earth science.

Relief. In descriptions of the surface, the term *relief* is often used. Beginning students sometimes confuse this term with altitude. As used in the description of landforms relief means *difference* in altitude, not absolute altitude. A region may be 5,000 feet above sea level and still have low relief, if all parts of the surface have nearly that altitude. In order to determine the relief of a region one must note the difference in altitude between the hill tops and valley bottoms. Relief of 500 feet or less is considered low, or gentle; 500 feet to 1,000 feet is moderate; and a difference of more than 1,000 feet constitutes high, or strong relief.

FIG. 24-1. William Morris Davis (1850-1934), pioneer in the explanatory description and genetic classification of landforms. *(Geological Society of America)*

CONSTRUCTIONAL LANDFORMS

Landforms of the First Order: Continents and Ocean Basins. The two most extensive topographic levels of the earth are the continental platforms and the ocean basins, two great units separated from each other everywhere by the abrupt continental slope. The ocean floor is covered with water which has an average depth of about 12,000 feet; mean elevation of the continental masses is about 2,300 feet above sea level.

As has been indicated earlier, the most likely cause for the existence of these two great topographic units is the difference in density of the substances composing them. The ocean floor, underlain by heavy basaltic material, tends to subside toward the center of the earth. On the other hand, the continental masses, consisting in large part of lighter rocks, are crowded upward, relatively speaking, between the sinking ocean basins.

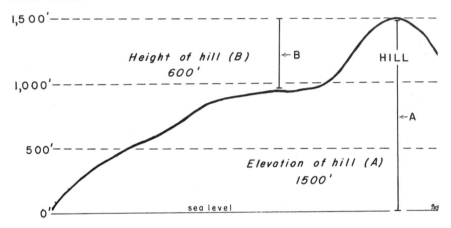

FIG. 24-2. In considering the relief of a landscape altitude or elevation (A) is differentiated from height (B).

All the continents possess certain characteristics more or less in common. Each has a broad interior lowland bordered by highlands toward the margins. These highlands are higher and of more recent origin on one side than on the other side. In North America and South America, for example, the ancient, low mountains are in the east and the high, youthful ones are in the west. In Europe, on the other hand, the old worn-down mountains are in the north and the rugged mountains of later origin are in the south. There is not only an alignment of the border highlands in each continent, but also a general parallelism in the trend of all the main features. Here in North America the trend, or grain, is north-south: the central lowland extends all the way from the Arctic Ocean to the Gulf of Mexico; the Cordilleran Highlands run from northern Alaska to Central America, and, in fact, continue to the southern tip of South America; and the eastern highlands can be followed from Newfoundland down to Georgia. In traveling from east to west, however, one crosses the structural grain of the continent and meets a succession of widely different topographic features. In South America and in Australia the principal structures and topographic features also have a north-south trend; but in Europe and Asia the grain is east-west.

Africa, however, exhibits the general features mentioned above to a lesser degree than the other continents.

Landforms of the Second Order. Within each continent there are regions which differ from each other in the structure of the bedrock. In some places the beds are essentially horizontal, in some others they have been disturbed in one way or another, in still others the rocks consist of cones of volcanic material. On the basis of these differences in structure, the continents are subdivided into the natural units of the second order called (1) plains and plateaus, (2) mountains, and (3) volcanoes. These are constructional landforms, produced by the great internal forces of diastrophism and volcanism.

Plains and Plateaus. A region where the rocks occur in distinct layers and lie in an approximately horizontal position is either a plain or a plateau. In most cases the rocks are uplifted sedimentary beds; but they may be volcanic in origin, in which case the region is a lava plain or a lava plateau.

Plains and plateaus are distinguished from each other on the basis of relief. In a plain, such as the Atlantic-Gulf Coastal Plain, the relief is low; the valleys are shallow and drained by sluggish streams. In a plateau, such as the Colorado Plateau, the relief is high, that is, the valleys are deep gorges or canyons. The top of a plateau must necessarily stand at a considerable altitude, in order that the streams may cut deep valleys and produce the necessary high relief. It does not necessarily follow that a plain must stand at low altitude. Most of them do, but some lie high above the sea and have low relief because the streams have not yet cut deep valleys.

Plains and plateaus are grouped together because they have the same fundamental structure, and erosion may convert one into the other. A region of horizontal rocks newly elevated to a high altitude might be called a plain as long as the valleys are shallow; when streams have cut deep gorges the region becomes a plateau; lastly, long-continued erosion may reduce the interstream areas nearly to the level of the valley bottoms and the region again becomes a plain.

The Cycle of Erosion in Plains and Plateaus. In the youthful stage of erosion, plateaus have broad, flat uplands between the gorges or canyons. As maturity is approached these interstream areas become narrow and deeply dissected by many tributary streams, so that the whole surface is eroded into steep slopeland. Such rugged, maturely dissected plateaus are popularly called mountains. The Catskill Mountains of New York, for example, are not mountains in the structural sense, but a maturely dissected plateau. With the coming of old age and the lowering of divides the plateau takes on the aspects of a plain, and were it not for the occurrence of monadnocks in the form of buttes and mesas, one would not recognize it as a former plateau.

Plains also pass through a regional erosion cycle from youth through maturity to old age. The features developed are similar to those of the corresponding stages in a plateau, except for the lower relief. In youth a plain has low, flat divides between narrow, but shallow stream valleys; in maturity the interstream areas become hilly; as old age approaches the valleys grow wide and flat and separated from each other by low divides and scattered monadnocks.

It is not to be thought that one can stand and observe a plain or a plateau or any other landform pass through a cycle of erosion. The process requires some millions of years. One can, however, observe different regions that are in various stages of the erosion cycle; and, by deduction, one can infer the sequence of events in any particular region. For example, the portion of the Atlantic Coastal Plain nearest the shore was only recently uplifted from the sea bottom and is now in the youthful stage of stream dissection. The inland portion of the same plain has been exposed to the agents of erosion for a longer time and has reached the stage of early maturity. It is reasonable to suppose that

FIG. 24-3. Most of the Badland region of South Dakota is maturely dissected, but parts of the original flat surface of the plain still remain. *(National Park Service)*

this inland portion was at one time in the same stage of development as the outer portion is now, and that the near-coast area will eventually, if stream erosion continues, reach the same stage as that of the inland area at the present time.

Mountains. Mountains are regions of disturbed or deformed rocks. They are differentiated into four types according to the nature of the deformation which created them. (1) Dome mountains result from the upbending of strata into the form of a dome. (2) Fold mountains consist of a series of long, more or less parallel wrinkles, or folds. (3) Block mountains are formed by the faulting and uptilting of angular blocks. (4) Complex mountains are made up of a number of disturbed structures.

Dome Mountains. The doming of strata may be accomplished either by compression from all sides, or by arching above an intrusion rising from below. On a newly formed, or young, dome the streams, following the dip of the strata and the slope of the surface, radiate outward from the center of the uplift.

As erosion proceeds to maturity the center of the dome, which stands

FIG. 24-4. Youthful dissection of a plateau. Canyon of the Little Colorado River, Cameron, Ariz. *(Photo by Barnum Brown)*

FIG. 24-5. Vertical view of the maturely dissected Appalachian Plateau in Kanawha County, W. Va. The scale bar represents about half a mile. (*U. S. Dept. of Agriculture, A. A. A.*)

FIG. 24-6. Dome structure at Sinclair, Carbon County, Wyo. The hogback ridges and annular valleys circle the center of the dome. (*U. S. Geological Survey*)

highest, is eroded most rapidly. After a time the topmost strata are cut through, and the upturned edges of different layers underneath are exposed. If there is an igneous intrusion beneath the uparched beds, this crystalline core is exposed. The edges of the strata that formerly covered the dome now form concentric rings around the center. Some of these beds are resistant and form ridges, called *hogbacks,* that have steep sides facing inward toward the center of the uplift and gentle slopes looking outward. Other beds are weak, and circular valleys are eroded on them, until an *annular* drainage pattern is developed. Some of the original streams still flow radially outward from the center through gaps in the hogback ridges, but their principal tributaries follow ring-like courses along the circular valleys. The dome is now maturely dissected. The Black Hills of South Dakota are a good example of a maturely dissected dome mountain, consisting of an uplifted central mass of ancient crystalline rocks surrounded by younger sedimentary beds. If erosion is allowed to continue to the old-age stage, this region will be reduced to a peneplane, and topographic evidences of the dome structure will be largely destroyed.

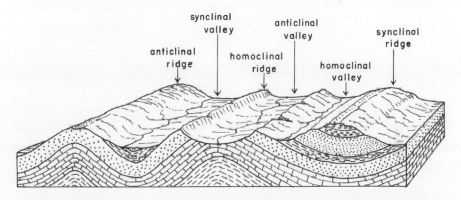

FIG. 24-7. Typical relationships between topography and pattern of rock outcrop in a maturely eroded region of simple folds.

Fold Mountains. Folds in the earth's strata result from compression. In a young folded mountain, that is, in a folded region newly exposed to erosion, the anticlines form long, narrow ridges, and the valleys between them follow the synclines, or troughs. The slopes of the surface thus correspond to the folds in the rocks. The drainage, too, is consequent to the folds, long streams following the synclinal troughs and their short tributaries flowing down the slopes of the anticlinal ridges.

The above conditions do not exist very long. Erosion soon cuts through the crests of the anticlines and exposes the edges of beds with different degrees of resistance. Now the rate of erosion will depend largely on the differences in resistance of the exposed rock formations. Weak beds are worn away rapidly and become the sites of valleys. Strong beds yield to erosion more slowly and make the ridges. Both ridges and valleys still have a linear and parallel arrangement, but their positions and the slopes of the surface do not necessarily correspond with the original folds. They depend on the distribution of the outcrops of resistant and weak beds. In this mature stage of erosion some of the ridges are anticlinal in structure and some are synclinal. The majority of them, however, are *homoclinal* ridges, formed by one limb of a truncated fold. Valleys also may be anticlinal, synclinal, or monoclinal. The mountains of western Virginia and central Pennsylvania are good examples of fold mountains in the mature stage of erosion.

Where fold mountains follow the trend of the continental border and are at right angles to the general slope of the land, streams must cross the folded structure in order to follow a direct course to the sea. In such cases one finds the master streams cutting through the resistant rock ridges in narrow gorges, called *water gaps.* Such gaps are commonly situated where the ridge-making formation is comparatively thin or ruptured by a fault or otherwise weakened. The main tributaries of the master streams follow the weak rock underlying the longitudinal valleys and enter the transverse master streams at right angles. In turn, the secondary tributaries flowing down the ridges on both sides join the main tributaries at right angles. This drainage arrangement, so typical of folded mountains, is called the *trellis pattern* of drainage.

It might be presumed that continued erosion would eventually reduce a fold mountain region to a peneplane in which both weak and strong rocks are worn down to a nearly uniformly low level, but no good examples of this kind of peneplane are known at the present time. If they have been developed in the past, such regions have been either rejuvenated or submerged.

Block Mountains. In Nevada, southern Oregon, and elsewhere in the Great Basin the rocks are broken into angular blocks by many faults. Some of the blocks are pushed up and tilted at various angles into block mountains. The depressed blocks between the uptilted ones are block basins.

The distinctive topographic features of block mountains are most easily recognized in the youthful stage of erosion. Young block mountains are angular, or block shaped. The crestline, which is the edge of the uptilted block, is straight and sharp. The baseline, where the mountain meets the lowland, is also straight and well defined. In most cases one side of the mountain, the fault surface, is steeper than the other. In a region of block mountains the principal streams tend to follow the fault lines and thus assume a rectangular pattern. Short tributaries flow down the steep faces of the blocks and longer ones down the gentler slopes.

In the mature stage of erosion, block mountains lose some of their youthful characteristics. In broad outline the angularity remains, but the simplicity of detail is lost. The mountain sides are cut by numerous ravines, gorges and small canyons; yet the ends of the main spurs still retain some of the original steep fault surface and form a straight line along the base of the mountain. The two sides of the mountain are still unequal in steepness, but the formerly clean-cut crestline becomes notched and irregular and is gradually shifted toward the gentler side. With the approach of old age, block mountains become smaller and more subdued, until eventually they appear as scattered, irregular hills surrounded by broad expanses of flat land covered by alluvium.

Complex mountains. As the name implies, complex mountains are made up of many different structures. Intricate folding, complex faulting, metamorphism, and a variety of igneous intrusions are commonly found. A typical complex mountain consists mainly of crystalline rocks, that is, of igneous intrusions and metamorphics. In North America the highlands of New England, the Adirondacks, the Blue Ridge, and most of the Rockies are good examples; in Europe the Scottish and Scandinavian Highlands are typical.

The rocks and structures of complex mountains are those that can usually be formed only deep beneath the surface. Consequently, such mountains now occur where there has been great uplift and erosion of the overlying material. Since these regions have been subjected to long erosion, we can not now observe the youthful stage.

Most complex mountains are maturely dissected. Erosion of a region of complex structure produces a variety of forms. The mountain peaks, bold and massive with rounded summits, are of various heights, and show no definite pattern of arrangement. Stream systems commonly branch out in an irregular tree-like, or *dendritic pattern,* except where prominent faults or joints give them a rectangular arrangement. If glaciers of the alpine type have been active, there are steep, rocky slopes, scoured and scratched rock outcrops, sharp peaks, valley lakes, and other typical glacial features.

If a region of complex mountains remains stationary for a sufficiently long time, it will, of course, be ultimately reduced to a peneplane. Although no examples of complex mountains now in the peneplane stage are known in this country, there is evidence that part of the New England region, except for remnants such as Mount Monadnock, was formerly peneplaned and later uplifted. The ruggedness of the present New England topography is largely the result of mature erosion of the uplifted peneplane surface. The Piedmont of the South, another region of complex structure, is also thought to have been peneplaned in the past and later uplifted and dissected to maturity.

Volcanoes. Volcanoes consist of conical layers of lava or ash disposed around the center of eruption. Although they are sometimes classified

FIG. 24-8. Ridges and valleys resulting from the erosion of folded strata, near **Laramie, Wyo.** *(U. S. Geological Survey)*

FIG. 24-9. Fault scarp with triangular facets, Kern County, Calif. *(U. S. Geological Survey)*

FIG. 24-10. The massive outlines of the Coeur d'Alene Mountains, Idaho, are typical of complex mountains consisting mainly of igneous rocks. *(U. S. Forest Service)*

FIG. 24-11. Mt. Assiniboine, in the Canadian Rockies, is maturely dissected by both streams and alpine glaciers. *(Geological Survey of Canada)*

as mountains, their structure and method of origin are sufficiently distinct to justify placing them in a separate group. Their conical structure is original and does not represent originally horizontal beds that have been deformed by mountain-making movements. As described before there are three types of volcanic cones, namely, cinder cones, lava cones, and composite cones. Each of these is subject to erosion by streams or glaciers and, if not built up and renewed by repeated eruptions, will eventually be worn away.

In youth a volcano has a more or less regular cone shape with a depression, the crater, in the top. Erosion has not greatly modified the original slopes of the surface. The modern inner cone of Vesuvius shows this youthful form.

Soon after exposure to erosion the runoff of surface water cuts gullies down the sides, and a *radial drainage pattern* develops. The gullies grow in size and number until little or none of the original surface remains. Perhaps even the crater is filled or its rim worn away. The volcano has now attained the mature stage of dissection. Mount Shasta and many of the other large volcanoes of the Pacific Coast mountains have been eroded to maturity, most of them by glaciers as well as by

FIG. 24-12. Undissected, snow-covered Alaskan volcano. *(U. S. Navy)*

streams. Unlike dome mountains, which develop annular drainage in
the mature stage, volcanoes retain the radial pattern.

With continued erosion to the old-age stage most of the cone is swept
away. Perhaps the only remnants of the former volcano may be a plug-
like mass of hard material that filled the throat and possibly some
radiating dikes that occupied cracks in the cone. Examples of these old
volcanoes are found in northern Arizona and New Mexico. Stark's
Knob, near Schuylerville, New York, is possibly an old volcanic neck.

We may now briefly tabulate the constructional landforms.

Tabular Summary of the Constructional Landforms

FIRST ORDER LANDFORMS

Continents—the great elevated portions of the earth, mostly above sea level
Ocean Basins—the great depressed portions of the earth, filled to overflowing
with sea water

**FIG. 24-13. Shiprock, near Farmington, New Mexico, a volcanic neck with radiating
dikes.** The rest of the cone has been carried away by erosion. *(Photo by Dr. Barnum
Brown)*

SECOND ORDER LANDFORMS

Plains—horizontal structure, low relief

Plateaus—horizontal structure, high relief

Mountains—disturbed structure
  Dome mountains: domed structure
  Fold mountains: folded structure
  Block mountains: faulted structure
  Complex mountains: complex structure

Volcanoes—conical structure

DESTRUCTIONAL LANDFORMS: LANDFORMS OF THE THIRD ORDER

The destructional landforms are the various features produced by the agents of erosion working on the constructional forms. Their characteristics are determined in part by the erosional agent and in part by the constructional landform on which the agent works. Some of these features, such as valleys, are produced directly by *erosion*, or the carrying away of material; others, like deltas, are the result of *deposition;* still others, as monadnocks, might be called *residuals*, for they are what is left after the surrounding material has been removed.

Inasmuch as the processes and results of erosion have been discussed in earlier chapters, a brief tabulation should be sufficient here. The most convenient method of tabulation of the destructional forms is to group them according to the agents of erosion and subdivide each group into erosional, depositional and residual forms.

Tabulation of the Destructional Landforms

FEATURES MADE BY WIND

Erosional	*Depositional*	*Residual*
Blowouts	Sand dunes	Mushroom rocks
Wind caves	Loess	Mesas and buttes
Blowholes		(in part)

FEATURES MADE BY STREAMS

Erosional	*Depositional*	*Residual*
Valleys of various kinds:	Alluvial fans and cones	Divides
gullies, ravines,	Floodplain deposits	Monadnocks
gorges, canyons,	Natural levees	Mesas and buttes
mature valleys,	Channel bars	(in part)
old valleys	Deltas	
Peneplanes		

FEATURES MADE BY GLACIERS

Erosional	*Depositional*	*Residual*
Glacial troughs	Terminal moraine	Matterhorns
Cirques	Ground moraine	Arêtes
Lake basins:	Drumlins	Hanging valleys
finger lakes	Glaciofluvial	
paternoster lakes	deposits:	
tarns	kames	
Rôches moutonnées	eskers	
	outwash plains	
	valley trains	
	kettle holes	

FEATURES MADE BY GROUND WATER

Erosional	*Depositional*	*Residual*
Caverns	Geyser cones	Natural bridges
Tunnels	Terraced spring	Natural chimneys
Sinkholes	deposits	

FEATURES MADE BY WAVES AND CURRENTS

Erosional	*Depositional*	*Residual*
Cliffed shorelines	Bars:	Stacks
Wave-cut benches	offshore bars	Arches
Sea caves	spits	
	tombolos	
	bay bars	
	Beaches	
	Tidal deltas	

LANDFORMS BASED ON SURFACE CHARACTERISTICS

A simpler classification of landforms than that given on preceding pages is presented below. This scheme has rather wide popular usage and is preferred by some geographers. For those whose interest is mainly in the relation of human activities to different types of surfaces, rather than in the origin and evolution of the topography, this simple classification is probably satisfactory.

Landform	*Nature of Surface*
Plain	Low relief; flat ground exceeds sloping ground
Hill Country	Low relief; sloping ground exceeds flat ground
Plateau	High relief; flat ground exceeds sloping ground
Mountain	High relief; sloping ground exceeds flat ground

LANDFORMS OF UNCERTAIN ORIGIN

In addition to the landforms listed above, on the basis of origin, there are some of uncertain origin. Chief among these are those depressions in the southern part of the Atlantic Coastal Plain, called the Carolina Bays, and such depressions as Meteor Crater (Coon Butte) in Arizona.

In the Coastal Plain of the Carolinas, Georgia, and northern Florida there are several hundred shallow, elliptical-shaped depressions, the origin of which is in dispute. Some think that they are meteor scars, formed by the impact of a swarm of meteors. Others think that these depressions were formed by the action of springs. There are still other explanations. A discussion of the merits of the various theories is beyond the scope of this book.

Near Holbrook, Arizona, is a depression about a half mile in diameter at the top and 600 feet deep. Some call it Meteor Crater because they think that it was formed by the impact and explosion of a large meteor. Others call it Coon Butte, because the upturned strata of the rim, as seen from a distance give it the appearance of a butte. Two theories of the origin of this depression are held. One is that it is a meteor scar and the other is that it is the result of the violent eruption of volcanic gases.

The examples given above show that there still is need for more examination and elucidation in the explanatory description of landforms.

FIG. 24-14. Meteor Crater, or Coon Butte, Ariz. *(Photo by Dr. Barnum Brown)*

Suggestions for Further Reading

ATWOOD, W. W., *The Rocky Mountains* (New York, Vanguard, 1945).

COTTON, C. A., *Volcanoes as Landscape Forms* (Christchurch, New Zealand, Whitcombe and Tombs, 1944).

FENTON, C. L., and M. A., *Mountains* (New York, Doubleday, 1942).

HINDS, Norman E. A., *Geomorphology* (Englewood Cliffs, N. J., Prentice-Hall, 1943).

LOBECK, A. K., *Geomorphology* (New York, McGraw-Hill, 1939).

PEATTIE, Roderick, *The Friendly Mountains: Green, White and Adirondacks* (New York, Vanguard, 1942).

———, *The Friendly Mountains: Great Smokies and Blue Ridge* (New York, Vanguard, 1943).

THORNBURY, William D., *Principles of Geomorphology* (New York, Wiley, 1954).

VON ENGELN, O. D., *Geomorphology* (New York, Macmillan, 1942).

WORCESTER, P. G., *A Textbook of Geomorphology* (Princeton, N. J., Van Nostrand, 1939).

— 25 —

Principles of Historical Geology

COMPARISON WITH HUMAN HISTORY

IN COMMON USAGE history deals with mankind. It is the story of races, nations and civilizations, of migrations and conflicts, and of the ideals, aspirations, and achievements of man. Most of our information about human history is obtained from written records, such as official documents, military records, and the writings of literary men. These are supplemented by legends, ruined cities, monuments and other man-made structures.

Human history is only one kind of history; it is but a short phase of the much larger history of the earth. This earth history, or geologic history, deals not only with the human race, but also with other animals, with plants, and with the physical earth back to the time of its beginning. Whereas human history is measured in thousands of years, earth history spans hundreds of millions of years. The record of this larger history can be read in (1) the surface of the earth, which has attained its present configuration through the operation of processes governed by natural laws, (2) the rocks of all types in the lithosphere, which reflect the conditions under which they were formed and the subsequent events that have affected them, and (3) the fossils of plants and animals entombed in the strata, which record the steps in the development of life on the earth. These evidences of former life bear witness not only of the kinds of organisms that lived at various times, but also yield important information as to the physical conditions under which they lived.

THE RECORD OF THE SURFACE

The various agents of weathering and erosion, discussed in Chapters 9-16, produce distinctive features which are easily recognized by the experienced observer. We can examine these features in their various stages of development at the present time; we also know the processes and conditions which make them. Sand dunes are the result of wind deposition and are formed only in certain kinds of localities. The vicinity of Albany and Saratoga Springs, New York, is not now the type of region in which sand dunes accumulate; yet we find old dunes there. They are a part of the record of past events and conditions. Stream valleys are also distinctive features which can be made only by the streams that flow in them. In the Columbia Plateau of Washington, in the vicinity of Sciotoville, Ohio, and at other localities, large river valleys are found without the corresponding rivers. The streams have abandoned their former valleys and taken new courses. This, too, is a part of the record of the past. Features resulting from glaciation are not easily confused with those resulting from any other cause. From the distribution of glacial till and other distinctive features we can trace the limits of glaciation during the Ice Age. The elevated shorelines of lakes and seas are easily recognized, even though the bodies of water that made them no longer exist. The extent of the several stages of ancient Lake Bonneville, of which Great Salt Lake is a shrunken remnant, can be traced from the positions of the old shorelines.

These as well as many other topographic features, are evidence of changes on the surface of the earth, but only of changes in the recent past. In the long view of earth history, however, surface features are transitory. They carry us back only a few million years. The landscapes of the more distant past are either destroyed by continued erosion or covered up by the deposition of sediment. In order to delve still further into earth history we must examine the rock strata and the fossils preserved there.

THE RECORD IN SEDIMENTARY
ROCKS

Sedimentary rocks cover about 70 per cent of the present continents. They reveal much history because they have been formed slowly, layer upon layer, and often contain remains of past life. By means of their type of bedding, texture, and composition they tell us of the conditions of their deposition and sometimes of the climatic conditions of the time. For example, a sandstone consisting of well-rounded and frosted grains and showing the eolian type of cross-bedding indicates ancient desert conditions. A coarse-textured sandstone containing angular feldspar fragments reveals that it was deposited fairly close to the highland area where weathering was occurring. A limestone containing shells of invertebrate animals of a kind found only in the seas today appears to be a marine formation. Our interpretations of rock history are based on man's observations of weathering, erosion, and deposition at the present time, and on a knowledge of living plants and animals in their present environments.

THE RECORD IN IGNEOUS ROCKS

By their textures, structures, and mutual relations to other rocks, igneous rocks reveal considerable history. Following the general principle of the relation between texture and rapidity of cooling of magma, we know that glassy and fine-textured rocks cooled rapidly at or near the surface. The medium textured and coarse ones cooled more slowly at

FIG. 25-1. View of the Unaweep Canyon. An ancient channel of a large river which has long ago had its course altered through an uplift of the earth surface which probably occurred when the Uncompahgre Plateau was formed. Uncompahgre National Forest, Colo. *(U. S. Forest Service)*

depth. The large masses of granite, whether caused by granitization of other rocks or by the cooling of magma follow the same principle. Great pressure and heat at depth have given these rocks a coarse texture. Vesicular portions of fine-textured igneous rocks tell us that they represent lava flows, even though they may now be covered with other solid rock. Intrusions are younger than the rocks they have intruded. A sill, the once molten material of which has altered the rocks below and above, is obviously younger than those rocks, and a dike is younger than the wall rock on both sides.

THE RECORD IN METAMORPHIC ROCKS

In regions where dynamic metamorphism has affected rocks, the intensity and direction of pressure can be determined by noting the

FIG. 25-2. Shore of Great Salt Lake near Black Rock Beach, looking south at Oquirrh Mountains. Old shorelines at higher levels can be seen on the mountain side. (*Salt Lake City Chamber of Commerce*)

textures, the structures, and the mineral composition of the metamorphic rocks. The gradational series from slate, through phyllite, into some type of schist, indicates increasing degree of metamorphism in that order. Within schists, minerals such as muscovite, biotite, garnet, cyanite, and sillimanite represent successively greater metamorphism. We can thus tell something about the nature of the crustal disturbance, the depth at which the changes took place, and the direction of the dynamic forces.

ORDER OF SUPERPOSITION OF STRATA

Sedimentary strata are laid down on top of older rocks in successive layers. It must therefore follow that in any series of undeformed rocks the oldest is at the bottom, the youngest is at the top, and the succession from bottom to top is one of age as well as position. This simple principle is the law of superposition.

Igneous rocks are often associated with sedimentary strata. Where they consist of material poured out, or extruded, onto the surface, as they do in the Columbia Plateau, they follow the law of superposition. Intrusions, however, are always younger than the rocks into which they are injected.

Each rock layer is a record of its time. A series of strata gives us the sequence of events over a long time. As in human history, not all of earth history is recorded in one locality. Areas of erosion and of deposition shift from time to time. In order to reconstruct the complete sequence of events, records from many regions must be pieced together in their proper position and order.

UNCONFORMITIES

Nowhere is there found a complete and continuous succession of rock formations from the most ancient to the most recent. Diastrophic movements shift the positions of the seaways. Igneous activity moves from one locality to another. Areas that were sites of marine deposition may be uplifted and exposed to erosion for a long or a short interval. The same area may again be submerged and receive a new series of sediments. Thus there is a time gap between the rocks below the erosional surface and those above. Such a gap is an unconformity.

Though an unconformity represents a time gap in the formation of rocks, it has historical value. During the uplift and erosion the older rocks may have been tilted, folded, faulted, or metamorphosed before subsidence allowed the accumulation of a younger series. Thus, an unconformity is an important part of the diastrophic history of a region.

Revolutions and Disturbances. The records of earth history show that long periods of relative tranquillity have alternated with shorter times of unrest, upheaval, and rapid change. The times of great unrest, called revolutions, are marked by most or all of the following characteristics: (1) widespread elevation of the continents and withdrawal of shallow seas; (2) mountain-making on a large scale; (3) great volcanism, either extrusive or intrusive or both; (4) changes in the distribution of climate, often marked by widespread extremes of glaciation or aridity; (5) rapid changes in organisms, the disappearance of many old types and the appearance of new ones.

Revolutions separate the great eras of geologic time. Disturbances differ from revolutions in being more limited in scope or of a lower order of intensity. They divide the eras into periods of time.

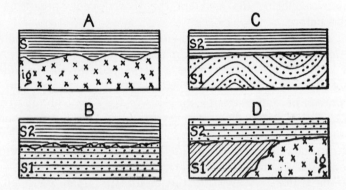

FIG. 25-3. Unconformities. A, Unconformity between igneous, ig, and sedimentary rocks, S. B, Parallel unconformity, or disconformity, between two
sedimentary series, s1 s2. C, Angular unconformity
or nonconformity between two sedimentary series.
D, Unconformity between igneous rock, ig, and
two sedimentary series; angular unconformity between the two sedimentary series, s1, s2. (New
York State Museum)

Both revolutions and disturbances are named from regions where mountain-making was especially marked during their times. Thus, the revolution at the close of the Paleozoic era is called the Appalachian revolution because the Appalachian Mountains were uplifted, folded, and faulted at that time.

Growth of the Continents. One of the grandest generalizations of earth history is that which says the continents have grown larger and higher. This growth has been neither uniform nor continuous. Instead, there have been many oscillations of level; the sea has transgressed and retrogressed repeatedly, but as a rule the transgressions of more recent times have been less extensive than earlier ones.

The growth of the continents has been cyclic. An era is ushered in by the continental uplift which closed the preceding era. At first the land stands relatively high, but with the passage of time it is worn down and shallow seas spread more and more widely over the lowlands. During the course of the era many local uplifts and warpings may shift the positions of some of the shallow seas and change the character of the sediments deposited in them. Some of these local disturbances are so marked that they provide the basis for subdividing the era into periods. Eventually, after long-continued and extensive erosion, great and wide-spread uplift of the continents takes place; most of the shallow seas are drained back into the ocean basins; the era is brought to a close. This time the lands are larger and higher than they were at the close of the preceding era. During the next era the seas do not spread as widely as they did before.

Search for a cause of these repeated and increasingly greater continental uplifts takes us back to isostasy. The uplift of the continents is probably only apparent, being due in large part to the periodic subsidence of the heavier ocean segments. After such an isostatic adjustment has taken place the stresses are relieved for a time and diastrophism ceases. Gradation wears down the lands and deposits the sediment in the ocean. The sea rises and spreads over the worn-down lowlands. Removal of material from the continents and its deposition in the ocean basins again upsets the isostatic balance. The ocean basins again subside. Much of the water is drawn off, the continents again stand high, and the lands are again subjected to erosion until the entire process repeats itself.

Dating Mountain-Making Movements. Continental movements are usually accompanied by mountain-making and other evidences of revolution. During the great uplifts which mark the close of eras the rocks are deformed on a grand scale. Large mountain systems rise, commonly near the borders of the continents where the stresses are greatest and the rocks must yield by folding, faulting, and upheaval.

Mountain-making is dated by the age of the rocks involved. In any mountain region the disturbance must have occurred *after* the formation of the youngest deformed rocks but *before* the deposition of the oldest undeformed rock of that region. Therefore, if one finds folded rocks of middle Cretaceous age he knows that the folding took place after middle Cretaceous time. If there are undeformed early Cenozoic rocks resting unconformably on the middle Cretaceous in the same region, the folding must have taken place before the Cenozoic rocks were deposited. The conclusion, therefore, is that the disturbance took place in late Cretaceous time.

Igneous activity, both intrusive and extrusive, is commonly associated with mountain-making, faulting, and continental uplift. The greater revolutions, such as those in late Precambrian time, the Laramide revolution in late Cretaceous time, and the Cascadian revolution during the Cenozoic have been accompanied by the intrusion of huge batholiths and laccoliths and by extensive lava flows.

Evidences of Past Climates. *Glacial Climate.* Glacial till, or its consolidated equivalent, tillite, is unmistakable evidence of glaciation. We see it deposited by glaciers today, and can find no other process which produces the same kind of material. The distribution of glacial till therefore indicates the distribution of glacial climate, and the age of the till as determined by its relationship to other rocks tells us the time of glaciation.

Arid Climate. Beds of rock salt, gypsum, and other salts precipitated from brine are considered good evidences of arid climate. These materials now being deposited in Great Salt Lake, the Dead Sea, and other bodies of water in dry climates can be precipitated from water only after a great deal of evaporation. Evaporation on a great scale can take place only where the climate is dry and also often hot. Wind-blown sand, another good indicator of dry climate, is often found associated with beds of salt and gypsum.

THE LAW OF FLORAL AND FAUNAL SUCCESSION

It has long been known that strata of different ages contain different assemblages of fossils. It is also known that more recent strata contain evidences of more complex organisms. At first these different assemblages in the strata of different ages were thought to represent successive creations, each a little higher than the preceding one. Now it is firmly established that organisms change, and that *the life of any epoch is descended from the life of the preceding epoch.* This is the law of floral and faunal succession.

FOSSILS

What Fossils Are. Fossils are the remains of plants and animals or some other record of their existence, such as imprints and tracks, naturally preserved in the rocks. In the past, plants and animals lived and died as they do now; after death some of them were buried by sediment which later hardened into stone. Where such rocks are now exposed to weathering and erosion these remains or other evidences of the presence of these organisms are being exhumed, and we can examine the life records of the past.

How Fossils Are Preserved. *Unaltered Remains of Organisms.* In rare instances the entire organism is preserved. Whole carcasses of the extinct wooly mammoth, including hair, hide, and flesh, have been preserved for several thousand years in the frozen soil of Siberia. Other specimens of the same animal have been found in a good state of preservation in oil seeps in Poland.

In most cases the only unaltered remains of organisms are their hard parts. Flesh and other soft parts soon decay, but such hard structures as shells, bones, claws, horns, and teeth may be preserved for millions of years with very little change. This is true especially of fossils imbedded in clay or other impervious material.

Most invertebrate animals which build shells of calcium carbonate have considerable protein included with the mineral matter. Vertebrates have protein in their bones and teeth. Recent studies show that some of this organic material in the form of amino acids may be preserved in fossils as old as 300 million years.

Altered Remains of Organisms. Circulating ground water often changes, or petrifies, the buried remains of organisms. One way in which this is done is by adding mineral matter to (permineralizing) the remains. If the original structure is porous the openings become filled with silica or calcite or some other mineral which makes the object heavier and more solid. Bones and some kinds of shells are often altered and preserved in this way.

Instead of merely adding mineral matter, the ground water often carries away the original

FIG. 25-4. James Hall (1811-1898), foremost American paleontologist of his time. Hall was state geologist and director of the New York State Museum for more than 60 years. Among his many important publications is *Paleontology of New York,* Vols. 1-8 (1847-1888), containing descriptions and classifications of many of the Paleozoic invertebrate fossils of New York. *(American Museum of Natural History)*

material and replaces it with something of an entirely different composition. In some cases the replacement is so exact in detail that all of the internal structures of the original object are retained. In the Petrified Forest of Arizona, for example, tree trunks which now consist of silica show the growth rings and the cell walls of the original wood.

Organic remains are also altered by a process of natural distillation, or carbonization. The volatile constituents of the original organic matter escape, leaving a residue of carbon. Many fossil leaves consist merely of thin films of carbon, all the other elements having been lost through distillation. Graptolites, animals whose remains resemble pencil marks on shales, are also preserved in this way.

FIG. 25-5. Tree trunks, buried long ago under sediment and slowly petrified, now uncovered by erosion. *(Frashers Photos)*

Inorganic Objects. In addition to the actual remains of organisms, altered, or unaltered, there are other objects which are unmistakable evidences of the former presence of these organisms. Walking and crawling animals leave *tracks* and *trails* in muddy sediment. These impressions preserved in the hardened rock are no less authentic records

FIG. 25-6. Slab of fossiliferous rock, a long-preserved record of the life of the past. *(Photo by Hardin, U. S. Geological Survey)*

of the animals that made them than actual bones or teeth. In some cases the tracks of an animal even give us certain information on its habits and manner of walking which cannot be obtained from an examination of a skeleton. For example, the two-legged dinosaurs had long hind limbs and short fore limbs like a kangaroo; but they did not jump as kangaroos do, for their tracks alternate.

A buried shell or other organic object may be entirely dissolved by the ground water, leaving only a *mold*, or cavity, as evidence of its former presence. The shape of the mold and the impression on its walls of the shell markings are usually ample evidence for identification. A leaf falling on soft sediment may make its *imprint*. If the leaf is later destroyed, the preservation of its imprint is just as valuable a fossil as the preserved leaf would be. The soft body of a worm has little chance of surviving through the ages, but its *burrow* made in sand may be preserved indefinitely in the hardened sandstone.

The tools, weapons, and utensils of early man are much more common fossils than are his skeletons. These *artifacts* not only indicate the presence of man in the localities where they are found, but they also give important information as to his habits and stage of culture.

Classification of Fossils. All organisms are classified into two great kingdoms, plant and animal, and these are in turn subdivided into successively smaller groups known as phyla, classes, orders, families, genera, and species. Although there are minor variations among individuals, all members of a species possess certain characteristics in common and are capable of interbreeding and reproducing their kind. All members of the modern human race, for instance, belong to the same species, but a number of racial groups are recognized on the basis of minor differences such as the color of the skin. The following classification of man according to the groups named above will serve to illustrate the classification of any plant or animal:

Kingdom—Animalia
Phylum—Chordata (Vertebrata)
Class—Mammalia
Order—Primate
Family—Hominidae
Genus—*Homo*
Species—*sapiens*

Fossils are classified in the same manner as living organisms. Since the soft parts are rarely preserved, their classification is based mostly on the structures of the hard parts. Of the fossil species almost none are identical with living forms, a few more belong to living genera, still more to present families and so on into the larger groups, until practically all of them can be grouped into phyla with living organisms.

Naming of Species. The technical, or scientific, designation of man is *Homo sapiens,* the genus and species respectively. That double name applies to all individuals of the present human race. Other animals and plants, both modern and fossil, are likewise designated by generic and specific name. In addition, many of them have common, or popular, names. The house cat is *Felis domestica*; the tiger, *Felis tigris,* belongs to the same genus but is a different species. Going back to a fossil form we find *Smilodon californicus,* the great saber-tooth tiger, which differs both generically and specifically from the house cat but still belongs to the same family.

Modern rules governing the naming of fossils specify that the generic and specific names should be derived from the Greek or Latin and should be descriptive of the organism. Both names should be printed in italics, the genus with a capital and the species with a lower-case initial letter. The name of the fossil is often followed by the name of the writer who first described it. More than 100,000 species of fossils have been named and described and new ones are still being discovered.

Limited Range of Species. One of the most important facts of earth history is that species of plants and animals are more or less limited in time. In the past, different species have made their appearance, lived for a time and then become extinct. Although some have lived longer than others, no single species has existed for a large portion of geologic time.

Since species come and go, the total assemblage of plants and animals now living on the earth is different from that of any time in the past. Likewise, the assemblage of any particular epoch of the past is different from that of any other epoch. The fossils contained in any rock formation represent the organisms that lived at the time that rock was formed. Consequently, rocks of different ages have different kinds and assemblages of fossils.

Let us consider a succession of rock formations, A, B, and C, each containing several species of fossils. Some of the species occurring in each formation are not found in either of the other two; other species are found in two adjacent formations, either A and B or B and C; and a few are found in all three. We see then that some fossils have a very narrow range in time, while others persist longer. Those with such a limited range that they occur only in a rock formation of a certain age are called *index fossils*.

In the latter part of the eighteenth century an observant civil engineer in England, named William Smith, discovered that the different fossiliferous rock formations there could be identified by their fossil content. Investigations since then have confirmed this principle and proved it universally applicable. Now it is not necessary to find strata superposed on each other nor to trace formations continuously from one region to another in order to determine their relative ages. If the rocks are fossiliferous their relative ages can be determined from outcrops in regions widely separated or even on opposite sides of the ocean.

Our knowledge of the types of organisms characteristic of different geologic times, and of their living habits, is very extensive. This knowledge is used to help decipher the earth's history. An interesting illustration of this may be found in reports of research being done in the ocean basins. West of the Hawaiian Islands in the Pacific Ocean there is a chain of submerged basaltic mountains with their tops at 5,400 feet below sea level. On their tops are sediments containing Tertiary corals, mollusks, and echinoderms. We know that reef corals now live in shallow water. Apparently, a chain of basaltic islands was submerged during Cretaceous time, so that their upper parts received Tertiary sediments. Later, the ocean floor sank still more, bringing the island tops down to 5,400 feet below sea level.

Changes in Living Things. Darwin's conclusion that living things change has been called "the grandest generalization of the nineteenth century." Before announcing this conclusion he had collected and studied abundant evidence to support it. The work of many investigators since Darwin has confirmed and established clearly his belief. Some things are still not clear as to *how* and *why* organisms change, but the fact that they do change is clear. Like many other natural changes, these changes in living things are so slow that they are scarcely recognizable in a short period of time. Looking back over the span of earth history, however, one commands a sweeping view of the great procession of life development.

Examination of the fossil record shows that the assemblage of organisms in any one period of time differs from that of any other period. This fact led to the early belief in universal catastrophes and multiple creations. It was thought that the organisms of each period had been destroyed by a cataclysm and those of the succeeding period were entirely a new creation. More detailed examination, however, reveals that the changes have been gradual and transitional, rather than abrupt, and that the plants and animals of any one period are descended from those of the preceding period.

The earliest organisms of which we have any record are simple types. From these simple forms of life, by gradual changes over long periods of time, have developed the higher or more complex kinds. Not all groups have progressed at the same rate, however, for many relatively simple types still persist. Even though some groups remain relatively simple for a long time, minor changes which differentiate the species of one age from those of another can nevertheless be seen. And, once a species becomes extinct, it never reappears at a later date. The fossil record further shows that the earliest organisms all lived in the sea and that land life is a much later development. It also shows that the highest forms have evolved on land, where the stimulus of varied environmental conditions is greatest.

Paleogeography. Ancient geography reconstructed by our study of rocks and fossils. Sedimentary rocks of marine and continental origin, deposited in areas now widely separated, may be correlated, or matched chronologically, by various methods. Within one continent, it is often possible to follow continuous outcrops of the same formation on the surface. This may also be done from a study of rocks found by drilling.

Sediments in widely-separated regions are correlated by means of index fossils. Several genera of Cambrian trilobites are found in Europe and North America, showing that in that period there were continuous shallow seaways linking what are now largely land areas.

By studying the ecology (environmental conditions) of present marine and land life, we can interpret the nature of the environment of ancient life. For example, abundant fossil reef-building corals in a limestone indicate that the sediment was formed in sea-water not deeper than 240 feet, and at a temperature of about 70°F. In the Mid-continent region of the United States, beds of Pennsylvania age consist of thin marine shales and limestones alternating with sandstones and shales containing fossil land plants and coal. This indicates that the region consisted of low-lying delta plains periodically invaded by shallow marine waters.

The positions of former shorelines are revealed not only by fossils, but also by different lithologic facies. Gravel and coarse sand show deposition near shore. Increasingly finer sediments indicate that the area of deposition was farther from the land. In this way, we can also interpret something about the topography of the lands which supplied the sediments.

ABSOLUTE AGES OF MINERALS AND ROCKS

In addition to dating rocks geologically, largely a relative matter in the past, it is now possible to actually determine the age in years of minerals found in the three classes of rocks on the basis of radioactivity. The rates of atomic disintegration of many elements, and the resulting products are known. The Uranium/Lead and the Thorium/Lead methods have given us the oldest dates so far. Uraninite and monazite from a pegmatitie dike in Precambrian rocks of Manitoba, Canada, show an age of about 3,360 million years. Clearly, the rocks intruded by this dike are even older.

A second method is the mass spectrometric analysis of the Strontium/Rubidium ratio. The preferred minerals for this are muscovite and biotite. Potash feldspar and hornblende have also been used, and give an age of about 1,000 million years for a syenite in Quebec, Canada. This intrusion was probably related to the orogeny which produced the Grenville rock metamorphism.

A third method of increasing usefulness is the Potassium/Argon method. It is most applicable to minerals older than 10 million years, and is most dependable when used on the micas. By this method, the crystalline gneisses, limestones, and schists of the New York City area are shown to have been metamorphosed about 366 million years ago. Potassium-bearing minerals such as sylvite (potassium chloride) and glauconite (potassium iron silicate) formed at the time of deposition of sediments, have yielded dates of 285 million years for the Middle Devonian of Canada, 142 million years for the Cretaceous in Canada, and dates ranging from 55 million to 12 million years for epochs of the Cenozoic in New Zealand.

For dating materials existing during the last 40 thousand years or less, we depend on radioactive carbon 14. This is applicable to pollen, wood, peat, and bone. Charcoal from a cave in France is thus dated as 15,500 years.

Suggestions for Further Reading

GOLDRING, Winifred, *Handbook of Paleontology for Beginners and Amateurs, Part I, The Fossils* (Albany, New York State Museum Handbook 9, 1950).

KNOPF, Adolph, "Measurement of Geologic Time," *Scientific Monthly,* November, 1957.

LULL, Richard S., *Organic Evolution* (New York, Macmillan, 1947).

SIMPSON, G. G., *The Life of the Past* (New Haven, Yale University Press, 1953).

TWENHOFEL, William H., *Principles of Sedimentation* (New York, McGraw-Hill, 1950).

ZUENER, F. E., *Dating the Past* (London, Methuen, 1953).

—26—

A Short Sketch of Earth History

THE PRECAMBRIAN ERAS

PRECAMBRIAN ROCKS everywhere form a basement beneath younger formations, and about 75 per cent of them are covered. Thousands of square miles of these ancient rocks are exposed in large areas such as the Canadian Shield and Fenno-Scandia. Smaller areas are exposed in mountainous areas where uplift has been followed by erosion. Such are the Vosges Mountains of Europe, parts of the Scottish Highlands, the Piedmont and Blue Ridge Provinces of eastern United States, the Adirondack Mountains of New York State, and the Black Hills of South Dakota. Deep erosion has exposed Precambrian rocks in the lower part of the Grand Canyon of the Colorado River in Arizona.

In some areas it is possible to recognize two groups of Precambrian rocks, Archeozoic, the most ancient, and Proterozoic, somewhat younger, separated by an unconformity.

The Archeozoic Era. The Archeozoic rocks are crystalline schists, gneisses, and marbles, with much igneous material. Radioactive minerals in a pegmatite dike in Manitoba, Canada, show an age of over 2,500 million years. The rocks intruded by the dike are, of course, older than the dike. Rocks of this era have suffered so much deformation and so much igneous intrusion, that their history is obscure. The only evidence of life is somewhat indirect, consisting of the presence of graphite in marbles and schists, probably derived from carbon of organic origin.

TABLE OF GEOLOGIC TIME

The larger time units into which the long span of earth history is divided are given in the table below. Study of this, the greatest of all histories, reveals the same times of crisis, of change and conflict, the same rise and fall of the ruling faction, the same growing dominance of certain trends that we know in our own human history.

Major Divisions and Duration of Earth History

II THE GEOLOGICAL OR GRADATIONAL EON

Era	Period	Minimum Duration in millions of years	Minimum Time since the beginning in millions of years
Cenozoic	Quaternary	1	1
	Tertiary	69	70
Mesozoic	Cretaceous	65	135
	Jurassic	40	175
	Triassic	40	215
Paleozoic	Permian	35	250
	Pennsylvanian	50	300
	Mississippian	50	350
	Devonian	40	390
	Silurian	30	420
	Ordovician	60	480
	Cambrian	80	560
Precambrian			
Proterozoic	Keweenawan	1,000	1,560
	Huronian	1,800	3,360
Archeozoic	Timiskaming	?	?
	Keewatin	2,600	?

I THE ASTRONOMICAL OR FORMATIVE EON

?	?	4,500	?

The Proterozoic Era. Proterozoic rocks are generally less metamorphosed than those of the Archeozoic. They contain more limestone along with quartzite and slate. In some areas they are strongly folded, but in others, such as the Little Belt Mountains of Montana, they lie essentially undisturbed and very little metamorphosed. Late Precambrian time was perhaps the greatest of all periods of igneous action. In the region of the western Great Lakes are lava flows more than 25,000 feet thick. There were also large intrusions similar to those of the Archeozoic. Throughout the vast Canadian Shield numerous batholiths of Precambrian Age, some of them of Archeozoic Age and some of

Proterozoic, most of them granites, have been uncovered by erosion.

Proterozoic limestones in the Rocky Mountains and in Arizona have well-preserved colonies of calcareous marine algae. No evidence of animals with shells has been discovered. It seems that marine animals had not yet developed hard parts, or that much of the geologic record between Proterozoic and Cambrian times may be missing. The earliest Cambrian rocks contain a great diversity of Arthropods, highest of invertebrate animals, indicating that there should be in earlier formations a long record of animal evolution.

Widespread glacial climates have occurred as far back in earth history as Precambrian time. Tillites of that age are found in such widely-separated localities as southeastern Canada, northern Utah, the Yangtze Valley of China, South Africa, and Australia.

Precambrian Mineral Wealth. Because of extensive volcanism, the Precambrian rocks are rich in gold, uranium, silver, nickel, cobalt, and copper. The sedimentary iron ores of the Lake Superior district are the world's greatest.

Two of the better-known areas will serve to illustrate the nature of Precambrian rocks, their history, and relations to younger rocks.

1. *The Lake Superior District*

Penokean orogeny. Killarney granite.

Keweenawan. Coarse clastic sediments and basaltic lavas. Native copper.
            Duluth and Sudbury intrusives. Nickel ores.
Unconformity

Huronian. Slates, Quartzites, dolomites. Much hematite as iron ore.

Great unconformity

Algoman orogeny. Granite intrusion. Gold-bearing quartz veins.

Timiskaming. Arkose, sandstone, and shale.

Unconformity

Laurentian orogeny. Granites.

Keewatin. Coutchiching sediments: sandstones, shales and limestones
            interbedded with greenstones, metamorphosed lava, and ash.
            Some iron ore.

2. *The Grand Canyon of the Colorado River in Northern Arizona*

Archeozoic rocks are exposed in the lower part of the inner gorge of the canyon. The formation is mainly a schist, named the Vishnu, with granite intrusions. Overlying the Archeozoic complex with great unconformity is the Proterozoic Grand Canyon System, consisting of conglomerate, quartzite, shale, and limestone. The Proterozoic formations dip gently and are only slightly metamorphosed. After their deposition, the region was uplifted and faulted, forming block mountains. The region was then much eroded before the subsidence which allowed the deposition of the flat-lying Cambrian sedimentary beds.

PALEOZOIC ERA

Cambrian Period. In this period there appeared in North America a structural and geographic pattern which persisted with many modifications through the Paleozoic Era. Where we now have the Atlantic Continental Shelf, the Coastal Plain, and the Piedmont Province was the eastern borderland, Appalachia. On the site of the present Appalachian Mountains from Newfoundland to Alabama lay the Appalachian trough, or geosyncline. At some times this was divided into several separate seaways. In the present Gulf Coast Region was the land-mass Llanoria, and to the north of it the Ouachitan Trough. A western borderland, Cascadia, occupied the present site of western Canada, Washington, Oregon, and California. To the east of this lay the Cordilleran Trough, where we now have the Rocky Mountains. The northeastern part of the continent was occupied by the Canadian Shield, Laurentia. The geosynclines sank from time to time as they received sediments from the adjacent borderlands, which were repeatedly uplifted.

FIG. 26-1. Charles Doolittle Walcott (1850-1927), paleontologist, with specialization on the Cambrian fauna. Director of the U. S. Geological Survey (1894-1906). Organized the Reclamation Service, the Forestry Service, and the Bureau of Mines. *(Columbia University Dept. of Geology)*

The continental interior was flooded repeatedly by shallow marine waters, called epeiric seas.

The Cambrian started with marine waters encroaching upon a low-lying and weathered Precambrian surface. The earliest sediments are sands, but as the seaways became deeper and more extensive, shales and limestones were formed.

Cambrian life was notable for its great diversity, and for the large percentage of animals now extinct, such as the trilobites. Many of the living invertebrate types were represented, but some of them differed markedly from their modern representatives.

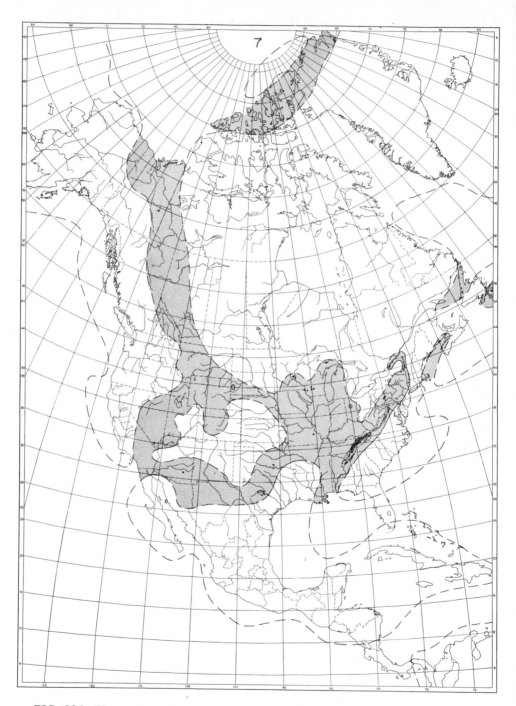

FIG. 26-2. Upper Cambrian paleogeography of North America. Shaded areas show the positions of epicontinental seas of that time; black areas show locations of outcrops of Upper Cambrian rocks. The small areas of the outcrops as compared with the large areas of the seaways are due to the facts that (1) extensive areas of Upper Cambrian rocks are concealed by overlying younger rocks and that (2) some of the rocks of this age have been removed by erosion. Dashed lines show inferred land boundaries. *(After Charles Schuchert, courtesy of John Wiley and Sons)*

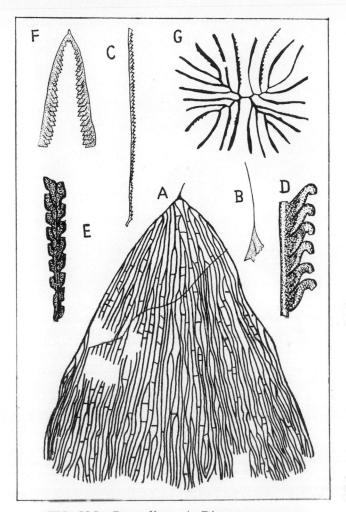

FIG. 26-3. **Graptolites.** A, Dictyonema, an attached, bushlike colony. B, Sicula of the same with budding first theca. C, Monograptus, a one-branched Silurian form with one row of thecae. D, The same, much enlarged. E, Climacograptus, one-branched form with two rows of thecae. F, Didymograptus, a two-branched form. G, Goniograptus, with many branches. *(New York State Museum)*

Ordovician Period. Marine waters overflowed the geosynclines and spread widely in broad epeiric seas across the central United States from the Arctic to the Gulf of Mexico. In this submergence, perhaps the greatest of all times, about half of present North America was flooded. Limestones and shales were the main deposits.

During later Ordovician time there appeared in what is now the

407

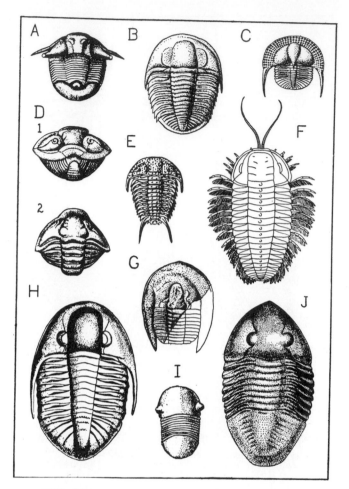

FIG. 26-4. **Ordovician trilobites.** A, Thaleops arctura. B, Proetus beecheri. C, Cryptolithus tessellatus. D, 1, 2, Calymene senaria. E, Ceraurus pleurexanthemus. F, Triarthrus eatoni (becki). G, Eoharpes ottawaensis. H, Bathyurus extans. I, Bumastus trentonensis. J, Isotelus gigas. *(New York State Museum)*

United States four stable areas which tended to remain relatively high throughout most of the Paleozoic. These were (1) the Highlands of northern Wisconsin, (2) the Ozark Dome of southeastern Missouri, (3) the Adirondack Dome in northern New York, and (4) the Cincinnati Arch, extending through Ohio, Kentucky, and Tennessee. This arch exerted an important control over sedimentation; it blocked the westward spread of clastic sediments from Appalachia. Toward the close of the period, uplift occurred in eastern North America from Newfoundland to New Jersey, as indicated by the coarse sediments washed into the

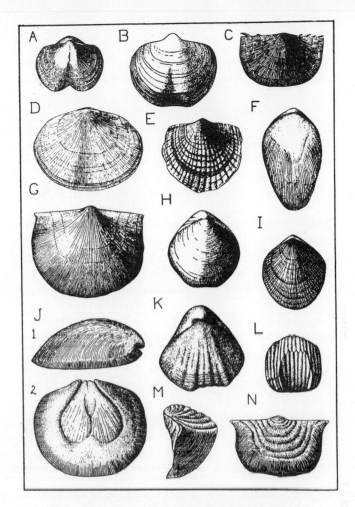

FIG. 26-5. Devonian brachiopods. A, Schizophoria striatula. B, Athyris spiriferoides. C, Chonetes coronatus. D, Rhipidomella oblata. E, Atrypa spinosa. F, Rensselaeria ovoides. G, Stropheodonta demissa. H, Meristella laevis. I, Atrypa reticularis. J, 1, 2, Hipparionyx proximus. K, Sieberella coeymanensis. L, Uncinulus mutabilis. M, N, Leptaena rhomboidalis. *(New York State Museum)*

Appalachian Trough from the east. This Taconian orogeny is also shown by an angular unconformity between Ordovician and Silurian rocks.

Great progress was made in the expansion of marine life. The graptolites, being floating creatures, had wide distribution. Trilobites were at the climax of their evolution. Brachiopods were numerous and varied. Among the molluscs, pelecypods and gastropods were expanding; the cephalopods, both straight and loosely coiled, became the largest animals of the time. The first true corals and bryozoa appeared. The stemmed echinoderms — cystoids, blastoids, and crinoids — became important.

Silurian Period. In this period seas spread almost as widely as in the preceding period. Reef-building corals lived in the limey seas from Alabama to the Arctic. Seas extending like this through wide latitude have often made it possible for animals suited to warm water to live in high latitudes. Toward the close of the period, a shrinking sea deposited salt and gypsum in the present region of Ontario, New York, and Michigan.

The Silurian Period closed quietly in most of North America; but in Europe the Caledonian disturbance formed a great arc of mountains extending through the British Isles and Scandinavia, and curving westward to northern Greenland.

Silurian marine life showed expansion among the corals, brachiopods, bryozoa, and crinoids. The Eurypterids, related to the scorpions, attained their climax in number and size. They seem to have been fresh-water forms. From the fossil evidence it appears that life first appeared on

FIG. 26-6. Representation of the transition from fish (lower) to amphibian (upper) which took place in the latter part of the Paleozoic Era. (*American Museum of Natural History*)

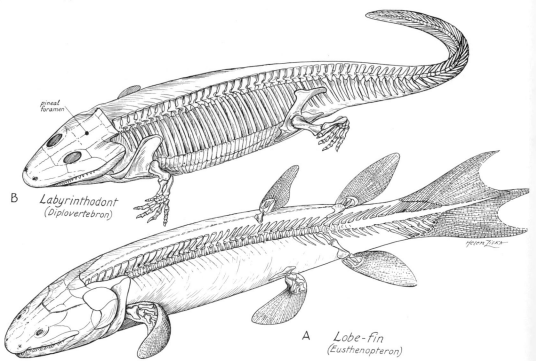

B   *Labyrinthodont*
     (*Diplovertebron*)

A   *Lobe-fin*
     (*Eusthenopteron*)

the lands in Silurian time. Remains of land plants are found in the Silurian of England and Australia. The first air-breathing animals, scorpions and millipeds, appeared. Partial remains of the first Chordates, the Ostracoderms, have been found in Ordovician rocks, but complete ones have been uncovered in the Silurian rocks of Europe.

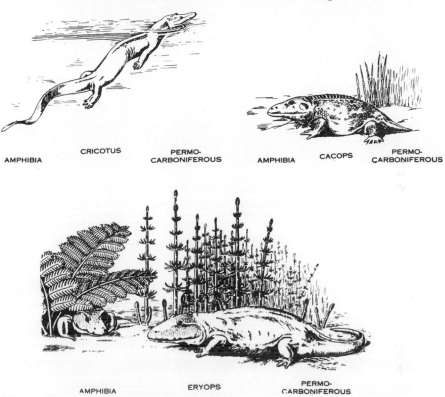

FIG. 26-7. Amphibia and vegetation of the late Paleozoic. *(American Museum of Natural History)*

Devonian Period. During Devonian time there was again flooding of central North America. From this time through the remainder of the Paleozoic Era, there was increasing crustal disturbance in the east, and marine waters came to be more restricted to central and western North America. In middle Devonian time began the Acadian disturbance, by which Appalachia was uplifted and folded. Great deltas were deposited to the west of these rising lands from Acadia southward to North Carolina. The northern part of the Appalachian Trough was filled with sediments and never again invaded by the sea. There was much extrusive vulcanism in the Acadian region, now evidenced by thick lava and tuff. Plutonic rocks were intruded, such as those which form the

FIG. 26-8. Fossil trunks and stumps of Devonian tree ferns are seen in the rocks in the foreground and a restoration of these ancient trees, with their foliage, in the background. Based on discoveries at the Gilboa dam, N. Y. The model from which this photograph was made is on display in the New York State Museum at Albany. *(Copyright J. A. Glenn, New York State Museum)*

FIG. 26-9. Restoration of Upper Devonian marine life. From left to right are glass sponges, coiled cephalopod, starfish, fishes, straight-shelled cephalopod, starfish, crinoid. Pelecypods and seaweeds are variously distributed. (*New York State Museum and Science Service*)

core of the White Mountains of New Hampshire. The deltaic deposits are well preserved in the Catskill Mountains of New York. In the central and western parts of the continent, shales and limestones were formed.

The first forests appeared during the Devonian. The Pteridophytes were well represented by ferns, seed-ferns, and the scale trees which were to become more important during Pennsylvania time. The first seed plants also appeared.

Among invertebrates, reef-building corals, especially large cup-corals and the honeycomb type of colonial corals were important. Brachiopods were at their climax; the spirifers were especially important. A great group of cephalopods, the ammonoids, got their start. This group developed bent and wavy partitions between the shell-chambers. The first ones were goniatites, represented by Tornoceras.

The vertebrates made great progress. The primitive jawless Ostracoderms, the Placoderms, and true sharks were common. Of greater significance from the evolutionary standpoint was the appearance of true bony fish, the Crossopterygians. These are thought to have been ancestral to the early Stegocephalian amphibians. The evidence lies in the structures of the limb (fin) bones, the skull, and the teeth. Remains of early amphibians have been found in the Devonian rocks of Greenland.

Mississippian and Pennsylvanian Periods (Carboniferous Period). The Appalachian area continued to receive continental sediments. With the filling of the geosyncline large swamp areas were developed, in which plants grew in such profusion as to form extensive beds of coal during Pennsylvania time. In the Mississippi Valley in Mississippian time, limestones were formed, but in the Pennsylvanian this region alternated between vast swamp-lands and shallow sea conditions. Llanoria was uplifted, supplying thick sediments to the Ouachita Trough. Strong pressure from the south folded these sediments into the Oklahoma Mountains. In Colorado, Utah, and New Mexico, the Colorado Mountains, not related to the present Rocky Mountains, were uplifted, and supplied detrital sediments to the seas around them. Because of the extensive swamp areas in various parts of the world, the Pennsylvanian is known as the time of greatest coal-making.

Among invertebrate animals, the echinoderms, especially blastoids, crinoids, and echinoids were important. The foraminifera became important rock-makers. Endothyra (a foraminifera) forms large portions of the famous Bedford (Indiana) building stone. The fusulines are so common in Pennsylvanian and Permian rocks that they are important index fossils for use in the petroleum industry. The lacy types of Bryozoa are distinctive of the upper Paleozoic. Among the Brachiopods, the robust, spiny productids were distinctive and common. Accompanying the growth of forests, insects became varied and large in Pennsylvanian time.

The first vertebrates well-adapted to a terrestrial life, the Reptiles,

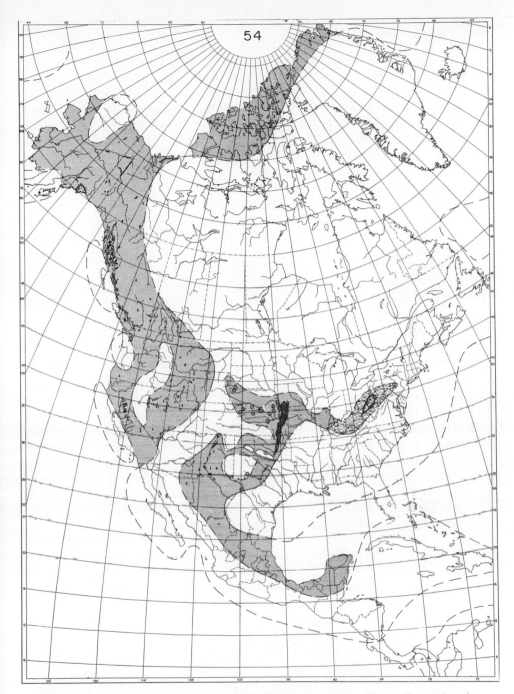

FIG. 26-10. Paleogeographic map of North America during Upper Pennsylvanian time. Shaded portions represent areas of deposition of marine strata. Dashed area shows nonmarine deposits. Outcrops are in black. Circles with center dots show oil fields. Dashed lines show inferred borders of the continent. *(After Charles Schuchert, courtesy John Wiley and Sons)*

415

appeared in the Pennsylvanian, while the Amphibians were still common.

Permian Period. The Appalachian Revolution at the close of the Permian Period forever put an end to the Appalachian geosyncline. Pressure from the east folded the thick sediments of the trough and thrust-faulted them, producing the structures seen in the present folded Appalachian Mountains. There was essentially no marine deposition east of Kansas. A Mid-continent seaway extended from Nebraska to Texas, but marine sediments gave way to lagoonal salt deposits. In western Texas and southeastern New Mexico, the Guadalupe Basin has 14,000 feet of Permian sedimentary rocks. The lower beds are chiefly marine limestones; the upper part is dominantly anhydrite, gypsum, and one of the world's great deposits of potash salts. The flat-lying Kaibab limestone of Permian age forms the rims of the Grand Canyon in Arizona.

The Permian was a period of contrasting climates. The southwestern United States had great aridity, as shown by dune sands, and salt deposits. Parts of Europe had similar climate. Southern Africa, Australia, India, and Brazil had glaciation.

Among invertebrates, the ammonoid cephalopods developed the ceratite and ammonite types of sutures. Reptiles evolved rapidly, becoming the ruling land animals. They were variously specialized for living in water or on land, and for carnivorous or herbivorous diets.

In the extensive swamplands of Pennsylvanian time, trees like Lepidodendron, Sigillaria, Calamites, Cordaites, and the seed-ferns had thrived. The arid and cold climates of the Permian greatly reduced these plants in size and number. The Cordaites type gave rise to the conifers, which soon became dominant.

The geographic and climatic changes were also difficult for many marine invertebrates. Types which became extinct were the trilobites, cystoids, blastoids, and several kinds of brachiopods.

MESOZOIC ERA

Triassic and Jurassic Periods. During the first two Periods of the Mesozoic Era, marine waters in North America were limited to the western part of the continent. Long seaways invaded the present west coast and Rocky Mountains regions. To the east of this area, from Wyoming southward into New Mexico there were deposited red sandstones and shales, gypsum, and eolian sands. Such rocks are seen in the Petrified Forest of northern Arizona and in Zion National Park, Utah. Eastern North America had a series of downfaulted basins from Acadia to North Carolina. In these basins continental red sandstones and shales, gray shales, and arkoses were deposited. Much igneous activity caused intrusion of dolerite sills and the extrusion of several basaltic lava flows. The nonmarine sediments of these periods are famous for dinosaur fossils.

At the close of the Jurassic, the Nevadian disturbance folded the rocks from British Columbia through California. There was much submarine volcanic action and the intrusion of great batholiths in the Coast Range and in the Sierra Nevada. The gold-bearing quartz veins of the Mother Lode in California were formed at this time.

Cretaceous Period. In the region of the present Rocky Mountains and High Plains, linking the Arctic with the Gulf of Mexico, lay the broad Rocky Mountain Geosyncline. Its waters were continuous with those covering the present Gulf Coast and Atlantic Coastal Plain.

The thick marine sediments formed in these seas are notable for a large quantity of chalk, from which the name of the period is derived. The Rocky Mountain Trough gradually filled with sediments carried to it from rising lands to the westward. As this great epeiric sea withdrew, there developed a swampy lowland from Alberta to Colorado rich in the vegetation which formed the important coal beds included within the Cretaceous. Similar to the Rocky Mountain Trough was a seaway in the region of the present Andes Mountains of South America.

One of the greatest revolutions of all time, the Laramide, uplifted, folded, and faulted the Cordilleran region in North and South America. In the Rocky Mountains of Colorado, Southern Wyoming, and Black Hills, the orogeny took the form of broad arches. In the northern Rockies, pressure from the west caused great thrust faults, such as the Lewis Thrust in Montana, in which Proterozoic rocks were thrust eastward over Cretaceous rocks of the High Plains. Also, the Pacific coastal belt was uplifted and volcanoes were active throughout this region. Large granitic intrusions formed batholiths in Idaho and Montana, and were responsible for the rich metallic mineral deposits of that area.

Mesozoic Life. Among invertebrate animals, the ammonoid cephalopods were at their culmination and the group of squid-like belemnoid cephalopods became important. Among echinoderms, the echinoids began a time of importance which continued into the Cenozoic. Many pelecypods and gastropods took on a more modern aspect.

During the Triassic and Jurassic Periods, cycads, ginkgos, and conifers were the dominant forest trees, but in Cretaceous time the Angiosperms, the higher flowering plants, became dominant. Their expansion was a helpful factor in the evolution of herbivorous mammals of this and the succeeding era.

The Mesozoic is called the Age of Reptiles. Dinosaurs, herbivorous and carnivorous, ruled the lands. Some reptiles, such as the Plesiosaurs, Ichthyosaurs, and Mosasaurs dominated the seas. Others, the Pterosaurs, developed the ability to fly. One line of reptiles gave rise to the birds in Jurassic time. Archaeopteryx, of the famous Solenhofen limestone of

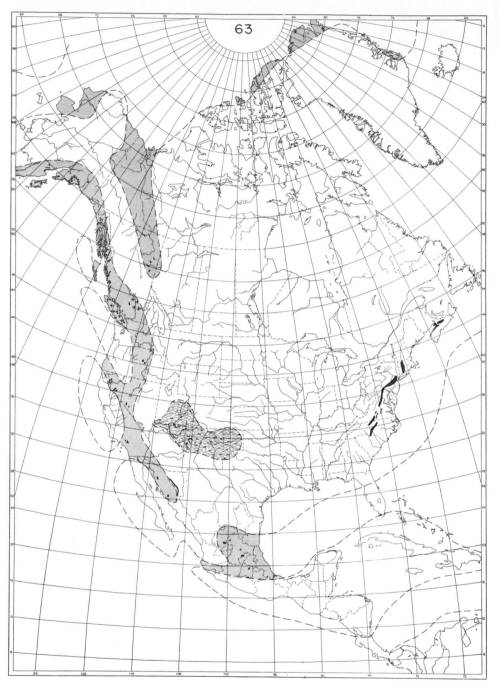

FIG. 26-11. Paleogeography of North America during Upper Triassic time. Shaded areas show marine deposits, with black spots indicating outcrops. The swamp symbols in the southwest and the black symbols in the east show areas of nonmarine deposits. *(After Charles Schuchert, courtesy John Wiley and Sons)*

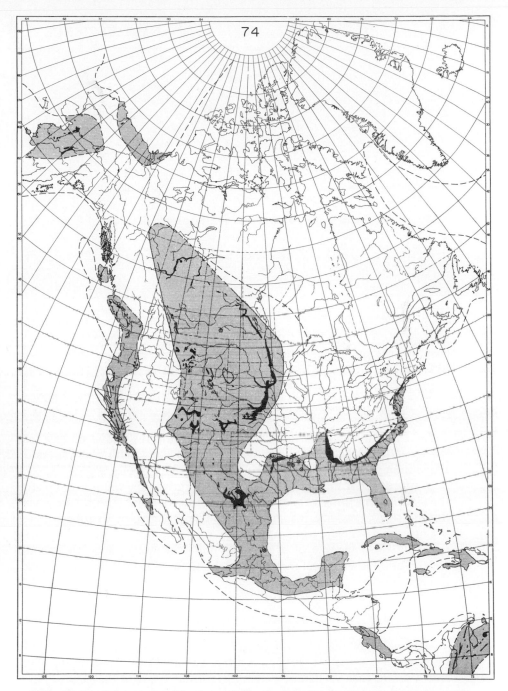

FIG. 26-12. Paleogeographic map of North America for Upper Cretaceous time.
Shaded areas show distribution of marine sediments, with outcrops in black. Circles
with center dots represent oil fields. Dashed lines represent inferred boundaries of
the land areas. *(After Charles Schuchert, courtesy John Wiley and Sons)*

FIG. 26-13. A restoration of the earliest-known bird, from the Upper Jurassic of Solenhofen, Bavaria. *(American Museum of Natural History)*

Germany, had teeth, but also feathers. With the restriction of seas and the general uplift of the continents which came with the Laramide Revolution great groups of reptiles died out.

It appears that mammals evolved from a group of reptiles in Triassic time. From the Jurassic beds of Europe, America, and Africa have come the remains of rat-size mammals called Pantotheres, or Trituberculates, because their molar teeth had three tubercles, or cusps. They were probably the ancestors of Marsupials and Placentals, the higher mammals. The first Placental mammals seem to have been Insectivores, like the present-day mole or shrew.

CENOZOIC ERA

Marine formations of the Cenozoic Era in North America are mostly restricted to a narrow strip along the Pacific Coast, and to the Gulf and Atlantic Coastal Plains. Nonmarine strata occur in the Great Plains, where sediments eroded from the Rocky Mountain uplift were deposited on the lowland to the east, and in such basins as the Green River and Bighorn in Wyoming. Later erosion of these poorly consolidated deposits has produced the striking badlands of some of these areas.

FIG. 26-14. Brontosaurus, a large herbivorous dinosaur from the Jurassic period. *(Harvard University Department of Geology)*

FIG. 26-15. A large carniverous dinosaur (Tyrannosaurus rex) from the Cretaceous period. *(U. S. Geological Survey)*

FIG. 26-16. Model of the head of a Triceratops, by Charles Lang. At the right of the picture is Otto Faulkenbash and at the left is Charles Lang. *(American Museum of Natural History)*

In eastern North America, the ridges and valleys of the Appalachians came into existence by differential erosion on the folded strata. The central part of the continent was rather stable. More exciting changes occurred in the west. The name Cascadian Revolution has been given to the changes that occurred in Cenozoic time. The Colorado Plateau was uplifted with normal faulting, thus bringing on the erosion which has produced the Grand Canyon. The Basin and Range Province and the Sierra Nevada owe their rugged topography to block faulting and to Cenozoic erosion on the fault blocks. The Columbia Plateau was formed by successive basaltic lava flows totalling some 5,000 feet thick and covering an area of 200,000 square miles. To the west of this plateau, the Cascade Mountains were uplifted, and large volcanoes such

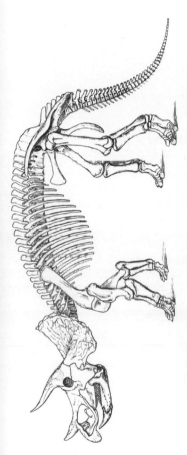

FIG. 26-17. Skeleton of the Triceratops, a Cretaceous horned dinosaur.
(*American Museum of Natural History*)

FIG. 26-18. Plesiosaurs and Icthyosaurs. Painting by Charles Knight.

FIG. 26-19. Restoration of an Upper Jurassic Pterosaur. *(American Museum of Natural History)*

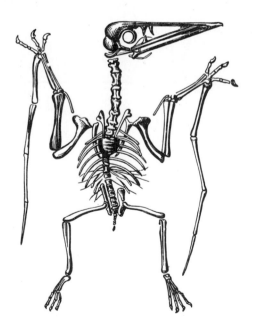

FIG. 26-20. Skeleton of a pterosaur (Pterodactyl), a flying reptile, from the Upper Jurassic strata of Solenhofen, Bavaria. *(American Museum of Natural History)*

as Rainier, Shasta, and Mount Lassen grew upon them. Along the Pacific border, the Coast ranges were folded and faulted. The fact that this is still an unstable region is shown by the present active faults, such as the San Andreas.

In other continents, too, the present relief features had their origin in this period. In South America, the Andes were eroded to a low level and later elevated and deeply dissected. Here, too, volcanoes, such as Chimborazo, rise high above the general level of the mountain summits. The Alpine system of Europe is largely of Cenozoic origin. Repeated thrusting from the south has made the structure in the Alps as complex as any on earth. Other mountains formed in Europe during the Cenozoic Age were the Apennines and the Pyrenees. The Himalayas of Asia owe their altitude to Cenozoic uplifts. The amount of uplift involved in these last-named mountains is indicated by finding early Cenozoic marine limestones at an elevation of 19,000 feet.

The Quaternary (Pleistocene), which began about 1,000,000 years ago, is most noted for four advances of continental glaciers in North America and Europe, and for the evolution of man.

The Cenozoic Era is named the Age of Mammals. Mammals have been better able to adjust themselves to different environments than have the other vertebrates. The important trends in mammalian evolution have consisted of a general increase in body size and relative brain development, specialization of the limbs and feet, and specialization of the teeth. The plant-eaters have developed longer legs for speed, and teeth suitable for eating grasses. The carnivores have developed claws and sharper teeth. Some, like the primates, have developed prehensile fingers and toes with nails. The earliest Primate is found in the Oligocene of Egypt. It appears that the higher Primates, apes and man, descended from ancestors similar to the Tarsiers, which now live in southeastern Asia.

Near the middle of the Cenozoic Era, the ancestors of apes and those of man took different lines of development. It is not thought that man has descended from the apes, but that both groups can be traced back to a common ancestry. A more erect posture has forced the human types to certain changes in the pelvis, limbs, and position of the skull on the vertebral column. Australopithecus, found in southern Africa and believed to be fairly close to man's ancestors, is of the early Pleistocene Age. This find and others make it seem that Africa was the continent of human origin. Pithecanthropus of Java and Sinanthropus of China lived in the early middle Pleistocene. They may have been the ancestors of Neanderthal man and Cro-Magnon man, who later lived partially contemporaneously in Asia and Europe. Man apparently did not reach the Americas until the upper Pleistocene.

The history of man's origin and early development is still somewhat obscure. In the study of this important phase of Man's history geology joins with biology, anthropology, and archaeology.

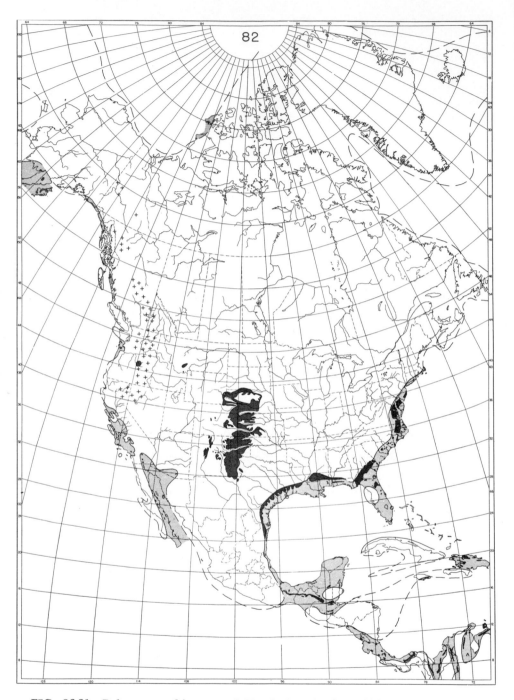

FIG. 26-21. Paleogeographic map of North America in Middle Cenozoic (Miocene) time. The shaded areas around the margins of the continent show marine overlap. Outcrops are in black. Black areas in the middle of the continent show nonmarine deposits. Cross marks are areas of volcanic rocks. Dashed lines show land outlines. *(After Charles Schuchert, courtesy John Wiley and Sons)*

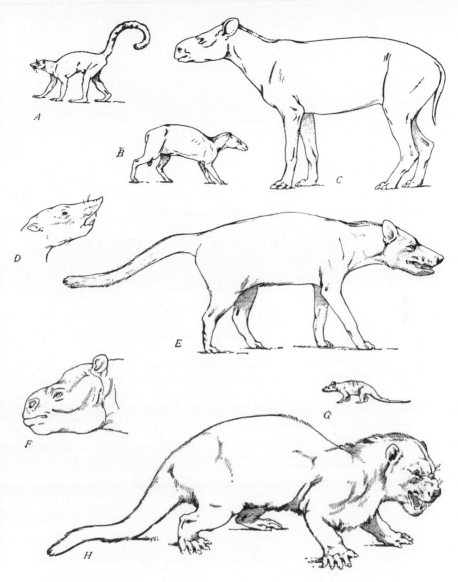

FIG. 26-22. Outline restorations to the same scale of contemporary Middle Eocene mammals. By Charles R. Knight. A, Notharctus, a primate, arboreal. B, Orohippus, a primitive horse, cursorial. C, Hyrachyus, a primitive rhinoceros. D, Tillotherium, a tillodont. E, Dromocyon, a creodont, cursorial. F, Palaosyops, a titanothere. G, Metacheiromys, an armadillo. H, Patriofelis, a creodont. (*American Museum of Natural History*)

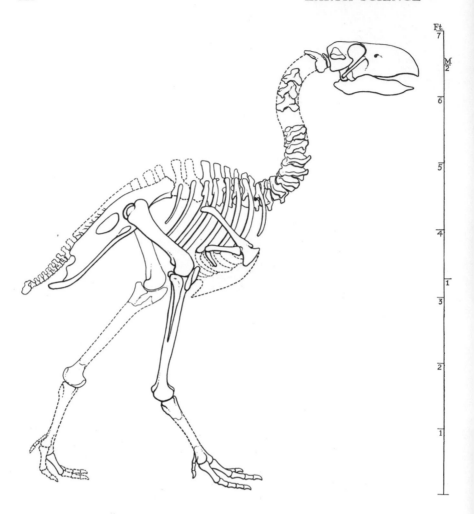

FIG. 26-23. Reconstructed skeleton of a Diatryma, an early Cenozoic flightless bird. *(American Museum of Natural History)*

Suggestions for Further Reading

DUNBAR, Carl O., *Historical Geology*, 2nd edition (New York, Wiley, 1960).

MOORE, Raymond C., *Introduction to Historical Geology*, 2nd edition (New York, McGraw-Hill, 1958).

SIMPSON, G. G., *The Life of the Past* (New Haven, Yale University Press, 1953).

FIG. 26-24. North American horses and elephants of the late Cenozoic. These animals became extinct in North America during the Pleistocene. *(American Museum of Natural History)*

FIG. 26-25. Representations of early man. From left to right: Pithecanthropus, Neanderthal, and Cro-Magnon. *(American Museum of Natural History)*

27

Useful Aspects of Earth Science

The sciences that deal with the facts and principles of nature have made and will continue to make important contributions to human progress and happiness. Even though some scholars appear to have no desire to put their knowledge and discoveries to practical use, sooner or later someone utilizes that information for the benefit of man. Paleontologists, for example, long boasted that their specialized knowledge could be of no practical value; now, however, people trained in that field are in great demand in the work of petroleum exploration. Some of the many useful aspects of the earth sciences will be briefly discussed here.

METEOROLOGY

Of all the elements in the natural environment, the weather is the most important; it affects directly or indirectly almost every human activity. Mark Twain's often-quoted statement that "Everybody talks about the weather but nobody does anything about it" is not entirely accurate. We do control the weather in our homes; and on many occasions the temperature over large areas of citrus fruit orchards is held above freezing and millions of dollars worth of fruit thereby saved from destruction by the process of smudging (burning oil in pots). It is true, of course, that we can not make any large-scale changes in the weather, but if given sufficient warning of its natural changes we can profit by its benign moods and protect ourselves and our property from its rigors.

In order to adjust our activities to the weather, advance information on its behavior is of the utmost importance. In this country the United States Weather Bureau is the agency chiefly responsible for performing this valuable service. From data gathered by more than 300 regular observing stations, the Bureau issues forecasts at least once daily and distributes them throughout the country by radio, television, telegraph, telephone, mail, and newspapers. At the present time, reliable forecasts can be made only a few days in advance, but these are nevertheless sufficient to enable us to save large sums in property and to avoid untold suffering.

Among the most striking eccentricities of the weather are the *hurricanes* which visit the Caribbean, Gulf of Mexico, and Atlantic Coast regions in late summer and autumn. The development and speed and direction of movement of these tropical disturbances are closely watched and storm warnings are issued by radio throughout those areas likely to be affected. On receiving warning of an approaching storm, ships at sea make for port and those in port remain there. Airplanes are grounded. Fishermen protect their boats and nets. The Coast Guard prepares for salvage and rescue work, and people are evacuated from danger areas.

River *floods* are another great source of danger to life and property. In times of excessive rainfall or rapid melting of snow, streams with flood plains are apt to overflow their banks and inundate the flat bottom lands. Generally the cause of a flood is of several days' duration and the rise of the water is gradual, so that ample warning can be given. When flood warnings are issued the farmers remove their livestock and harvested crops from the bottom lands. Warehousemen and merchants move their goods to upper floors. Dams, locks and levees along the river are inspected and repaired and, if necessary, reinforced. As the flood waters rise, there is a general exodus of the inhabitants and their movable property from those areas where inundation is expected.

Cold air masses sweeping in from the north bring frosts and destructive *cold waves* to a large part of the country. Among the activities most affected by these sudden cold waves are those concerned with the production and distribution of foodstuffs. Advance notice of an approaching cold wave is of tremendous importance. Farmers then have opportunity to set out smudgepots in their orchards and to cover up their tender plants; ripe fruit and vegetables are picked before the freeze; livestock is driven in from the range and meat animals are slaughtered. Transportation companies protect perishable goods by heating, or rush them to their destination in advance of the cold wave; if this is not possible, the shipments are held until the freeze is over. Heating and lighting companies prepare to meet increased demands. Ice factories curtail their output. Merchants advertise cold-weather articles. The common man pours antifreeze into the radiator of his automobile, checks his fuel supply and heating system, and gets out his warm clothing.

Protracted *rainy spells* are a potential source of much damage and inconvenience, but those who take advantage of the forecasts are least annoyed and best prepared to turn the wet season to advantage. At planting time, for instance, the farmer likes to get his seed in the ground just before a rain. By keeping in close touch with the forecasts for his region, he can usually time his seeding to the best advantage. At harvesting time hay, wheat, oats, and most other cereals must be kept dry after they are cut. If he can expect a few days of dry weather, the farmer may be able to cut his crop and haul it into the barn before rain spoils it; if rain is forecast, on the other hand, the crop is best left uncut until the wet weather is over. The efficient fruit grower does not spray his orchard just before a rain; the rain washes the spray off and only doubles his work. If rain is predicted at picking time, however, he will make every effort to gather the crop before the rain and ship the fruit dry. The activities of many people are affected more or less by the prediction of protracted rainy weather. The building contractor rushes the completion of the roof on the building; the merchant goes over his stock of overshoes and umbrellas; the field worker delays the start of his trip or, if he is already in the field, hastens its conclusion; and the camper shortens his vacation.

In military operations, too, the weather affects the conduct and course of war in many ways. Violent storms ground aircraft and keep surface vessels in port. Fog conceals movement, giving advantage to the attacking force and also aiding the escape of the defeated. Heavy rains and sudden thaws slow up the movements of ground troops and supplies. Cold waves interfere with the operation of machines and bring severe discomfort to the soldiers, especially to the wounded. Leaders who plan and execute military undertakings, whether on land, sea or in the air, are constantly alert to the probabilities of weather conditions. In fact, so important a factor is the weather in modern war that strict censorship is imposed on all forecasts that might be useful to the enemy.

In numerous instances storm, fog, or cold wave have determined the course of important operations, or even the outcome of a war. It is highly probable that William the Norman would have lost the battle of Hastings in 1066 had he sailed from Normandy on schedule, for Harold the Saxon was waiting for him in southern England with a large and well-equipped army. However, strong storm winds delayed William's sailing for several weeks. During this delay another invader, Harald Hadrada, landed on the northeast coast of Britain, and Harold marched northward to meet and defeat this enemy in the Battle of Stamford Bridge. When William landed a few days later, Harold's tired and depleted troops made forced marches to meet him. In the ensuing battle, the Normans won by such a narrow margin that it seems safe to say that the invasion would have been unsuccessful had William sailed

FIG. 27-1. Oil derrick on the prairie lands of southern Alberta. *(Geological Survey of Canada)*

on schedule and met Harold's forces while they were fresh and undepleted. Other oft-quoted cases in which storms influenced the course of history are the destruction of the Persian fleet in its attempt to invade Greece in 490 B.C. and of the Spanish Armada when it set out to conquer England in 1588.

It is reliably reported that heavy fog in the Mediterranean saved Napoleon from either capture by the British fleet or self-destruction when he was returning from Egypt in 1799. It had been decided that the crew of the vessel which carried Napoleon would blow up the ship if they were intercepted by the patrolling British fleet, rather than surrender their leader. But the concealing fog allowed them to slip through the blockade unseen and unmolested. When one stops to think that the Napoleonic Wars had not yet, and therefore never would have, occurred the influence of that fog on the course of history seems profound. Thirteen years later, however, the weather was not so kind to Napoleon when he underestimated the rigors of the Russian winter.

In World War II the failure of the Germans to reach Moscow in 1941 was due in no small part to the early arrival and severity of the cold winter weather. And the stealthy attack on Pearl Harbor by the Japanese was greatly aided by fog. Also, the time of landing of the Allies on the Normandy beaches was strictly governed by weather forecasts.

MINERAL DEPOSITS

Importance in Civilization. Since the dawn of human history, minerals and rocks have been used in ever increasing quantities. Their importance in the development of civilization is suggested by the fact that the successive cultural stages are named from earth materials. In the early Stone Age, crude implements and utensils were fashioned from chert, flint, and other varieties of quartz and also from obsidian and other dense rocks. Later in the Stone Age still other rocks, such as soapstone and limestone, were used, and greater skill was acquired in shaping them. As man's knowledge of earth materials continued to increase, as he developed more and more skill in utilizing them, there followed in order, the Copper, Bronze, and Iron Ages. In terms of metals we are still in the Iron Age; even though we use many other metals, iron is still by far the most important.

In this country, as well as in several others, the extraction and processing of earth materials is an industry second in importance only to agriculture. The value of mineral products produced in the United

FIG. 27-2. Limestone quarry, Drummond Island, Mich. Quarrying is facilitated by the rectangular jointing. *(Photo by Russell, U. S. Geological Survey)*

States amounts to more than 14 billion dollars annually. Along with the increased demand for minerals and the consequent exhaustion of old sources of supply, the services of the mining geologist have become increasingly necessary in the discovery and evaluation of new deposits.

Origin and Occurrence of Mineral Deposits. That branch of earth science called economic geology deals with the methods of origin and conditions of occurrence as well as with the distribution and utilization of economically valuable mineral deposits. These commercial mineral deposits include: (1) metallic minerals, such as the ores of iron, copper, tin, lead, zinc, gold, silver, and other metals; (2) building materials, such as granite, marble, slate, and limestone; (3) fuels, such as coal and petroleum; (4) fertilizers, such as nitrates, phosphates, and potash; (5) chemical minerals, such as sulphur, salt and fluorite; and (6) the gems.

In general we may say that the economic mineral deposits are parts of, or are associated with, the igneous, sedimentary, and metamorphic rocks. They are therefore formed by the process of volcanism, sedimentation, and metamorphism. Some of the common rocks are of economic

FIG. 27-3. The Golden Chest mineral vein (white), Coeur d'Alene, Idaho. This vein contains silver, lead, and other metals, and is mined through shafts and tunnels. *(Photo taken in one of the mine tunnels by Ransome, U. S. Geological Survey)*

FIG. 27-4. Mining a placer gold deposit by hydraulicking, which washes away the lighter materials and concentrates the heavy gold, Idaho County, Idaho. *(Photo by Capps, U. S. Geological Survey)*

value in themselves; granite and limestone often make up the outer walls of buildings, marble trims the interiors and slate covers the roofs. More commonly, however, the valuable mineral deposits represent concentrations of materials that are relatively scarce in the lithosphere.

Those mineral deposits which are of igneous origin are concentrations of certain minor but valuable constituents of magmas. These minerals may either be more or less segregated in certain parts of the parent rock or else be injected into the surrounding rock as *mineral veins*. Many of the metallic mineral deposits are the result of igneous action.

In sedimentary mineral deposits the valuable materials are concentrated by the mechanical and chemical processes of gradation. These processes of weathering, erosion, and deposition sort matter: heavy minerals are left behind while the lighter materials are carried away; hard minerals persist while the soft ones are ground to bits; and insoluble matter remains after the soluble has been carried away in solution. Valuable concentrations of heavy and insoluble metals, such as gold and platinum, are sometimes concentrated in gravel and sand along streams that are eroding the rocks in which these metals were originally formed. Such accumulations are called *placer deposits*.

Metamorphism plays a relatively minor role in the actual formation of mineral deposits, though it is often important in changing the character of those that were originally formed by igneous or sedimentary processes.

Exploration for Mineral Deposits. In the past many of our valuable mineral deposits were discovered by accident or by prospectors who had

FIG. 27-5. Modern cold-water thawing plant and dredging operations in the Klondike placer gold-mining district of Yukon. Here the ground is frozen to a depth of as much as 200 feet and must be thawed before dredging. (*Geological Survey of Canada*)

little or no formal training in geology. Now that most of the easily discovered deposits have been found, it is necessary for those who would discover new deposits or appraise the value of old ones to be well trained in economic geology. The prospector must be able not only to identify the various useful minerals when he sees them; he must also know their modes of origin and habits of occurrence. He must know the kinds of rocks in which to search for certain mineral deposits and be able to judge the extent and value of these deposits beneath the surface. Although individual prospecting is still important, much geological exploration is now carried on by organized federal and state surveys and by mining companies. Exploring parties ordinarily consist of several members and are provided with the various instruments necessary for both surface and subsurface prospecting. In times of war, when mineral products are demanded and used on a vast scale, the tempo of geological exploration is greatly accelerated and a large percentage of the geologists of the country temporarily augment the staffs of the surveys and the mining companies.

Much of the exploration for economic mineral deposits, including the metallic minerals as well as oil and gas, is now done by subsurface methods. These methods involve the use of physical instruments, such as the seismograph, the gravimeter, and the magnetometer. People trained in both physics and geology are required in these operations. Thus the union of geology and physics has evolved into the important and rapidly growing science of geophysics.

437

FOSSIL FUELS

Coal and petroleum are designated as fossil fuels because they are the residues of past life.

Coal. Plants that grow and die in swamps are the main source material of coal. In such an environment the dead plants undergo a process of *carbonization*, instead of the oxidation that decays the dead plants on drier land. The cellulose of plants has the composition of $C_6H_{10}O_5$, that is, about 44 per cent carbon. On being buried in swamps the cellulose undergoes slow change. The principle products given off in this change are carbon dioxide (CO_2), methane (CH_4), and water (H_2O). In this process the hydrogen and oxygen are lost at a more rapid rate than is the carbon, so that the percentage of carbon remaining becomes higher and higher. The percentage of carbon in bituminous (soft) coal is usually 75 to 85, and in anthracite (hard coal) it may be as much as 95. Since animals, such as amphibians, also live in swamps, their remains are incorporated with those of the plants.

Although time is important in determining the degree of carbonization, it is not the only factor. Diastrophism and thermal condition may be more important. Coal of the same age may be of different grades in different localities. For example, from the subbituminous area of Iowa eastward to the anthracite region of eastern Pennsylvania coal of the same age increases in the degree of carbonization. Still farther east, in Rhode Island, completely carbonized material of the same age occurs in the form of graphite. Clearly, the degree and nature of the disturbance of the earth's crust are closely related to the degree of carbonization of the organic material.

The Pennsylvanian Period is called the Great Coal Age. During that time large areas of the earth were emerging from the oceans and producing low-lying swamp lands. Plant evolution had reached the stage in which many plants were suited to growing luxuriantly in those swamps. Widespread mild climate was favorable to the plant growth. Oscillations of the land level, either by the subsidence of the swamps or by the elevation of regions nearby, allowed the accumulated organic matter in the swamps to be covered by inwashed sediment and thus preserved. In some localities the oscillations occurred a number of times, for several coal beds occur separated by layers of other sedimentary beds.

Although the Pennsylvanian Period was the great coal-forming age, some coal is found in the rocks of the preceding (Mississippian) period and in the rocks of more recent periods. The rocks older than the Mississippian are not known to contain productive coal beds. Therefore, the geologist, or prospector, in search of coal deposits confines himself to regions where the rocks are Mississippian or younger in age. Furthermore, he would confine his search to those rocks that are nonmarine in origin.

FIG. 27-6. World-famous Utah Copper Division Mine of Kennecott Copper Corporation at Bingham Canyon, Utah. The operating area covers 972 acres, and the mine consists of a series of levels with connecting switchbacks. The vertical distance from the bottom level to the top level on the west side is 2,210 feet. The mining area contains about 177 miles of standard gauge track, most of which is moved frequently to meet operating needs. *(Salt Lake City Chamber of Commerce)*

Aside from wood and charcoal made from wood, coal was for many years our most important fuel. It is still important for many purposes, such as the smelting of iron ores and the production of gas and electric power. In recent years, however, the use of petroleum as a fossil fuel has surpassed that of coal.

Petroleum. Petroleum, that is, natural oil and gas, is mainly the decay products of marine animals, though members of the Plant Kingdom, such as diatoms, may contribute.

Petroleum consists of hydrocarbons, many of them, and constitutes a large part of the material for organic chemistry. It is not a simple compound, but a mixture of many hydrocarbon compounds. When these many compounds are partially separated, either in nature or by man, there results three physical states of the hydrocarbons, that is, gaseous, liquid, and solid. The gaseous fraction is called natural gas, the liquid part is oil, and the semisolid part is asphalt or paraffin.

In nature the petroleum generally occurs as oil. From the oil many products are obtained by fractional distillation. On heating, the lighter hydrocarbon compounds go off first and are collected and used as natural gas. The next compounds to vaporize are collected and separated and condensed to the various liquid products of petroleum, ranging from the light napthalene and benzene through the grades of gasoline and then through the grades of lubricating oils. The residue of the distillation of most natural oils is asphalt; it is used in the construction of macadam roads.

In contrast with coal, petroleum-bearing strata have few outcrops. Being mobile, the petroleum, if not trapped, migrates to the surface and evaporates, leaving a deposit of natural asphalt.

Organic matter buried in marine muds forms petroleum. The fluid may migrate to more porous beds and form a *pool*. A pool is a porous stratum, or series of strata, more or less saturated with oil. As a rule there is ground water beneath the oil: the oil, being lighter, rides on top of the water. Natural gas often accumulates above the oil. It is necessary to have a structural trap in order to localize the oil sufficiently to form a pool. Such a trap might be a structural dome, an anticline, the flanks of an impervious intrusion, certain types of faults, and unconformities. In any case there must be a rising porous bed to contain the oil and the underlying water and an overlying impervious bed to prevent the oil from escaping.

The tasks of the oil geologist are to locate the favorable strata and the favorable structures. Much of this work can be done by the examination of surface exposures. For stratigraphic and structural conditions at great depth the oil geologist is depending more and more on geophysical exploration. Inasmuch as oil is of marine origin and no commercial quantities have been found in the Precambrian rocks, the geologist and geophysicist in search of petroleum limit their activities to regions of marine strata that are younger than the Precambrian.

CARTOGRAPHY

In practically all walks of civilized life, maps of some kinds are used, often so commonly that their importance may be overlooked. The constructing of maps and especially the collecting of necessary map information requires training in the earth sciences. Progress in cartography has come largely with the acquisition of more detailed and accurate knowledge of the earth.

General maps, such as road maps and political and physical maps, are published by commercial companies and widely distributed; yet few people realize the great amount of geographical research on which they are based. The daily weather map issued by the United States Weather Bureau and published in newspapers all over the country represents a summary and analysis of information contributed by several hundred widely scattered observers. The importance of this map and of the forecasts based on it have already been discussed.

Some maps, however, are more limited in distribution because special training is required to read them. Yet many of these specialized maps, such as the topographic and the geologic maps, are tremendously important.

The topographic contour map is the most accurate means of representing the relief of the earth's surface. It is essential to explorers and aviators, real-estate men and civil engineers, teachers and soldiers and to many others. The information that makes up a topographic map is gathered by trained topographers in co-operation with experienced surveyors. The geologic map is in some respects even more fundamental for it portrays the nature of the bedrock on which the topography largely depends. The data for such a map are amassed by experienced geologists who make detailed surveys. The geologic map is used by mining and civil engineers, oil prospectors, agriculturists, army officers and others whose activities depend on the nature of the bedrock.

Topographic maps often serve as a base on which other types of maps are constructed. The compiler of data for various other maps must be familiar with topography and skilled in the recognition of landforms as shown by contour lines. For example, the most common type of military map is a topographic map on which is superposed other information valuable from a military standpoint. In World War II the demand was urgent for military maps of various parts of the world, and large numbers of geographers and geologists were engaged in compiling information and constructing maps for the armed forces. Included in the initial shipment of supplies for the armies invading North Africa were 140 tons of maps sent by the Army Map Service.

The Military Geology Unit of the United States Geological Survey was sometimes considered our most important "Civilian Task Force." Consisting of more than a hundred of the country's most able geologists, this unit prepared maps and supplied the other essential information that made possible the many successful invasions in remote parts of the world. On these maps the geologists put such data as the kind of topography, nature of the ground, sites suitable for airfields, location of springs, deposits of gravel and stone for road building, kind of vegetation, desirable observation posts, distribution of population, roads, railroads, telegraph lines, and countless other items of military information.

ENGINEERING GEOLOGY

Engineering operations of many kinds require the services of well-trained geologists for their safe and economic execution. Many of the dangers attending the building of large engineering structures are of geological origin. One of the chief responsibilities of the geologist is to recognize such dangers and to point them out to the engineers in time to avoid accidents. These dangers include falling rock in tunnels, the failure of rock to support the weight of dams or piers and caving in of ground in various excavations. Because of inability to predict or explain them, some of these accidents were formerly considered "acts of God." Now most of them are avoided because advance knowledge of local geological conditions is secured and proper protective measures taken.

Since the collapse, shortly after its completion, of the foundation of the St. Francis Dam of the Los Angeles water-supply system in 1927, no great public work dealing with earth materials has been planned or constructed without competent geological advice. Private engineering organizations are also using the services of geologists more and more in the building of railroads, bridges, tall buildings, and other large structures. Most of the large undertakings of this kind are public projects. They include municipal water-supply systems, flood-control programs, irrigation systems, power plants, river and harbor improvements, subway tunnels, bridges, and buildings of unusual weight. Among the larger public agencies which require the services of engineering geologists are municipal boards of water

FIG. 27-7. Charles P. Berkey (1867-1955). Leader in the application of geological knowledge and principles to the field of engineering. Consultant to the U. S. Bureau of Reclamation, the New York City Board of Water Supply, and other programs. (Geological Society of America)

supply, departments of sanitation, and the United States Bureau of Reclamation. In recent years, this federal agency has constructed numerous power, flood-control, and irrigation projects in the western part of the United States.

Modern war could not be effectively waged without the information supplied by engineering geologists. For the army in the field the geologist provides data and interpretations on such problems as water supply, sewage disposal, mining, entrenchments and other earthworks. His understanding of terrain and its advantages and disadvantages for particular military purposes and his ability to construct and interpret maps are of critical value to the field commanders.

Among the unsung heroes of World War II were the geologists who selected the particular Normandy beach from which the European invasion was launched by the Allies in June, 1944. Secretly taken ashore at night at various places along the coast, they crawled over the beaches examining the materials of which they are made and collecting samples for laboratory tests. On their recommendation was chosen the beach most likely to support the large tanks, trucks, bulldozers, and other heavy equipment necessary for successful landing.

In recent years the search for uranium and petroleum has occupied many gelogists. The main use of petroluem is as a fuel, though there are many by-products. Uranium has been used mainly in weapons of destruction, but it is hoped that its tremendous energy will be turned more and more to peaceful purposes.

FIG. 27-8. Boulder Dam and Lake Meade, one of the great flood control, irrigation and power projects of the West. (*National Park Service*)

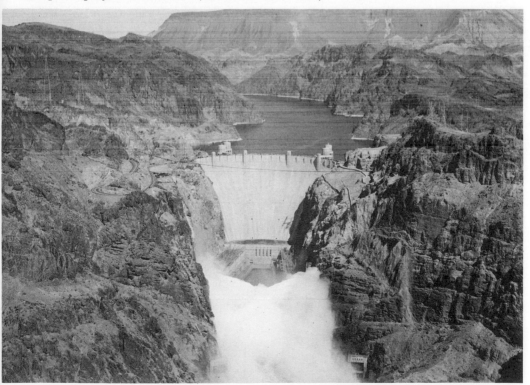

Suggestions for Further Reading

BATEMAN, Alan M., *Economic Mineral Deposits* (New York, Wiley, 1950).

GREENHOOD, David, *Down to Earth: Mapping for Everybody* (New York, Holiday House, 1951).

HOTCHKISS, W. O., *Minerals of Might* (Lancaster, Pa., Jacques Cattell Press, 1945).

KELLOG, C. E., *The Soils That Support Us* (New York, Macmillan, 1941).

LOBECK, A. K., and TELLINGTON, W. J., *Military Maps and Air Photographs* (New York, McGraw-Hill, 1944).

MATHER, K. F., *Enough and to Spare* (New York, Harper, 1944).

UNITED STATES DEPARTMENT OF AGRICULTURE, *Climate and Man, 1941 Yearbook of Agriculture* (Washington, D. C., 1942).

VAN ROYEN, William, and BOWLES, Oliver, *Atlas of the World's Resources, Vol. II: The Mineral Resources of the World* (Englewood Cliffs, N. J., Prentice-Hall, 1952).

APPENDIX A

Subdivisions of Earth Science

Mathematical geography—the earth as a planet, its shape, motions, size, latitude, longitude and mapping.

Meteorology—the study of the composition and behavior of the atmosphere; the various factors that produce weather and climate.

Climatology—a description and explanation of the different climates on the earth and the effects of climate on life.

Oceanography—the area, depth, composition, movements, etc. of the oceans and their effect on climate and life.

Submarine geology—the configuration, composition, and structure of the ocean floor.

Geomorphology—the distribution, characteristics, origin and evolution of the surface features of the lithosphere.

Mineralogy—the crystal form, physical and chemical properties, origin and distribution of the mineral constituents of the solid earth.

Petrology—the composition, structure and modes of origin of the rocks of the earth.

Historical geology, including **paleontology** and **stratigraphy**—the history of the earth and its inhabitants from the beginning to the present.

Geophysics—the study of earthquakes and other phenomena of the interior of the earth by the use of such instruments as the seismograph, torsion balance and magnetometer. Meteorology might well be considered a branch of geophysics.

Geochemistry—has to do with the chemical composition of the rocks and minerals in the earth. Geochemists are especially interested in identifying the isotopes and the decay products of the radioactive elements in the earth.

Economic geology—including the study of ore deposits, petroleum, coal and other useful minerals.

Engineering geology—the relation of geologic conditions to various engineering undertakings, such as tunnels, dams, canals, bridges, and other heavy structures.

Pedology—the study of soils.

Ecology—the relation of life to its physical environment, with a special view toward interpreting past environments.

Sedimentation—observation of the processes and environments of deposition of present sediments, with the aim of interpreting the processes and environments of the past.

Structural geology—examination and interpretation of the architecture of the earth, that is, the arrangement and distribution of materials, with a view toward an understanding of the diastrophic history.

445

American Earth Science Publications

American Association of Petroleum Geologists, *Bulletin* (Tulsa, Okla.).

American Geophysical Union, *Transactions* (Washington, D. C.).

American Meteorological Society, *Bulletin* (Milton, Mass.).

The American Mineralogist (Menasha, Wis., The Mineralogical Society of America).

Annals of the Association of American Geographers (Lancaster, Pa., The Science Press Printing Company).

Economic Geology (Lancaster, Pa., Economic Geology Publishing Company).

Geographical Review (New York, American Geographical Society).

Geological Society of America, *Bulletin* (New York).

Journal of General and Applied Geophysics (Houston, Texas, The Society of Exploration Geophysicists).

The Journal of Geology (Chicago, University of Chicago Press).

Journal of Geophysical Research (Washington, D. C., American Geophysical Union and Carnegie Institute).

Journal of Meteorology (Milton, Mass., American Meteorological Society).

Journal of Micropaleontology (Chicago, The Paleontological Society).

Journal of Sedimentary Petrology (Tulsa, Okla., The Society of Economic Paleontologists and Mineralogists).

Rocks and Minerals (Peekskill, N. Y., Peter Zodac).

Seismological Society, *Bulletin* (Stanford University, Cal.).

United States Geological Survey, Washington, D. C.:

> Annual Reports
> Bulletins
> Geological Atlas Folios (now discontinued)
> Geological Quadrangle Maps
> Monographs
> Professional Papers
> Water-Supply Papers

Publications of state geological surveys

Publications of university geology and geography departments

Articles in various general science publications, such as *The American Journal of Science, American Scientist,* and *The Scientific Monthly.*

Summary of Rock-making Plants and Animals

All recognizable evidences of past life are important as fossils. This summary lists only those forms whose remains have been most important as rock-makers.

PLANT KINGDOM

Group*	Composition of Hard Parts	Times of Abundance	Kind of Rock
Lime-secreting Algae	Calcareous	Proterozoic Cambrian Recent	Algal limestone (Reef limestone)
Diatoms	Silica	Cenozoic Recent	Diatomaceous earth (Infusorial earth) Diatomite
Ferns, Seed-ferns	Cellulose, now carbonized	Pennsylvanian	Coal
Horsetails	Cellulose, now carbonized	Pennsylvanian	Coal
Club Mosses	Cellulose, now carbonized	Pennsylvanian	Coal

ANIMAL KINGDOM

Group*	Composition of Hard Parts	Times of Abundance	Kind of Rock
Foraminifera	Calcareous	Mississippian Pennsylvanian Permian Cretaceous	Foraminiferal limestone, chalk

	Calcareous	Cenozoic Recent	Reef limestone
Corals	Calcareous	Silurian Devonian Mesozoic Cenozoic Recent	Reef limestone
Bryozoa	Calcareous	Ordovician to Recent	Reef limestone
Crinoids	Calcareous	Ordovician Silurian Devonian Mississippian Pennsylvanian	Crinoidal limestone
Brachiopods	Calcareous	Ordovician Silurian Devonian Mississippian Pennsylvanian	Coquinite (shell limestone)
Molluscs:			
Cephalopods	Calcareous	Mesozoic	Shell limestone
Gastropods	Calcareous	Mississippian Cenozoic-Recent	Coquina
Pelocypods	Calcareous	Mesozoic Cenozoic Recent	

* The student interested in a more detailed classification and in the evolution of the groups named should consult more intensive books on historical geology and paleontology.

INDEX

Boldface numbers refer to illustrations

451